ANGLO-AMERICA:

a regional geography

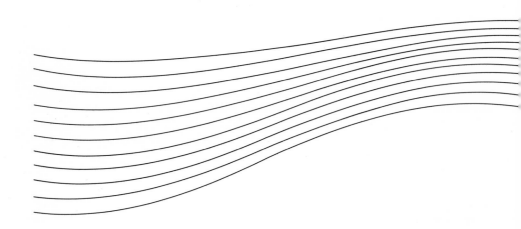

NEW YORK · LONDON   JOHN WILEY & SONS, INC.

ANGLO-AMERICA:

a regional geography

EARL B. SHAW Professor of Geography
State Teachers College, Worcester, Massachusetts

Cartography by
JAMESON MAC FARLAND

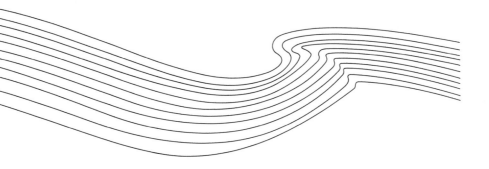

Preface

In this textbook on regional geography, I have given most attention to Anglo-America, the title of the book; but I have also included a chapter on Greenland, Danish America, and a chapter giving an overview of the entire continent of North America.

The overview is given in order to point out major geographic features of the continent and to show the relationship between Anglo-America and North America as a whole. Danish America has been included largely because of its regional simplicity. I believe that regional teaching should start with a simple region, possessing relatively definite boundaries such as those of an island, general economic uniformity, and easily understood geographic relationships. After such an introduction, regions with greater complexity may be understood more easily.

Emphasis is placed on regional land use. Since land use may show clear relationships to the physical environment, the description of regional physical features precedes the analysis of regional activities.

Some geographers may believe that careful examination of the regional core gives sufficient understanding of a region; however, in spite of the fact that many regional boundaries are changing and, at best, are transitional, the student may learn more if he considers regional boundaries as well as the regional core. With this thought in mind, boundaries of several regions are delineated.

Comparison and contrast among various areal divisions encourage learning. For that reason, comparison and contrast are utilized in several places, for example, the Corn Belt and the Cotton Belt, and the Willamette Valley and the Puget Sound Trough. The student should be encouraged to make more comparisons and contrasts.

No attempt has been made to include all available information in the description of any region; however, emphasis is placed on geographic relationships, and on enough factual material to give the student familiarity with the geography of Anglo-America. A large number of references follows each chapter. These are added to give more geographic information than is possible to include in any one book. Careful study of these references will expand student knowledge of Anglo-America greatly.

A list of questions follows each chapter. These are added to provide an outline for reviewing the text and to give opportunity for further study. In the latter case, attention is called especially to such questions as (1) those on the location and growth of regional cities and towns; (2) those suggesting the reading of definite references; (3) those concerning population distribution; and (4) those that will provide additional information by the reading of listed and unlisted references.

Illustrations have been chosen for two main purposes: to emphasize topics described in the text, and to add information that otherwise cannot be included. Attention is called to the black and white regional maps. Most students need to see a regional map before they can (1) understand the size and shape of a region; and (2) learn its location with reference to other regions and to the continent as a whole.

I am indebted to many persons for ideas, information, and illustrations; I have borrowed from former teachers, colleagues, students, government agencies, and business firms. To all who have contributed, I am extremely grateful.

EARL B. SHAW

Worcester, Massachusetts
June 1959

Contents

1 · North America – Overview

The geography of North America may be studied in a number of ways. The student may follow a topical outline with such headings as agriculture, commerce, forestry, and manufacturing; he may study the large political units or political subdivisions; or he may subdivide the continent and its countries into regions.[1]

Geographers stress several advantages for the regional approach. (*a*) It gives a better understanding of a large unit by a systematic examination of parts showing considerable similarity. (*b*) The regional approach provides a good method of organizing factual material about a continent, its people, and their activities. (*c*) By the use of regional techniques, regions of like characteristics throughout the world can be compared and contrasted.

Geographic regions may be delimited on many bases: on land forms, climate, vegetation, soil, etc.; or they may be set apart from one another on the basis of land use—in short, into economic regions. The latter approach will be followed in this text (Fig. 1); and since economic regions are based upon many factors, both physical and man made, a better understanding may be gained by first examining the location, size, topography, climate, vegetation, and soils, before studying the regional economy. It also seems best to look at the continent as a whole before attempting to break it into various parts of economic uniformity.

Location, Shape, Area, and Population

Location. North America extends from beyond 80° north in both Ellesmere Island and Greenland to within a few degrees of the equator in

---

[1] A region is an area possessing enough homogeneity in its physical environment to encourage either actual or potential unity in its man-made features.

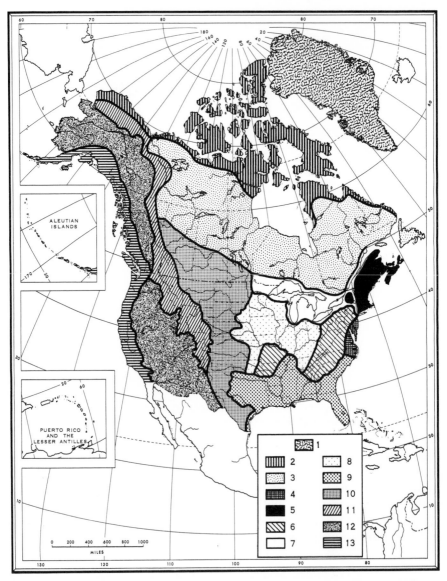

Fig. 1. Land Use Regions of Anglo-America. (1) Greenland; (2) the Tundra of Canada and Alaska; (3) the Taiga or Subarctic Region of Canada; (4) the Middle Atlantic Coastal Plain; (5) the Northeast; (6) the Southwest Appalachians; (7) the Interior Seaboard; (8) the Central Farming Region; (9) the South; (10) the Great Plains; (11) the Rocky Mountains; (12) the Inter-montane Plateaus; (13) the Pacific Borderlands.

southern Panama; the great stretch of approximately 80° of latitude, all north of the equator, totals more than 5,000 miles. The 20th meridian west passes through eastern Greenland; and the Aleutian Islands extend to about 170° east. Thus the continent also spreads over a long distance in an east-west direction.

Europe lies less than 2,000 miles across the Atlantic from Newfoundland on North America's eastern borders, and South America joins on the south by means of the Isthmus of Panama. Several thousand years ago, a land bridge connected Eurasia to the Alaskan Peninsula (Fig. 2); now less than 60 miles of Bering Strait separate the two land masses. Eurasian animals, plants, and men probably first reached America by way of the old land bridge. North Africa is not far distant from North America, but Australia lies much farther away.

Shape. North America is shaped like a triangle, and in this respect resembles South America, Africa, and Europe. One of the most significant facts about the continent is that it tapers into the tropics from a broad area lying within the middle and high latitudes. Europe and Asia also have large sections lying within the middle latitudes; but Asia's latitudinal advantage is lessened by high mountains and plateaus to a much greater extent than that of the two smaller continents.

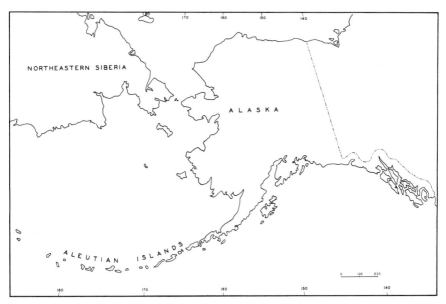

Fig. 2. North America Lies Close to Asia. About 50 miles of water separate the North American continent from Asia at their closest points, between Alaska and Siberia. The Diomede Islands form stepping stones across the short span of Bering Sea. Russia's Big Diomede Island is only three miles distant from Little Diomede Island, belonging to the United States.

The narrow shape of the southern portion of North America made practical the digging of a transcontinental canal across Panama. This waterway makes enormous savings of distance in both commercial and military ocean shipping. During World War II, the canal and surrounding areas became of great significance in Allied defense strategy (Fig. 3).

Although North America's coastal indentations are fewer and less penetrating than those of Europe, the continent's shore line is far from regular. Irregularities include water areas such as the American Mediterranean—the Gulf of Mexico and Caribbean Sea—Hudson Bay, the Gulf of Lower California, the Gulf of St. Lawrence, and Chesapeake Bay; among the peninsulas are those of Labrador, Alaska, Lower California, Nova Scotia, Florida, and Yucatan; scores of islands border the coasts of the Northwest, the North, and the Southeast.

Area. The continent's 9,435,000 square miles equal about half those of Asia, and about four-fifths those of Africa; these two continents are the only ones that exceed North America in size. Two nations, Canada and the United States, Anglo-America, comprise 7,500,000 square miles, with

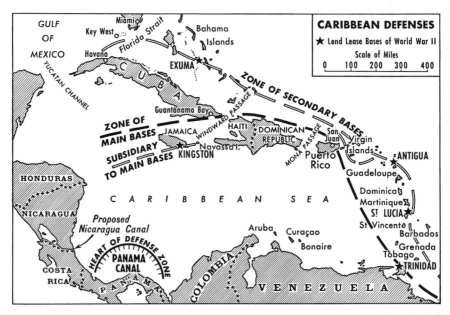

Fig. 3. Caribbean Defenses. Compare the thousands of miles east-west width of the United States and Canada (Fig. 1) with that of the narrow isthmus of Panama. Only about 51 miles separate the deep water of the Atlantic from that of the Pacific along the northwest-southeast route of the canal. The Panama waterway provides a sea route between United States coasts 7,800 miles shorter than the route around Cape Horn. (Source: Etzel Pearcy, *World Political Geography,* Thomas Y. Crowell Co., 1957.)

Greenland and the Latin American portion—Mexico, Central America, and the West Indies—accounting for the remainder.

Population (Fig. 4). More than 175,000,000 of the continent's approximately 250,000,000 people live in the United States; Canada has 16,000,000, Mexico about 30,000,000, the West Indies nearly 20,000,000, and Central America more than 10,000,000 (1958). Although the majority of the population belongs to the white race, many Negroes live in the United States and in the West Indies. Indians are most numerous in Mexico and Central America, but some Indian and Oriental people live in all countries. Race mixtures of mulatto, mestizo, etc. are widespread, especially in the Latin American portion of the continent.

Various languages are spoken; English is official in the United States, Canada, and in some of the West Indies; French is official in Canada, Haiti, St. Pierre, Miquelon, and in the French West Indies; Spanish is official in Mexico, Central America (except British Honduras), Cuba, Puerto Rico, and in the Dominican Republic. Dutch is spoken on Saba and St. Martin; and Danish is official in Greenland. Many Indian dialects appear in Mexico, Central America, and in Canada. Eskimo dialects may be heard in Greenland, northern Canada, and Alaska.

Surface Features

The land forms of North America (Figs. 5, 6) fall into three major subdivisions, all showing a general north-south trend. On the west, a great cordillera of mountains and plateaus extends from Alaska to Panama. On the east, the Appalachian system reaches its southern limit in Georgia and Alabama and its northern one in Labrador. Between the two highland units, plains reach from the Arctic and Hudson Bay to the Gulf of Mexico.

In the United States, the western cordillera may be divided into the Pacific mountain system, the Intermontane Plateaus, and the Rocky Mountains. The Pacific system slightly resembles a capital letter H. The Coast Ranges form the left upright, the Sierra Nevada and Cascades the right one, and the Klamath Mountains the cross bar that ties the two uprights together. The Great Valley of California lies south of the cross bar and the Willamette Valley lies to the north. Intermontane Plateaus include the Columbia, the Colorado, and the Basin and Range physiographic provinces; and for convenience in study, the United States Rocky Mountains may be divided into the Northern, Middle, and Southern Rockies (Fig. 6).

In Canada and Alaska, the western cordillera is narrower than in continental United States, although all major subdivisions, Pacific mountain system, Intermontane Plateaus, and Rocky Mountains are represented. Many of the coastal ranges have been affected by subsidence and form

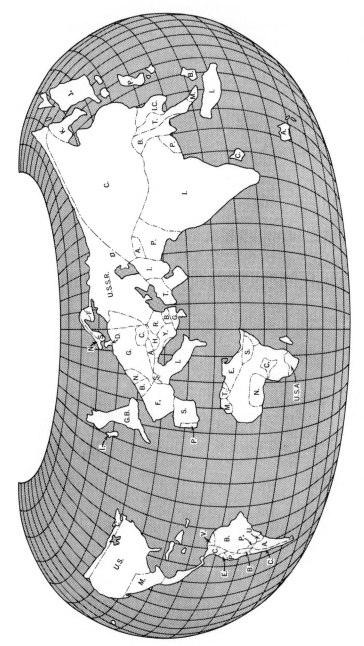

Fig. 4. Size of Continents and Countries According to Population. Distorted map of the world showing each continent and selected countries on a scale proportionate to population in 1950. Uninhabited and sparsely populated areas of the Arctic and Antarctic do not appear. Note the size of North America in comparison to the other continents and to China and India. Notice also the size of the United States in comparison with Canada, Mexico, Central America, and the West Indies. (Courtesy The Twentieth Century Fund.)

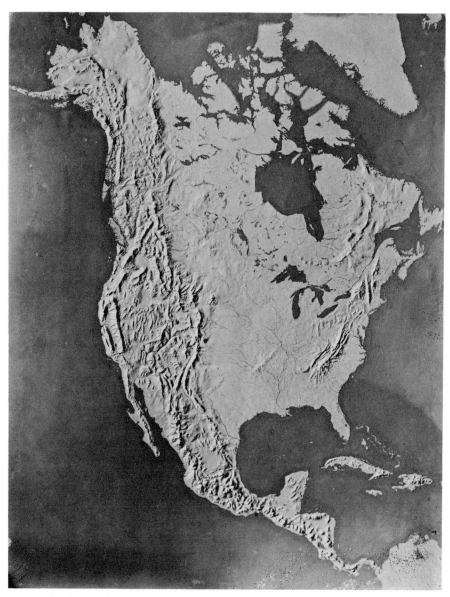

Fig. 5. The Relief of North America. Point out the Appalachians, the Ozarks, the Western Sierra Madre, the Eastern Sierra Madre, the Sierra Nevada, the Klamath Mountains, the Cascades, and the Intermontane Plateaus. (Courtesy U. S. Geological Survey.)

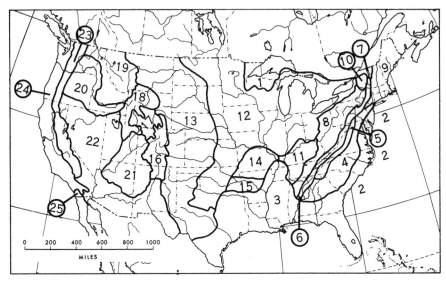

Fig. 6. Major Physical Regions of the United States. Nevin M. Fenneman divides the United States into 25 major physical provinces, which are further subdivided into a total of 86 land form regions. The 25 include (1) Superior Upland; (2) Continental Shelf; (3) Coastal Plain; (4) Piedmont; (5) Blue Ridge; (6) Valley and Ridge; (7) St. Lawrence Valley (including Lake Champlain); (8) Appalachian Plateaus; (9) New England; (10) Adirondacks; (11) Interior Low Plateaus; (12) Central Lowland; (13) Great Plains; (14) Ozark Plateaus; (15) Ouachitas; (16) Southern Rockies; (17) Wyoming Basin; (18) Middle Rockies; (19) Northern Rockies; (20) Columbia Plateaus; (21) Colorado Plateaus; (22) Basin and Range; (23) Sierra Cascade; (24) Pacific Border; (25) Lower California. (Source: Nevin M. Fenneman, *Physical Divisions of the United States.*)

mountainous islands almost enclosing the famous water route to Alaska, the Inside Passage. The Fraser and the Yukon are important among the plateaus that separate coastal mountains from the Rockies to the east (Fig. 5).

In Mexico, mountain ranges continue in Baja California, which is separated from the mainland by a graben, the Gulf of California. On the mainland, other elements of the western cordillera include the Sierra Madre Occidental, and the Sierra Madre Oriental, which are separated from one another by Mexico's Northern Basins and Ranges, an equatorward extension of North America's Intermontane Plateaus. The Western and Eastern Sierra Madre come together in a complex highland mass in the vicinity of Mexico City. To the south and east are the Sierra del Sur and the Chiapas Highlands. The western cordillera, much narrower, continues through Central America to join the Andes of South America (Fig. 5).

Several of the mountains of southern Mexico and Central America have a structural trend in an east-west direction; and these east-west trending continental ranges are connected by submarine ridges, showing the same trend, with the east-west mountain backbones of the Greater Antilles. Most of the West Indies are mountainous. In general, the islands may be divided into two great arcs, an inner arc of volcanic islands with medium to high altitudes, and an outer arc of low-lying limestone islands.

North America's Appalachian system is shorter in a north-south direction, narrower in an east-west extent, and its highest elevations, approximately 6,700 feet, are far lower than those of the western cordillera, more than 20,000 feet. The system may be divided into the Southwestern Appalachians and the New England-Acadian ranges. In the United States, an Atlantic Coastal Plain borders the Southwestern Appalachians on the east and south; in Mexico and Central America, a continuation of this plain is much wider than the narrow plain along the Pacific. An outlier of the Southwest Appalachians, the Ozark-Ouachita province, forms a separate physiographic unit within the Interior Plains.

The Interior Plains comprise the Laurentian peneplain, a horseshoe-shaped remnant of erosion almost encircling Hudson Bay; the Great Plains, lying just east of the Rockies and extending from the Arctic to Texas; and the Central Lowland, which borders the Appalachians to the east, the Great Plains to the west, and the Laurentian Shield to the north.

Many Canadian and United States surface features were greatly affected by Pleistocene glaciation (Fig. 7). The equatorward boundary is approximately as follows: it extends from Long Island to Pittsburgh where it follows the Ohio south to its confluence with the Mississippi. From there the edge of the glacial ice turned north along the Mississippi to the mouth of the Missouri. The latter stream forms the approximate equatorward boundary west of the Mississippi. Within the general area of continental glaciation are at least two sections unaffected by ice action. One is located in southwest Wisconsin, northeast Iowa, southeast Minnesota, and northwestern Illinois; it is called the Driftless Area. The other includes a broad expanse in central Alaska. High mountains south of the glacier's general equatorward boundary were covered with an extensive ice blanket in Pleistocene time.

A significant service of glacial action for North America was the formation of the greatest inland waterway system in the world, the American Great Lakes. Moreover, the great ice rasp dug thousands of smaller lakes, and with its diggings it blocked drainage patterns so as to form thousands more. Numerous waterfalls developed when the continental ice sheet interrupted stream courses. Canadian and northern United States surface features afford many striking evidences of Pleistocene ice.

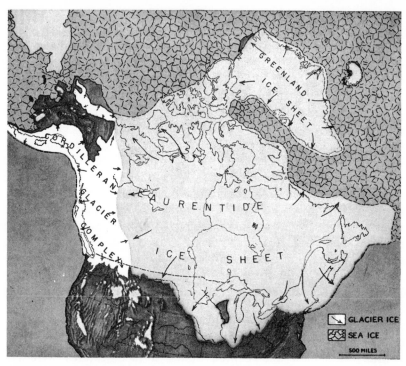

Fig. 7. Extent of Glaciation of North America at the Maximum of the Glacial Ages. This map is somewhat generalized, and the boundaries between glacier ice, sea ice, and open sea are conjectural; however such boundaries are based on modern analogies. Arrows show general directions of ice flow. Note the relation of the Ohio and Missouri rivers to former ice margins. (Source: C. R. Longwell, A. Knopf, and R. F. Flint, *Physical Geology*, 3rd ed., John Wiley and Sons, 1948.)

Climates

(Figures 8, 9, 10, 11)

Land forms provide one of several controls that affect the climates of North America. The western cordillera bars moisture-laden oceanic air from the interior, and desert and steppe climates occur over wide areas to the east. Most of the Pacific moisture, carried by the prevailing westerlies, is dropped upon the Pacific-facing slopes.

Cordilleran altitudes also affect temperature. Mt. McKinley rises 20,300 feet in Alaska; Mt. Logan reaches 19,850 feet in Canada; Mt. Whitney, highest in the contiguous United States, lifts its head to 14,495 feet; and Mt. Orizaba, in Mexico, measures 18,701 feet above the sea. Since the average temperature decline is about 3° F. per thousand feet increase in altitude, the cordillera influence upon temperature is significant.

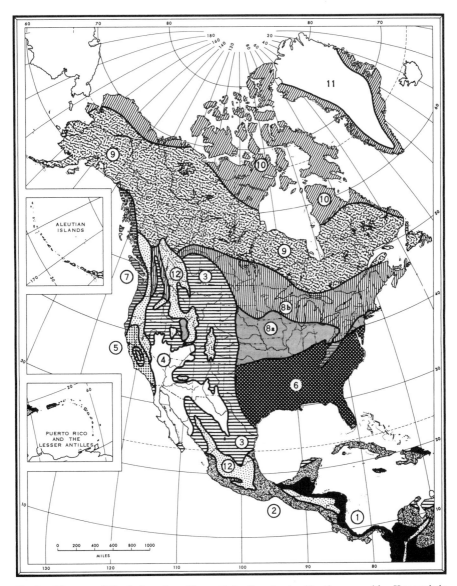

Fig. 8. Climates of North America. Trewartha's climatic classification resembles Koppen's in most respects. Included on the above map are (1) Tropical Rainforest, Af, Am; (2) Tropical Savanna, Aw; (3) Steppe, BSh, BSk; (4) Desert, BWh, BWk; (5) Mediterranean, Cs; (6) Humid Subtropical, Ca; (7) Marine West Coast, Cb; (8a) Humid Continental Warm Summer, Da; (8b) Humid Continental Cool Summer, Db; (9) Subarctic, Dc; (10) Tundra, ET; (11) Ice Cap, EF; and (12) Undifferentiated Highlands. (After G. T. Trewartha, *An Introduction to Climate,* McGraw-Hill, 1954.)

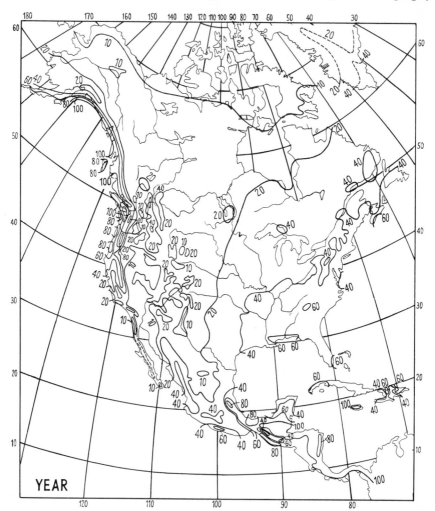

Fig. 9. Mean Annual Rainfall (in inches). Note the influence of land forms, mountains as barriers, prevailing winds, distribution of land and water, cyclonic storms, and ocean currents on distribution of precipitation. (Source: W. G. Kendrew, *The Climates of the Continents,* Oxford University Press.)

East of the Rocky Mountains, one can travel from the Gulf of Mexico to Hudson Bay at elevations of no more than a thousand feet above sea level. Here altitude does little to encourage low temperature. However, the lack of an east-west mountain barrier in central North America permits easy movement of huge masses of cold Polar Continental air from the Arctic to the Gulf of Mexico; Tropical Gulf air (Fig. 12) can use the same unobstructed path to bring warmth and moisture over the continental interior.

Lower temperatures and heavier precipitation occur east of the central plains, partly because of the Appalachian Mountain system. However, lower altitudes than those of the western cordillera make the Appalachian influence upon cooler temperatures less significant than that of the mountains of the West.

In Central America and the West Indies (Fig. 13), mountains as barriers, aligned at right angles to the northeast trade winds, force moist

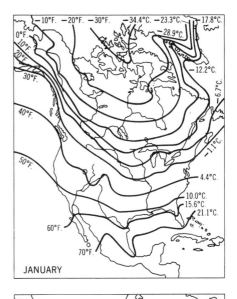

JANUARY

Fig. 10. Mean Temperature. Note the larger number of isotherms on the January map than on the July map. Explain. (Source: W. G. Kendrew, *The Climates of the Continents,* Oxford University Press.)

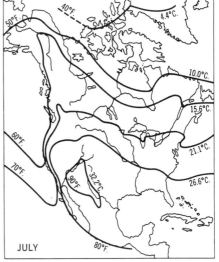

JULY

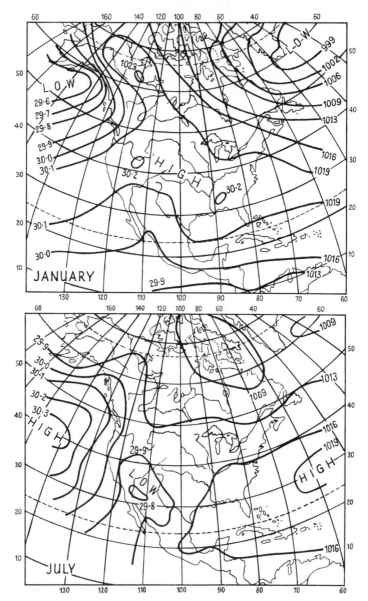

Fig. 11.   Mean Pressure (in inches and millibars).   Explain the contrast in pressure on the two maps.   (Source: W. G. Kendrew, *Climates of the Continents*, Oxford University Press.)

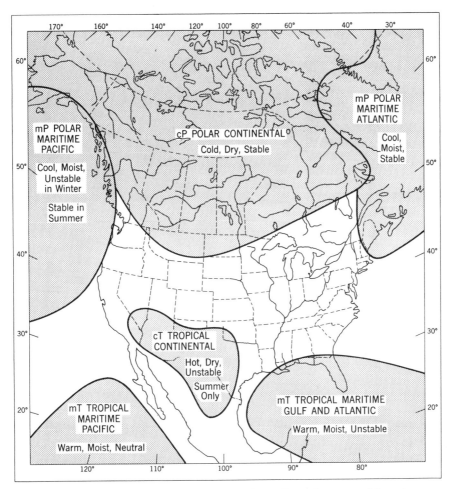

Fig. 12. North American Air Masses and Source Regions. Learn the names of these air masses which exert so much influence upon North America's weather. (Source: G. T. Trewartha, *An Introduction to Climate,* McGraw-Hill Book Co., 1954.)

tropical air to rise, cool, condense, and give up heavy precipitation on windward slopes. Moreover, great differences in altitude provide the well known tierra caliente, tierra templada, and tierra fria climatic and vegetation zones of the Latin American section of the continent (Fig. 14).

Warm and cold currents, which bathe continental shores, exert an important climatic influence (Fig. 15). Southern California summers are cooler because of the cold California current along shore. Alaska's Panhandle receives more rainfall as a result of warmth of the nearby N. Pacific current. Labrador's coast is colder than England in the same latitude partly because of the cold Labrador current; and finally, the Gulf Stream

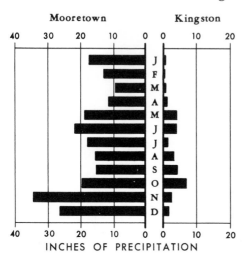

Fig. 13. Contrasts in West Indies Rainfall. Mooretown, a few miles northeast of Kingston, Jamaica, lies on the windward side of the east-west trending Blue Mountains while Kingston is situated on the leeward side. Northeast trades rising over Blue Mountains as barriers cause heavy orographic precipitation at Mooretown; northeast trades descending on the leeward side of the Blue Mountains leave Kingston comparatively dry.

influences the temperature and precipitation of the southeastern part of the continent.

Not only do ocean currents affect the continent's climates, but the bordering seas also exert a strong marine influence upon North America. It must be remembered, however, that North America is third largest among the continents; and because of large size, continental climates occur in areas far from the ocean (Fig. 8).

The cyclonic storms of the westerly wind belt, which at some time of the year spreads over all of North America except the tropics, vitally affect the continent's climates; and on no other continent are these extra-tropical cyclones better developed. Associated with the westerly wind belt and its sequence of cyclones and anticyclones is the jet stream which has much to do with the continental weather.

The great north-south extent of North America between approximately 7° north and 84° north provides a strong latitude control. In the far north, a climatic region, the Ice Cap Region (Fig. 8), has no month with an average temperature as high as 32° F., but along the windward coast of Central America, the Tropical Rainforest climate has no month with an average temperature below 64.4° F.

Natural Vegetation

In a continent as large as North America, with its diversity of climates and land forms, broad contrasts in natural vegetation occur. Vegetation ranges from the deciduous forest of eastern United States to the short grasslands of the American Great Plains; from the tundra vegetation among the snow-capped peaks of the Rockies, Sierras, and Cascades, and the northern Canadian plains to the tropical rainforests of the wet windward slopes of Mexico, Central America, and the West Indies; and from the luxuriant coniferous forests of Oregon, Washington, British Columbia, and the Panhandle of Alaska to the barren deserts of southeastern California and northwestern Mexico.

In the United States (Fig. 16), forests form two broad belts, one extending inland from the Atlantic Ocean, and the other extending inland from the Pacific Ocean. The eastern forest is relatively continuous, but the western one is broken by many areas of non-forested land. The main break in the western forest occurs in the dry Intermontane Plateau region which lies between the forested Coast Ranges, Sierras, and Cascades on the west and the forested Rocky Mountains on the east. The characteristic desert

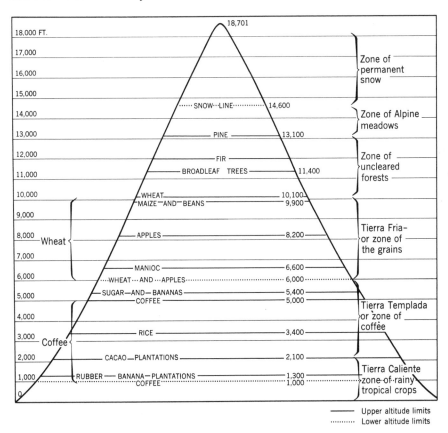

Fig. 14. Temperature Zones on Mount Orizaba. Mount Orizaba is located at 19° 0′ N. and 97° 15′ W. The upper limits of each zone extend higher the closer a location is to the equator. (After Karl Sapper and Preston James, *A Geography of Man,* 2nd ed., Ginn and Co., 1959, p. 434.)

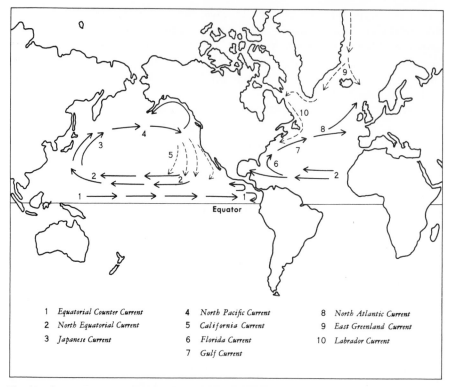

Fig. 15. Ocean Currents Affecting North America's Climates. Ocean currents along the border of the continent provide an important climatic control. Explain.

scrub of the Intermontane Plateau broadens toward the south, and along the Mexican boundary it forms an almost continuous strip extending from the Pacific Ocean to the Gulf of Mexico. Only here and there is it interrupted by forest at high elevations.

A great central grassland area lies east of the Rockies, with the tall grass subregion bordering the Atlantic forest region and the short grass subregion bordering Rocky Mountain forests (Fig. 16).

Both Atlantic and Pacific forest belts of the United States extend into Canada (Fig. 17). In southern Canada they are separated from one another by grassland, which is a northward extension of the Great Plains grasses; but in central Saskatchewan and Alberta, grasslands give way to trees which join eastern and western Canadian tree belts into an almost continuous cross-country coniferous forest. North of the 50° F. isotherm for the warmest month and at high altitudes throughout western North America, forest changes to tundra. Five-sixths of Greenland is covered with an ice cap, which gives way to a narrow belt of tundra along most coastal sections.

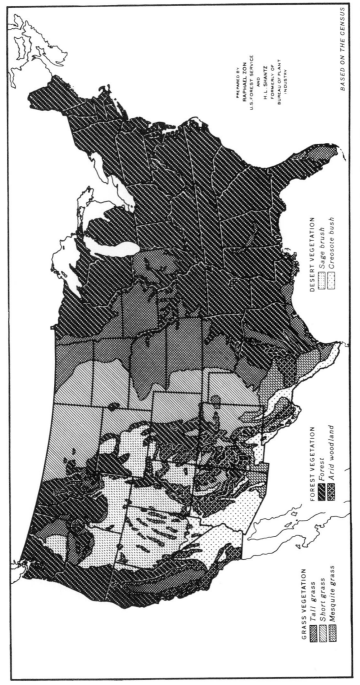

Fig. 16. Native Vegetation. Note the relation between the distribution of vegetation types and climatic regions. (Courtesy Bureau of Agricultural Economics, U. S. Department of Agriculture.)

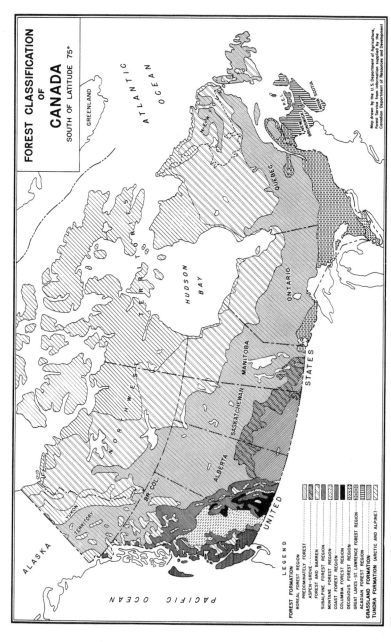

Fig. 17. Canadian Vegetation Regions. The boreal forest, mostly coniferous, covers more area than does any other tree vegetation. Note the tundra vegetation on high altitudes as well as in high latitudes. Mixed forests and deciduous trees occur in southeastern Canada. (Courtesy U. S. Department of Agriculture.)

Alaskan vegetation may be divided into four major regions. (*a*) Coastal forests occupy the Alaskan Panhandle from the British Columbia border to Cook Inlet; (*b*) in the interior, forests less luxuriant than those on the coast are better developed along stream courses than on interstream areas; (*c*) forests give way to grasses on the Pacific coast of the Alaskan peninsula and on the Aleutian Islands to the west; and (*d*) the remainder of Alaska is characterized largely by tundra vegetation.

South of the United States, in Mexico (Fig. 18), great diversity in land forms, altitudes, and climates results in varied types of vegetation. Tropical forest covers much of the Mexican Gulf Coast as well as the Pacific border equatorward from the Sonoran Desert. Coniferous forests occur on higher elevations of the Western and Eastern Sierra Madre, with broadleaf deciduous trees occupying the foothill country. Mexico's Basin and Range physiographic province between the Sierras changes from desert to steppe as rainfall increases from north to south.

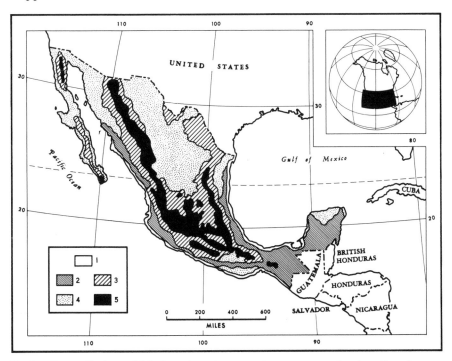

Fig. 18. Forest Regions of Mexico. Area 1 represents mangrove and palms; 2, mahogany, mountain mahogany, ceiba, chicle, cedar, and many other wet tropical species; 3, oak, copal, piñon pine, senna, alder, arbutus; 4, agave, cactus, mesquite; and 5, pine, white cedar, cypress, and fir. Note the general correlation between land forms and climate on the one hand and vegetation zones on the other. See Fig. 5; also Fig. 9. (After map in *Boletin del Departamento Forestal y de Caza y Pesca, No. 8,* 1937.)

Central America includes three main vegetation regions; (*a*) the tropical rainforest of the Atlantic coastal plain and the Atlantic facing mountain slopes; (*b*) the tropical scrub and savanna of the leeward Pacific coastal plain and Pacific-facing slopes; and (*c*) the central mountain region with vegetation varying according to altitude and exposure to prevailing winds (Fig. 19).

In the West Indies, tropical savanna occupies most of Cuba, which has no east-west mountain backbone. However, on windward eastern and northern slopes of mountainous Puerto Rico, Jamaica, and Hispaniola, the natural vegetation is largely tropical rainforest; leeward positions are characterized by steppe or desert plants. Windward and leeward slopes of most mountainous Lesser Antilles possess a vegetation distribution similar

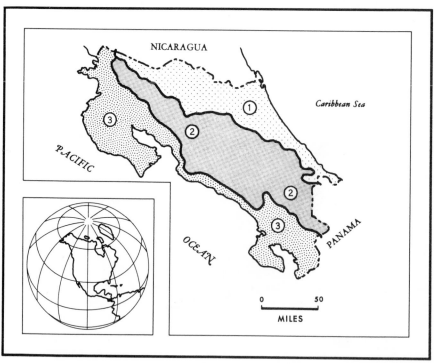

Fig. 19. Vegetation Zones, Costa Rica. Costa Rica's three vegetation zones are almost synonymous with the three major topographic regions, and they may serve as an example of plant distribution in Central America. On (1), the Caribbean Lowlands, dense tropical broadleaf-evergreen rainforest occurs; on (2), the Central Highlands, a semideciduous forest is characteristic; and on (3), the Pacific Littoral, vegetation diversity of tropical evergreen forest, dry forest, and savanna results from contrasting topography and precipitation. (After map by Paul C. Morrison, "Notes on the Regional Geography of Costa Rica," Tokyo Geographical Society, *Journal of Geography,* Vol. 65, No. 2, 1956.)

to that of mountainous Greater Antilles; but plant life resembling that of Cuba occurs on the relatively flat limestone islands such as Barbados.

Soils

(Figure 20)

The 100th meridian in the United States is the approximate boundary between the pedocal or lime-accumulating soils and the pedalfer or non-lime-accumulating soils. Soil distribution is influenced by the fact that east of the meridian annual rainfall averages more than 20 inches, whereas west of the line the yearly average is generally less (Fig. 9).

Three eastern United States pedalfers, the podzols, the gray-brown podzolic and the red and yellow earths all have developed under forest cover. Their east-west extent is greater than that to the north and south. Most of the fourth pedalfer belt in eastern United States, the prairie soil, developed under tall grass vegetation and extends farther in a north-south direction than in one trending east and west.

The pedocals lying west of the 100th meridian, especially (1) the chernozems and reddish chestnut soils and (2) the chestnut, brown, and reddish-brown soils, occupy approximately the same area as that of the United States short grasslands. Both soil belts extend north into Canada. However, podzol and tundra soils occupy most of Canada, as well as Alaska, and that portion of Greenland not covered by an icecap.

Mexican soils, with the exception of those in the south, show the influence of low precipitation, and belong largely to dry land types. They are deficient in humus, strong in mineral constituents, and may require careful handling to guard against a rise of saline materials toward the surface.

In southern Mexico and in most of Central America and the West Indies, heavy precipitation encourages soils belonging to the latosol group. Laterites are leached of their mineral constituents by heavy rains. Such soils are also low in humus, but not because of the lack of plant life. In this heavily forested area, leaves of the evergreen broadleafs are not the best source of humus; furthermore, the active work of aerobic bacteria destroys much humus. Again, destructive oxidation of organic matter takes place quickly, and significant amounts of organic material are carried away in solution rather than becoming incorporated into the soil.

The chernozems, chestnut, brown, and reddish-brown soils of the United States and Canada are probably the most fertile of North American soils; but they lie in a rainfall belt that is marginal for successful humid agriculture. The marginal rainfall helps make the soils fertile, but it also makes them a risk area for farming.

The best of the North American pedalfers are the prairie soils. Grass

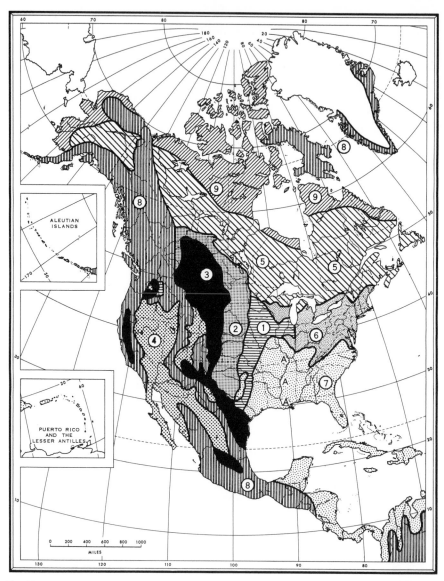

Fig. 20. Soils of North America.   The following soil groups are shown on the map: (1) Prairie
Soils, Degraded Chernozem; (2) Chernozems and Reddish Chestnut Soils; (3) Chestnut, Brown,
and Reddish-Brown Soils; (4) Sierozems, Desert, and Red Desert Soils; (5) Podzols; (6) Gray-
Brown Podzolic Soils; (7) Latosols and Red-Yellow Podzolic Soils; (8) Soils of Mountains and
Mountain Valleys; (9) Tundra Soils; (A) Alluvial Soils.   Many small but important areas of
alluvial soils are not shown on the map; the same can be said of the bog and half-bog soils.   The
map is taken from schematic soil map of the world by Charles E. Kellogg and Arnold C. Orvedal,
1956.   (Courtesy U. S. Department of Agriculture.)

vegetation, supported by these soils for thousands of years, has contributed fertility both in the form of grass roots and in grass stalks. Prairie soils may not be quite so fertile as chernozems, but the larger annual rainfall of the prairie region together with greater rainfall dependability give better assurance for successful farming.

The North American podzol region occupies practically the same area as that of the conifer belt of northeastern United States and the Taiga region of Canada. Conifers contribute less to soil fertility and to soil structure than do the deciduous broadleafs. Moreover, the low temperatures of the podzol region do not encourage adequate development of soil forming organisms, such as earthworms, so active in the broadleaf forests of the Middle Atlantic states with their gray-brown podzolic soils. North of the podzol belt, in Canada, Alaska, and Greenland, the tundra soils are low in fertility, poor in structure, limited in organic life, and have poor drainage. South of the gray-brown podzolic belt of the United States, heavy rainfall and warm temperatures encourage development of red and yellow earths. These soils are less fertile than the gray-brown podzolics.

Glaciation exerted an important influence upon soils in Canada and northern United States. Ice stripped soils from Canada's Laurentian Plateau and carried many of them on to the prairies of northern United States; Pleistocene ice also cut down the hills and filled in the valleys of the preglacial rolling topography of Iowa, Illinois, and other Corn Belt states; at the same time, Corn Belt soils profited by mixing during the leveling process; and retreating glacial ice ponded huge lakes like Lake Agassiz, which left rich lacustrine soils over wide expanses in the Dakotas and prairie provinces of Canada.

In northwest United States, soils of the Columbia plateau are richer because of recent lava flows.

Little opportunity exists for the early development of a heavy soil cover or a mature soil profile on the large areas of North America's mountainous terrain. Long periods of geologic time will pass before mountain lands are changed to plains—plains where soil can accumulate with little danger of erosion.

In retrospect it may be noted that all the basic factors of soil formation are active on North American soils. These include relief, climate, vegetation, parent material, and time.

Regional Geography

In the following chapters, North America is divided into geographic regions and subregions for further study. Major regions include Greenland, the Tundra, the Subarctic or Taiga, the Middle Atlantic Coastal Plain, the Southwest Appalachians, the Northeast, the Interior Seaboard, the Central Farming Region, the South, the Great Plains, the Rocky Mountains, the Intermontane Plateaus, and the Pacific Borderlands (Fig. 1).

QUESTIONS, EXERCISES, AND PROBLEMS

1. What is a geographic region? What are the advantages of the regional approach? Read E. W. Gilbert and Preston James, references cited.

2. Is the great latitudinal extent of North America an advantage? Are there geographic advantages in the fact that North America is broad in the middle latitudes and narrow in the tropics? How does South America compare with North America in this respect?

3. Describe North America as to location, area, total population, racial character, languages, independent countries, and European holdings. Look in a good atlas and compare the number of countries in North America with the number in South America, in Europe, in Asia, and in Africa. How do Canada and the United States compare in area and population with other large countries of the world?

4. List and locate the major mountain groups, plateaus, and plains in North America. Indicate in some detail the area covered by Pleistocene glaciation. What influences did glaciation contribute? What and where are the major soil regions? Compare major surface and coastal features of North America with those of South America, Europe, Asia, Africa, and Australia; examine some good physical maps of the continents to do this.

5. What air masses influence the continent's climates? Name and locate the climatic regions. Each of the following physical features influences the climates of North America: ocean currents, altitude, latitude, prevailing winds, mountains as barriers, cyclonic storms, distribution of land and water, permanent and semipermanent highs and lows. Give a few specific examples showing the influence of each.

6. Describe briefly the major vegetation features of Canada, the United States, Mexico, Central America, and the West Indies.

7. Which is better situated for world commerce, Europe or North America? Name the 10 leading exports and the 10 leading imports for the United States. Do the same for Canada. Study the position of the United States and Canada in the production of food supplies, forest products, minerals, and power resources. How do the United States and Canada rank among the leading manufacturing nations of the world?

8. Identify the following: pedalfer, graben, pedocal, peneplain, climax vegetation, mestizo, cordillera, driftless region, Pleistocene, the wind belts which influence North America's climates, laterite, and Agassiz.

SELECTED REFERENCES

Alexandersson, Gunnar, *The Industrial Structure of American Cities: A Geographic Study of Urban Economy in the United States,* University of Nebraska Press, 1956.

Atwood, Wallace W., *The Physiographic Provinces of North America,* Ginn and Co., 1940.

Ball, Max W., and others, "Possible Future Petroleum Provinces of North America," *The American Association of Petroleum Geologists,* 1951.

Bogue, Donald J., "The Geography of Recent Population Trends in the United States," *Annals of the Association of American Geographers,* June 1954, pp. 124–134.

Borchert, John R., "The Climate of the Central North American Grassland," *Annals of the Association of American Geographers,* March 1950, pp. 1–39.

Borchert, John R., "The Surface Water Supply of American Municipalities," *Annals of the Association of American Geographers,* March 1954, pp. 15–32.

Brown, Ralph H., *Historical Geography of the United States,* Harcourt, Brace and Co., 1948.

Calef, Wesley C., and Howard J. Nelson, "Distribution of Negro Population in the United States," *Geographical Review,* January 1956, pp. 82–97.

Clark, Andrew H., "Contributions to Geographical Knowledge of Canada since 1945," *Geographical Review,* April 1950, pp. 285–308.

Dewhurst, J. Frederic, and associates, *America's Needs and Resources: A New Survey,* The Twentieth Century Fund, New York, 1955.

Dominion Bureau of Statistics, *Canada Handbook,* 1958.

Fenneman, Nevin M., *Physiography of Eastern United States,* McGraw-Hill, 1938.

Fenneman, Nevin M., *Physiography of Western United States,* McGraw-Hill, 1931.

Fenneman, Nevin M., and others, *Physical Divisions of the United States,* (map), U. S. Geological Survey, Department of the Interior, 1930.

Geddes, Arthur, "Variability in Change of Population in the United States and Canada, 1900–1951," *Geographical Review,* January 1954, pp. 88–100.

Geographical Record, "Timber Supply and Demand in the United States," *Geographical Review,* July 1956, pp. 409–411.

Geographical Record, "Tree Farming in the United States," *Geographical Review,* October 1953, pp. 564–565.

Gilbert, E. W., "Geography and Regionalism," *Geography in the Twentieth Century,* edited by Griffith Taylor, Methuen and Co., 1957.

Haystead, Ladd, and Gilbert C. Fite, *The Agricultural Regions of the United States,* University of Oklahoma Press, 1955.

Higbee, Edward, *American Agriculture,* John Wiley and Sons, 1958.

Higbee, Edward, *The American Oasis,* Alfred A. Knopf, 1957.

Ireland, Gordon, *North America: Boundaries, Possessions and Conflicts in Central and North America and the Caribbean,* Harvard University Press, 1941.

James, Preston, *Latin America,* Odyssey Press, 1959.

James, Preston, "Toward a Further Understanding of the Regional Concept," *Annals of the Association of American Geographers,* September 1952, pp. 195–222.

Jones, Clarence F. and Ellen Churchill Semple, *American History and Its Geographic Conditions,* Houghton Mifflin Co., 1933.

Kendrew, W. G., *The Climates of the Continents,* Oxford University Press, 1953.

Lobeck, A. K., *Physiographic Diagram of North America,* C. S. Hammond and Co., 1950.

Lobeck, A. K., *Geologic Map of the United States,* C. S. Hammond and Co., 1941.

Lobeck, A. K., *Physiographic Diagram of the United States,* C. S. Hammond and Co., 1957.

Marbut, C. F., *Soils of the United States,* U. S. Department of Agriculture, 1935.

Meigs, Peveril, "Water Problems of the United States," *Geographical Review,* July 1952, pp. 346–366.

Olmstead, Clarence W., "American Orchard and Vineyard Regions," *Economic Geography,* July 1956, pp. 189–236.

Patton, Donald, "The Traffic Pattern on American Inland Waterways," *Economic Geography,* January 1956, pp. 29–37.

Platt, Robert S., "Field Approach to Regions," *Annals of the Association of American Geographers,* Vol. 25, 1935, pp. 153–174.

Price, Edward T., "A Geographic Analysis of the White-Negro-Indian Racial Mixtures in Eastern United States," *Annals of the Association of American Geographers,* June 1953, pp. 138–155.

Putnam, Donald F., and Donald P. Kerr, *A Regional Geography of Canada,* J. M. Dent and Sons, 1956.

Renner, G. T., and M. P. Renner, "Regionalism in American Life," *Teachers College Record,* Vol. 43, February 1942, pp. 337–357.

Robinson, J. Lewis, and M. Josephine Robinson, *The Geography of Canada,* Longmans, Green and Co., 1950.

Shantz, H. L., and Raphael Zon, *Natural Vegetation of the United States,* U. S. Department of Agriculture, 1924.

Stewart, George R., *U. S. 40: Cross Section of the United States of America,* Houghton Mifflin Co., 1953.

Thomas, Morley K., *Climatological Atlas of Canada,* National Research Council and Meteorological Division, Department of Transport, Canada, 1953.

Ullman, Edward L., "The Railroad Pattern of the United States," *Geographical Review,* April 1949, pp. 242–256.

Ullman, Edward L., *U. S. Railroads: Classified According to Capacity and Relative Importance* (map), Simmons-Boardman Publishing Corp., 30 Church Street, New York.

U. S. Department of Agriculture, Yearbook of Agriculture: *Soils and Men,* 1938; *Climate and Man,* 1941; *Science and Farming,* 1943–47; *Grass,* 1948; *Trees,* 1949; *Crops in Peace and War,* 1951; *Insects,* 1952; *Water,* 1955; *Soil,* 1957; *Land,* 1958.

Van Cleef, Eugene, "Finnish Settlement in Canada," *Geographical Review,* April 1952, pp. 253–266.

Visher, S. S., *Climatic Atlas of the United States,* Harvard University Press, 1954.

Zelinsky, Wilbur, "A Method of Measuring Change in the Distribution of Manufacturing Activity: The United States, 1939–1947," *Economic Geography,* April 1958, pp. 95–126.

2 · Greenland

(Figure 1)

The regional geography of Greenland is relatively simple in comparison to that of other regions of the North American continent. In the first place, Greenland is an island with boundaries much more definite than those of regions lying within the continent. Second, approximately five-sixths of Greenland's surface is covered with ice, and the other one-sixth has a tundra climate. These two facts sharply limit economic development. Third, the island's population is one of the most sparse of any large region in North America. And finally, the occupations of Greenland's people lack the complexity of industries in most continental regions; thus, most geographic relationships are direct and easily understood.

An example of these relationships may be noted in Greenland's location. The island's position relatively near Iceland and the European continent encouraged early exploration and colonization. Settlement occurred in the tenth century, 500 years before Columbus touched islands off North America's southeast coast.

Today, in the age of jet planes, Greenland's location near the top of the world (Figs. 2, 3) makes it an important base for both commercial and military aviation. In fact, the island has become extremely significant to the United States in military strategy. It is probably unfortunate that America did not follow Seward's advice to purchase the island in the 1860's, at the same time Alaska was purchased. Although there has been little difficulty in leasing bases on the Danish island, we could use a quitclaim deed to the northeast rampart as well as the one we hold on the Alaskan outpost to the northwest.

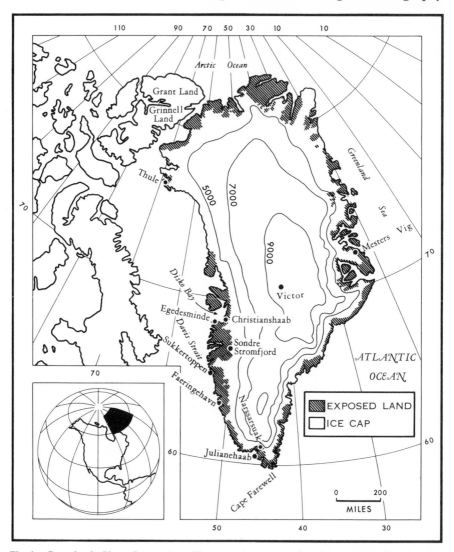

Fig. 1. Greenland: Place Geography. The map shows most locations described in the text. Note that Greenland's icecap rises to high elevations; contours of 5,000, 7,000, and 9,000 feet are somewhat generalized.

Area and Location

Greenland has an area of 840,000 square miles and an icecap large enough, if melted, to raise world sea level more than 25 feet. The island is almost one and one-half times the size of Alaska, largest state in the Union, and over twelve times the size of the six states forming New England.

The world's largest island extends from 60° north to 84° north, a distance of approximately 1,650 miles, as far as the distance between the northern tip of Maine and southern Florida. East-west measurements of the island, at its greatest width, are from 10° 20′ west to 70° 20′ west, or as far as from Boston to Detroit, approximately 700 miles. Greenland's most western point is about due north of Worcester, Massachusetts; and the

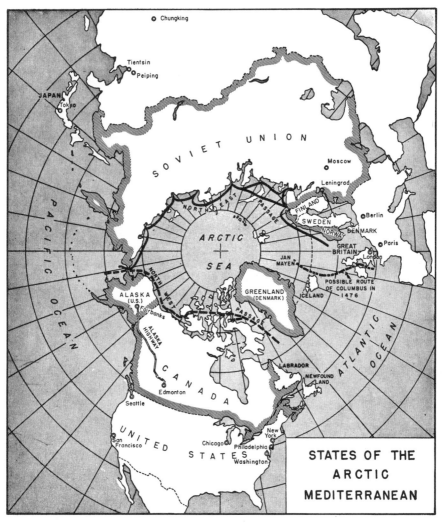

Fig. 2. States of the Arctic Mediterranean. The short distance between Eurasia and Greenland may be noted on this polar map projection. Greenland's location gives it advantages for use as a commercial and military air station. (Source: Etzel Pearcy, *World Political Geography,* Thomas Y. Crowell Co., 1957.)

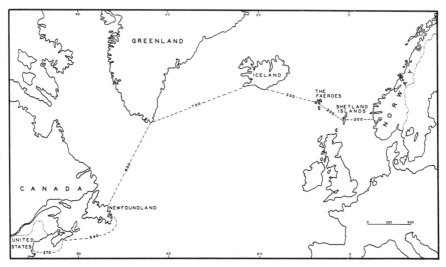

Fig. 3. Islands as Stepping Stones. During World War II, United States military defense considered the possibility of German invasion of North America by way of the stepping-stone route. At present, Greenland, Newfoundland, and Iceland serve as useful military and commercial air bases.

island's eastern extremity, farther east than the eastern tip of Iceland, is almost directly poleward from Cape Clear, Ireland, and Liberia in western Africa. The southern latitude is approximately the same as that of Seward, Alaska; and the northern tip is within 400 miles of the North Pole.

Population

As previously indicated, Greenland is one of the most sparsely populated lands. If population were evenly distributed, each of the approximately 25,000 people would have about 40 square miles of elbow room. But people are not evenly distributed.

Most of the population live along the southwest coast where more than 100 small settlements are located. The 1951 census lists 180 settlements with 22,095 people on the southwest coast, 29 settlements with 1,660 persons on the east coast, and only 12 settlements and 363 people on the north coast.

The most favorable town sites are along the margins and flats of fiords, or on the leeward sides of islands and peninsulas. Such situations offer protection, drainage, opportunities for trade, and most important of all, close proximity to good fishing grounds. For example, settlers in Julianehaab and Godthaab took advantage of pocketlike basins in the slightly elevated seaward edge of long, slender-shaped, rugged peninsulas. These towns have a south to southeast-facing exposure, which offers a greater amount of solar warmth and direct light. Each of the two settlements occupies a river mouth site. Here the distribution of dwellings is influenced in part by the axes of the rivers and the flatness of the river mouth area, and in part by the amount of relatively flat land bordering fiord margins adjacent to deep water.

Surface Features

Greenland's icecap is shaped like a shield, with its crest a little east of the longitudinal center of the island. The ice is thicker in the south than in the north, and the largest continuous areas of land not covered by snow occur in Pearyland on the poleward section. This situation results from the fact that snowfall is heavier in the south than in the north.

Over large areas, the glacier is relatively flat, but there are crevasses, hummocks, and deep valleys cut by intermittent surface streams which disappear in englacial and subglacial passages. Here and there, nunataks stand out above the ice, and their sun-heated rocks melt water to produce ice gullies. Icebergs break away from valley glaciers (Fig. 4) at the heads

Fig. 4. The Birthplace of Icebergs. Along the coast, Greenland's valley glaciers break off as icebergs, which menace North Atlantic shipping. The "unsinkable" Danish ship *Hedtoft,* with 95 passengers and crew, sank after hitting a Greenland iceberg in January 1959. (Courtesy Robert F. Ashe.)

of fiords; some bergs are as tall as ten-story buildings and fall thunderously into the sea from ice fronts that terminate in steep escarpments.

Ice-free coastal areas have been scoured and plucked by the ice. Steep slopes are girdled with cirques and U-shaped valleys. Most of the marginal valleys are filled with glaciers still actively scouring the lowlands. Talus at the foot of exposed earth slopes gives evidence of active physical weathering.

The island rim is extremely irregular, with peninsulas, fiords, islands, and skerries. Flat surfaces are limited to the heads of fiords, where glacio-fluviatile sediments are being deposited. Local relief shows more variety on the east coast than upon the west. Mountains are higher, plateau surfaces show more dissection, fiords are deeper and steeper walled, and the narrow lowland shoreline lies almost at right angles to the steep coastal-facing escarpments. In spite of these local differences, the overall work of ice gives major uniformity to island surface features.

Climate

Like the topography, the island's climate shows considerable unity. (*a*) The entire island lies in high latitudes. (*b*) Most of the surface is covered with ice that rises in places to 10,000 feet; the large amount of ice encourages a more or less permanent high atmospheric pressure, and this glacial anticyclone sends out intermittent surges of cold air over the island's coastal rim. Downdraft winds, flowing out radially from the highest slopes, result from the increasing density of chilled surface air. (*c*) Temperatures are consistently low with warmest month averages below 32° F. over the icecap (Fig. 5) and between 32° and 50° F. over ice-free coastal lands. (Fig. 6.) (*d*) Precipitation is meager everywhere, partly because the air is so cold that it cannot hold much moisture. (*e*) Great seasonal contrasts exist between length of day and night (Fig. 7). At Etah, 77° north,

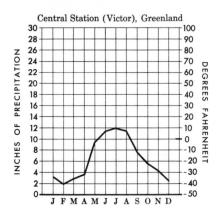

Fig. 5. Central Station (Victor), Greenland (70° 57′ N., 40° 42′ W.; altitude 9,950 feet; mean annual temp. −19° F). Most of Greenland's climate belongs to the Icecap variety, EF, with no month averaging as high as 32° F. Only the temperature is shown on this chart.

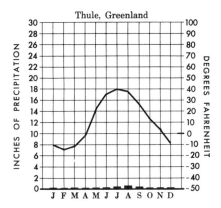

Fig. 6. Thule, Greenland (76° 33′ N., 68° 49′ W.; altitude 121 feet; mean annual temp. 10.7° F.; mean annual precip. 2.55 inches). Almost all of coastal Greenland, to which Thule belongs, is characterized by a Tundra climate, ET, with temperatures for the warmest month averaging between 32° and 50° F.

the sun remains below the horizon constantly between October 21 and February 21st; and even at the Arctic Circle, which crosses southern Greenland, there is at least one 24-hour period of darkness and one day with 24 hours of sunlight.

Obviously climatic differences exist between the equatorward and

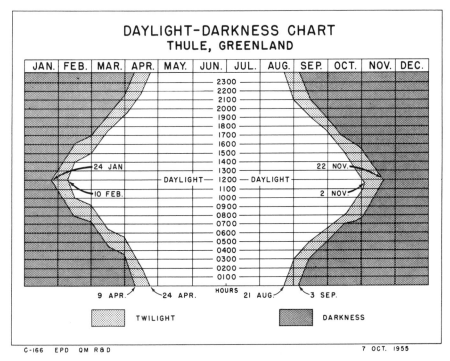

Fig. 7. Daylight and Darkness, Thule. The 24-hour day and the 24-hour night are important factors in Greenland's geography. (Courtesy Headquarters Quartermaster Research and Development Command, Natick, Mass.)

poleward sections of an island with a 1,650-mile north-south extent, even if all Greenland lies within the high latitudes; and, of course, climatic contrasts exist between the icecap and the exposed land. Koppen and Trewartha (Fig. 8, Chapter 1) classify the climate of the former as EF and the climate of the latter as ET.

Vegetation and Soils

Tundra vegetation occurs only on ice-free surfaces. Stunted trees, including birch, willow, alder, juniper, and mountain ash may appear in the south among hardy grasses which mature during the short growing season. Farther north, mosses and lichens occupy large areas and trees are less numerous and smaller. In the northern coastal lands, vegetation is less consistent, with fewer species, and with a lower order of plants; all vegetation is influenced by low temperatures, scanty precipitation, and limited soil.

Soils are of little economic importance in a region where climate discourages agricultural development. They may be classified as tundra soils with much semifluid material resting on permafrost; soils are low in humus, leached, generally acid, and poorly drained.

Sequence Occupancy

The Eskimo Period. Prior to European settlement at the end of the tenth century, Greenland was truly the land of the Eskimos. These primitive but ingenious people supported themselves primarily by hunting and fishing. Seal, walrus, and narwhal were staple articles of diet, supplemented by arctic hare, the flesh and eggs of sea fowl, fish, and other items. Animals from land and sea furnished materials for harpoons, spears, boats, and other hunting equipment, as well as for clothing; stone was used for knives, spear points, etc. Shelters were constructed of stone, turf, driftwood, and even from blocks of snow and ice. Seal oil was used for light and heat. Relationships between man and the environment were clear and direct. There was little choice in gaining a livelihood, and geographic determinism featured Eskimo life of the pre-tenth-century period.

European Settlement, First Period, 1000 to 1500 A.D. During the latter portion of the tenth century, people from Iceland, under the leadership of Eric the Red, established settlements along the southwest coast of Greenland. They brought dairy cattle, sheep, goats, and horses which were fed on hay and forage raised during the short summers. Farms were established on nearly level to gently rolling ground at the inner edges of the fiords. In places, streams from the interior entered the fiords, depositing sediments useful for planting hardy farm crops; these waterways also furnished fresh water and contained fresh water fish.

Steep valley walls gave protection from cold winds occurring frequently at higher elevations. Fiord location gave access to the sea, a contact useful for communication with the homeland and one that provided fish and other sea life necessary for food, shelter, clothing, and export. Shelter for man and beast was fashioned from local stone, turf, and drift wood. Exports included butter, cheese, fish, seal oil, skins, furs, and walrus tusks. Imports featured knives, repairs for boats, breeding animals, malt, flour, and other foodstuffs.

Regular communications with Europe continued for a few centuries, but were discontinued in the first part of the sixteenth century. When the second European settlement occurred early in the eighteenth century, only the abandoned villages remained. Settlers may have been killed, starved to death, or mingled completely with the Eskimos.

The Second European Settlement, 1721–1920. In 1721, Hans Egede, a Danish missionary, was the leader of an organized group of colonists who settled in the southern part of the island. Shortly afterwards, in 1743, the Danish government established trading posts where blubber, seal oil, furs, skins, fish, eiderdown, and other export products could be sold. Denmark continued to take a great interest in the colony and carefully handled government action in favor of natives and colonists. As a result, settlement was encouraged and population increased. As with previous settlements, most of the economic life continued to focus on the sea. Until about 1920, sealing remained almost as important as fishing. Both activities contributed significantly to an exchange economy that had been of little importance before European settlement.

Modern Greenland

Strategic Location. World War II brought one of several changes that make life in Greenland today different from that in the island of yesterday. In early 1940, Hitler sent reconnaissance planes and ships to study Greenland meteorology. Since cyclonic storms in middle and high latitudes move from west to east, predicting European weather is more successful with information from a western outpost like Greenland. The Allies quickly learned of German activity, and Denmark granted rights to the United States for the establishment of weather stations and air bases.

After the war, in 1951, Denmark and the United States made a treaty that gave the Americans use of bases at Thule, Sondre Stromfjord, and Narssarsuak. Greenland contractors and laborers with first-hand experience in Arctic construction did most of the building at the various bases. Previously these workers had constructed meteorological stations for the International Civil Air Organization. Workers prepared electricity and water facilities, factories, and houses for the new towns. In 1954 and 1955, nearly 8,000 men were constructing bases at Narssarsuak, in south Greenland, and in Sondre Stromfjord, in the central part of the island. In 1956, large-scale building work started on the American base at Thule.

People in the United States were somewhat surprised at prices paid American labor who assisted in building the Thule base. Common labor received as high as $13,000 a year. This situation emphasizes (*a*) the influence of isolation, sparse population, and an unfavorable climate upon wages; and (*b*) that labor is an extremely mobile factor in industry.

Denmark has built a naval station in southwest Greenland for two main purposes: for defense, and to patrol the rich fishing grounds that attract hundreds of trawlers from almost every European nation.

Continuance of the cold war with the Soviets has made the Free World increasingly aware of Greenland's strategic location. Thule is only 2,200 miles from Moscow, and approximately the same distance from Russia's industrial heartland. This base provides an eastern anchor for a North American radar screen guarding against a sneak air attack; and Thule could be used for launching an attack against an enemy.

Another change related to Greenland's strategic location concerns the interest in peaceful intercontinental air transport. The island lies across the shortest route between northern Europe and parts of the American Pacific Coast region. Recently commercial air lines began to make use of this fact. Scandinavian Airlines opened a route over Greenland in 1954, and maintains regular service from Copenhagen, via Sondre Stromfjord (where an airport hotel has been built) and Winnipeg to Los Angeles. A saving of approximately 1,000 miles and two or three hours flying time is possible over this route. Although storms may rage over the icecap and along the West Greenland coast, use of alternative landing grounds in Labrador and Iceland is seldom necessary.

Scandinavian Airlines, first scheduled Europe-to-Tokyo plane to travel the north polar route, arrived in Tokyo the last of February 1957. A sister airplane starting from Tokyo for Copenhagen passed the Tokyo-bound plane near the pole. The elapsed time, including the refueling, was 32 hours and 31 minutes. This schedule compares with 52 hours for the lines on the older Tokyo-Copenhagen route via south Asia.

Canadian Airlines have also established a route from Vancouver to Amsterdam via Sondre Stromfjord, and probably other airlines will soon follow.

Fishing. The two changes just described are man made, but another important change involves an alteration in the physical environment. The North Atlantic Ocean bathing Greenland's southwest coast began to grow warmer in the 1920's. This encouraged a poleward movement of seals and a northward migration of cod. Prior to the twentieth century, the seal was a dominant factor in Greenland's economy. It was a source of food, clothing, oil for light and heat, and bone for implements. Sealing was a subsistence occupation and it provided the hunter with so many of his necessities that he needed little contact with the commercial world. Now the seal has moved away from Greenland's major centers of population.

The present-day emphasis upon cod fishing differs from the former sealing economy; commercial fishing requires a different set of tools and techniques from those employed in catching seals; and since the fisherman cannot live directly from the cod as he did from the seal—now he sells his catch of fish—he has learned about a money economy.

Today, Greenland fishermen use motor boats more than kayaks. They burn petroleum products instead of seal oil. At Faeringehavn are located storage tanks of the Greenland Oil Company. From this depot small craft carry kerosene, diesel fuel, gasoline, lubricants, etc., to many communities. In 1953, 200 foreign fishing vessels called at Greenland ports for fuel and supplies. Not long before no Greenland harbor would have been open to such trade; for Greenland long was a closed colony, deliberately isolated to protect its then-generally-unsophisticated people from exploitation. Now, under careful government regulation, modern Greenland welcomes visitors on legitimate business.

Until the 1950's the native cod-fishing industry was limited to local waters navigable for small boats. Now, with the help of loans the government is encouraging investment in larger vessels that are suitable for extended cruising. There are local boat building and repair yards as well as fishing stations with filleting and freezing plants. Fishermen are also urged to exploit the 1948 discovery of huge shrimp and prawn beds in Disko Bay. Shrimp canneries have been built, and the one at Christianshaab handles several hundred tons each year. Filleting factories may be seen at Egedesminde and Sukkertoppen, where cod are processed.

Other Industries. By 1955, more than 20,000 sheep grazed the summer pastures in the south; and attempts are being made to establish a reindeer industry by importing breeding stock from Norway. There is little soil for agriculture, but a few home gardens may be noted. It is possible that trees can be grown in selected locations. In 1955, 15,000 seedlings of selected hardy species were set out; if this experiment succeeds, Greenland may some day have a small but badly needed local supply of lumber, every stick of which today is imported.

A state-owned mine, located in the northwest, supplies coal, the principal fuel for houses and public buildings. A cryolite quarry at Ivigtut has long provided mineral exports for making aluminum, but these cryolite deposits in the southwest of Greenland are nearing exhaustion, and bauxite has taken the place of cryolite in aluminum production almost everywhere.

There are known deposits of lead, copper, zinc, iron, wolframite, and graphite; and lead and zinc mining is now in the development stage at

Mesters Vig in the northeast. These deposits were discovered in 1948 and are being exploited by a corporation, the Nordisk Mineselskab (Northern Mining Company) with Danish, Swedish, and Canadian capital. Shaft mining is necessary and enormous machine rooms have been quarried out of solid underground rock. Ice closes coastal waters most of the year, but ore shipments can be made during the summer months. The first minerals moved out in 1956 and plans have been made to ship 20,000 tons of lead and zinc concentrates annually for several years. Cargo is carried by modern ice breakers, a highly specialized type of transport. Since a great deal of mineral exploration is in progress throughout the island, it is probable that mining may develop an important source of wealth.

Government, Education, and Health. Greenland is no longer a colony of Denmark, but in 1953 became an integral part of that country. Greenlanders do not like to be called Eskimos. It should be noted that the original population, which Hans Egede met when he first started his work of colonization more than 200 years ago, has since received a large admixture of Danish blood. During the first 150 years of the colonization many Danish craftsmen, coopers, carpenters, smiths, and seamen were sent to Greenland. As a rule they married native girls and, as was usual at that time, had a lot of children. These children were given a good home and a good upbringing. The descendants of these mixed marriages made their mark on the population during succeeding centuries, so that now there are few pure-blooded Eskimos. Most Greenlanders can claim both Danish and Eskimo ancestry.

Greenlanders point with pride to progress in education and health. Illiteracy hardly exists. Since 1925, school attendance at elementary schools has been compulsory for children from 7 to 14 (Fig. 8); libraries and secondary schools have been built in the larger communities. The lower schools are taught in the native language, but children learn Danish as well; this is done because of difficulties in translating general literature and technical writing into the Greenlandic language.

Undoubtedly as a result of the geographic factor of isolation, Greenlanders have been disastrously susceptible to some common infectious diseases occasionally carried into the country from abroad. But they have been active in improving both health and sanitation. The expansion of medical services has been pressed steadily and new hospital construction was the largest single item in the 1953 budget. All in all Denmark should be commended for its enlightened stewardship of Greenland.

Summary and Conclusions

In summary, the world's largest island shows regional unity in surface features, which have been and continue to be shaped by glaciation; in

Fig. 8. Greenland School Children. All Greenland children between the ages of 7 and 14 attend school, and provision is made for further education. Schools are coeducational. These youngsters are about 12 years old. (Courtesy Danish Information Service.)

climate, controlled largely by high latitude, high altitude, and an icecap; in vegetation, which, where present at all, belongs to primitive types stunted by cold and physiological drought; and in soils, which may be described as some of the world's poorest.

Regional unity also occurs in island population. As previously indicated, most Greenlanders carry both native and Danish blood in their veins, and the few Eskimos of the far north may soon be replaced by descendants from Eskimo and European parents, both of whom are now working on military installations.

Human use of the land and adjoining sea shows considerable uniformity in an emphasis upon simple economic activities. Catching cod and other marine organisms may be classed as a simple extractive industry; mining belongs to the same class; the processing of local raw materials is manufacturing of the simplest type; and sheep grazing shows little agricultural complexity.

In case sea temperatures return to a colder regime, cod and seal may migrate equatorward and economic emphasis may return more to sealing. If land temperatures change to a colder cycle, the present interest in livestock may lessen. However, Greenland's location is not so variable as land and ocean temperatures, and military and commercial aviation are probably here to stay. That phase of the island economy is likely to expand rather than contract. Moreover, man's need for minerals is growing rapidly, and further search may locate valuable metals to aid in an expanding minerals market.

QUESTIONS, EXERCISES, AND PROBLEMS

1. Why is Greenland a good area for introducing the subject of regional geography? Summarize conditions that make for regional unity. Could the island be divided into subregions?

2. Compare the location, area, population, surface features, climates, vegetation, and occupations with those of your home area. How would clothing, diet, housing, recreation, transportation, schools, health, light and darkness, heating, etc., differ from the conditions in your local environment? Make a comparison of both the physical and man-made environments of Greenland and Antarctica.

3. Prepare a climatic chart for your own city and compare it with the Greenland climatic charts. Point out any similarities and differences and the causes for them.

4. Trace the sequence occupancy of the island from the discovery period to the present time. How have aviation and location influenced island economy? Point out relationships to the geographic environment in the fishing, mineral, and animal industries. Describe military activities and their relation to the geographic environment.

5. What are the opportunities for farming in Greenland; for forestry; for manufacturing; for commerce?

6. Read one of Peter Freuchen's books on Greenland and the Arctic, or the works of some other well-known writer on the Arctic, and note relationships between man's activities and the geographic environment.

7. Identify the following: Seward, nunatak, fiord, skerries, littoral, solifluction, geographic determinism, Eric the Red, Hans Egede, kayak, cryolite, cirque, Thule, Godthaab, Julianehaab, Mesters Vig, Christianshaab, Sondre Stromfjord, Narssarsuak, Sukkertoppen, Egedesminde, Disko Bay, and Cape Farewell.

SELECTED REFERENCES

Boyd, Louise A., and others, *The Coast of Northeast Greenland: With Hydrographic Studies in the Greenland Sea,* American Geographical Society, 1948.

Boyd, Louise A., and others, *The Fiord Region of East Greenland,* American Geographical Society, 1935.

Danish Government, Statistical Department, *Denmark, Statistical Yearbook,* 1958.

Danish Ministry of Foreign Affairs, *Greenland,* 1958.

Friis, Herman R., "Greenland: A Productive Arctic Colony," *Economic Geography,* 1936, pp. 75–92.

Headquarters Quartermaster Research and Development Command, *Climatic Information Sources for Greenland, Research Study Report RER-11,* U. S. Army, Natick, Mass., January 1957.

Headquarters Quartermaster Research and Development Command, *Handbook of Thule, Greenland, Environment, Technical Report EP-34,* U. S. Army, Natick, Mass., 1956.

Howarth, David, "Secrets of the Unknown War," *Saturday Evening Post,* Aug. 3, 1957.

Lloyd, Trevor, "Progress in West Greenland," *Journal of Geography,* Vol. 49, 1950, pp. 319–328.

Miller, David H., "The Influence of Snow Cover on Local Climate in Greenland," *Journal of Meteorology,* Vol. 13, No. 1, February 1956, pp. 112–120.

Powers, William E., "Polar Eskimos of Greenland and Their Environment," *Journal of Geography,* Vol. 49, 1950, pp. 186–192.

Roseberry, Cecil R., "Men Against the Icecap," *Saturday Evening Post,* April 7, 1956.

Therkilsen, Kjeld Rask, "Danish Achievement in Greenland," *Progress,* Autumn, 1956.

3 · The Tundra of Canada and Alaska

Most of us, when we think of deserts, call to mind wide expanses of hot, sunny, dry lands of middle or low latitudes with large sand dunes and a scarcity of vegetation. But if we use the term *desert* in its botanical sense—an area of sparse and highly specialized plant life—we can apply the name just as appropriately to the poleward sections of North America north of the tree line.

The Tundra resembles low and middle latitude deserts in several ways. These regions are similar in (*a*) low precipitation; (*b*) scanty vegetation; (*c*) limited agriculture, manufacturing and commerce; (*d*) considerable dependence of man upon animals; (*e*) sparse population—in some places nomadic, in other places centered around mines or military installations; and (*f*) a relatively primitive stage of civilization, especially in the more isolated sections.

Location and Boundaries

The equatorward boundary of the Tundra is the poleward limit of tree growth or the 50° F. isotherm for the warmest month (Fig. 1). In northern Canada, between the Alaskan-Canadian boundary and the 110th meridian west, the Tundra occupies a narrow coastal strip approximately 100 miles wide; this strip broadens to several hundred miles as it approaches the western shore of Hudson Bay. It continues its broad north-south extent to include the Ungava Peninsula and that portion of the Labrador Peninsula east of Ungava Bay. On the Labrador coast, tundra takes over from forest because cold winds off the Labrador current are unfavorable to tree growth. Islands north of Hudson Bay, including Baffin, Victoria, Banks, Ellesmere, and Baird belong to the Tundra region.

Alaska's triangular-shaped Tundra plain is only 15 to 20 miles wide at the Alaska-Canada boundary. Near Barrow the lowland reaches a 200-mile north-south width; but it narrows again near Cape Lisburne.

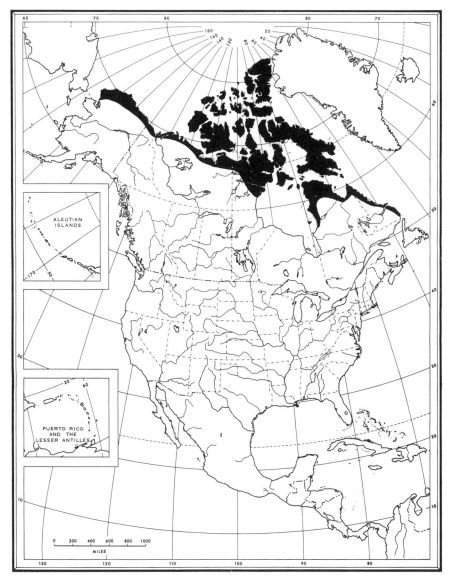

Fig. 1. The Tundra of Canada and Alaska. The southern boundary of the Tundra approximates that of the 50° isotherm for the warmest month.

Surface Features and Climate

Most of the Tundra is a lowland plain with such slight relief that it is difficult for the unaided eye to judge which way the land slopes. In some sections hummocky surfaces do occur. These hummocks, all of low eleva-

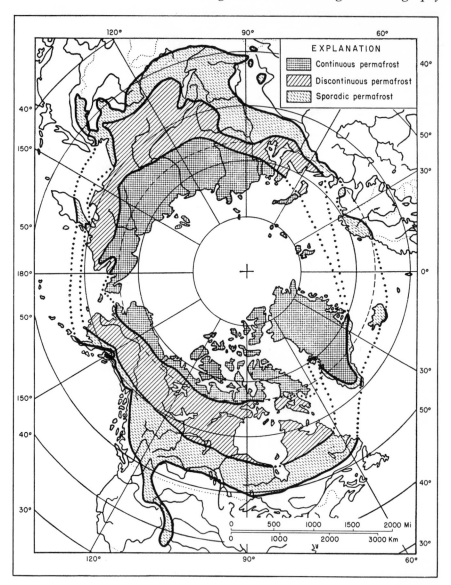

Fig. 2.   Contemporary Extent of Permafrost in the Northern Hemisphere.   (Source: Richard Foster Flint, *Glacial and Pleistocene Geology,* John Wiley and Sons, 1957.)

tion, may show a varied pattern of circles, polygons, or strips. Mounds several feet high, called pingos, result from the squeezing of layers of unfrozen soil between frozen top soil and the underlying permafrost (Fig. 2). Pressures may be so great that when release comes, a hill shoots up.

In some parts of the Tundra, mechanical weathering, particularly frost action, may shatter and dissect large areas of bare rock. Thousands of lakes and swamps are scattered over the surface, contributing wide expanses of water during the short summer, and ice during the long winter. It may seem strange that the Arctic, with an average annual precipitation of about 10 inches, has numerous lakes, marshes, and swamps. But water surfaces result primarily from poor drainage encouraged by permafrost.

Climate has a greater influence upon the landscape than that of any other factor in the physical environment. Climatic change encouraged Pleistocene glaciation, which smoothed the more rolling preglacial topography over wide areas. Low temperatures (Fig. 3) probably caused much of the permafrost, which interferes with the construction and operation of bridges, roads, and buildings. Enormous stretches of surface water encourage millions of mosquitoes (Fig. 4). In summer there are several times as many mosquitoes per square mile over at least two-thirds of the Tundra as there are over an equivalent area in the tropics. Polar climates also sharply limit vegetation, and make all but impossible any significant development of agriculture.

High latitude causes a low sun in both summer and winter. The noonday sun is never closer than within 43° of the zenith even at the Arctic Circle; and it is 90° from the zenith on one day of the year at 66½° north. Low altitude of the sun at all times and short daylight periods or no daylight at all during the winter half-year cause some of the world's coldest mean annual temperatures.

Precipitation is low because (*a*) cold air can hold but little moisture; (*b*) descending air of the more or less permanent high pressures discourages precipitation; and (*c*) there are few cyclonic storms and little convectional activity. Most of the precipitation falls in summer.

Polar climates have high winds during the cold season. These are

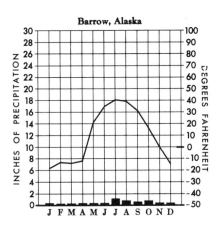

Fig. 3. Barrow Alaska (71° 15′ N., 156° 12′ W.; altitude 10 feet; mean annual temp. 10° F.; mean annual precip. 5.6 inches). Barrow temperatures and precipitation illustrate high-latitude desert climates. Note that no month averages as high as 50° F.

Fig. 4. Mosquitoes on Army Caps, Churchill, June 1947. Churchill is located in the transition zone between forest and tundra. The ground is permanently frozen a short distance beneath the surface. For a good description of mosquito problems see "Study of the Biology and Control of Biting Flies," *Arctic,* April 1950. (Courtesy C. R. Twinn, Arctic Institute of North America Collection.)

likely to be stronger than winds in the great conifer forests to the south, partly because there is little vegetation to obstruct the gales. High winds and low precipitation keep large areas entirely free from snow.

The huge size and general uniformity of the Tundra make it an important source region for polar continental air. This air mass greatly affects all Canadian climates as well as those of the United States (Fig. 12, Chapter 1).

Soils and Vegetation

Since climate alone limits agricultural production, soils are of little significance. Most mature soils are low in plant food, leached of mineral constituents, and become fluid during the short season when temperatures average slightly above freezing. Glacial erosion left broad expanses of bare rocks.

Plant life resembles that of the dry deserts in several respects. Leaves are small; root systems may expand in a horizontal direction like those of the desert; the plant makes this adjustment to take advantage of thawing, which reaches only a few inches below the surface during the summer. Plants are compact, stunted, and make haste to complete their life cycle as quickly as possible during the short growing season.

As an adaptation to the short Arctic summer, almost all truly Arctic plants are perennial and develop the next year's flowering buds before the onset of winter. Summer is too short for annual species to complete a life cycle in one season. The failure of a single seed crop might exterminate the species in a local population. Most Arctic plants require many years from germination to the first flowering. Many do not depend entirely on seed production for their propagation, but are protected against unfavorable seasons by various means of vegetative reproduction.

In the Arctic there are no climbing plants, plants that sting or poison, nor any that are protected by spines or thorns. The implication, of course, is that such protection is not needed. Many are xerophytes, that is, plants adapted to withstand prolonged drought by having rather small, leathery leaves, often covered by densely matted hairs that provide a feltlike covering for the stomata.

Arctic plants numbering more than a thousand species were identified by the beginning of the twentieth century—250 species of mosses, 330 of lichens, and 760 of flowering plants. Flowering plants outnumber the non-flowering, and in tonnage the preponderance of flowering is still greater. Of the most northerly of the flowering plants, many found within a few hundred yards of the north coasts of the most northerly islands, the following have been cited by various authorities: bluegrass, timothy, goldenrod, dandelion, buttercup, poppy, primrose, anemone, alpine chickweed, purple saxifrage, heather, arnica ferns, shinleaf, bluebell, rhododendron, cranberry, curlewberry, and catspaw.

Plants in the Arctic do not grow haphazardly among one another. Those having similar requirements as to soil, moisture, and wind or snow protection generally grow together in more or less well-defined communities. Four such major plant communities may be recognized in the North American Arctic, each capable of subdivision into a number of more or less distinct associations, the relative importance of which depends upon the geographic environment. These include (*a*) the rock desert or fell-field communities which may be subdivided into rock desert, unstable screes and stone creeps, and gravelley river flats and fans; (*b*) Tundra communities whose subdivisions include dwarf-shrub heath, lichen and moss heath, grassland, willow and alder thickets, marsh and wet tundra, and snow flushes; (*c*) strand communities with three major subtypes: lagoon and salt marsh subject to floods, sand dunes and gravel beaches, and rocky shores; and (*d*) vegetation of fresh waters, including ponds, lakes, brooks, and rivers.

Perhaps the most striking of these communities is the rock desert, which occupies vast areas of rock-strewn, barren flats that from the air look entirely devoid of vegetation, but which, each summer for a short time, may be transformed into veritable rock gardens. The tundra community, which is best developed on the mainland, differs from the rock desert by having a more continuous plant cover; some of it is grasslike in character and provides grazing for caribou and musk oxen. Strand communities and fresh water vegetation furnish but little feed for grazing animals.

Plants and Human Economy

Only a few native plants show a direct relationship to man's economy. None of the woody species is large enough for constructional use by the Eskimo, who, formerly at least, obtained what little wood he needed chiefly from driftwood. However, heather and berry bushes, stunted willows, alder, and ground birch are used for cooking; and nearly all the larger lichens are highly inflamable when dry and may be used to cook food. Raw peat, particularly heath turf but also partly decomposed sphagnum moss, is available nearly everywhere, and is an important source for fuel.

Indirectly vegetation is of great importance to man because, as previously indicated, it furnishes feed for grazing animals. Seeds, winter buds and roots, and stems or leaves of many species are eaten by birds and small rodents that, in turn, constitute the feed of some of the fur-bearing animals. Likewise, the comparatively rich marine plant life indirectly furnishes feed for the sea mammals long so important in the economy of the Eskimo.

Among the Eskimos, the dependence on plant food varies from group to group, according to tradition and according to what natural vegetation is available; thus, to the most northerly Canadian tribes, the use of vegetable food is purely incidental and largely limited to the partly fermented and predigested content of the rumen of caribou, whereas in the diet of the Eskimos of Alaska, Labrador, and Greenland, vegetable food constitutes a regular, if not very large, item. Moreover, it is a valuable source of ascorbic acid and thiamin.

Animal Life

Canada (Fig. 5). Throughout the Tundra, wild life is important to the native economy. Both the Indian and the Eskimo trade fur for the white man's goods, and eat the flesh of both land and sea animals. Natives use skins of large mammals for clothing and bedding. They make harpoon lines and ropes from hides and intestines of various animals. They use ivory, teeth, bones, and sinews for many purposes.

At present, with Eskimo hunting efficiency increased through the use

Fig. 5. Dog Team in the Tundra. Dog teams are often the safest way—and sometimes the only way—of getting from place to place in the far north. Beyond the tree line, teams may be hitched fan fashion, as in the above picture taken at Baker Lake, Northwest Territories. (Courtesy Department of Northern Affairs and National Resources, Canada.)

of firearms, it is most important that wild life resources be utilized carefully. Both Canadian and United States governments have enacted laws to preserve wild life and to make sure that it is used only by those who need to exploit it. One of the most important of regulations is called the Northwest Territories Game Ordinance. This law controls the taking of mammals in the Northwest Territories, and, under it, vast areas have been set aside as game preserves. The Arctic Islands Game Preserve, for example, contains 772,302 square miles of land. Over all the Arctic islands only natives or half-breeds can hunt, with the exception that scientific permits may be granted under special conditions for the taking of animals by other persons, and in real emergencies game can be taken by anyone. Other important regulations include the Migratory Birds Convention Act and the Fisheries Act.

The most valuable land mammal in the Canadian Northwest Territories for Indian and Eskimos is the barren-ground caribou, *Rangifer arcticus* (Fig. 6). It provides them with food, and its skin excels that of all other mammals for winter clothing and sleeping robes. Its meat is excellent, either fresh or dried; its antlers and bones provide material for tools and implements; its sinews are used for sewing and other purposes; and its fat is used for fuel and food. Natives even eat the brains and marrows of caribou as well as the contents of their stomachs. The largest herds are found on the mainland and thousands migrate from one seasonal range to another. In summer most caribou feed on the barrens, but in winter they browse in the wooded sections to the south. On the northern islands, natives hunt a small light-colored animal, Peary's caribou.

Before the advent of modern firearms, the musk ox was an important source of food and clothing. This large gregarious animal, whose thick coat is a defense against both winter cold and summer insects, is not as migratory as the caribou; but he can forage under winter snow just as well. With heavy horns, great strength, agility, and a shoulder to shoulder defense, he can fight any animal except man. Today, he is seldom seen except on the Arctic Archipelago.

Among the marine mammals, several varieties of seals contribute significantly to Eskimo economy. Fish life is also plentiful; species may not be so numerous as in the tropics, but quantity will compare favorably. Large numbers of insects afford plenty of feed for thousands of ducks, geese, and other migratory birds, particularly in summer.

The Fur Trade. Economic statistics for the entire Tundra region as a unit are difficult to obtain, but those for the Northwest Territories, which

Fig. 6. Caribou in Yukon Territory. Caribou still supply food and other necessities for the natives. This herd has been known to cross the Richardson Mountains, in the background, and to appear west of Aklavik in the Northwest Territories. (Courtesy D. A. Munro, Department of Northern Affairs and National Resources.)

make up much of the region although including some of the Taiga, provide useful information. The Territories' fur trade averages about \$2,000,000 annually, which amounts to about 7½ per cent of the total Canadian catch. Although furs were the most important commodity in the Northwest Territories from the latter part of the seventeenth century to 1939, minerals now exceed animal products in value.

Muskrats lead the fur-bearing animals of the Northwest Territories in value of pelts. Nature has created a fine habitat for them in the complex of lakes and rivers of the Mackenzie River delta. Rat feed is plentiful, and despite an annual harvest of about a half million skins, these animals have maintained their numbers well. Natives also trap beaver, mink, ermine, marten, colored fox, lynx, otter, squirrel, wolf, wolverine, bear, and white fox.

For a long while, the white fox was one of the few products that the Eskimo could trade for white men's food, clothing, utensils and other equipment. But in the decade 1942–52 prices showed a steady decline. Fifty thousand pelts brought \$1,317,575 in 1942 and the same number brought \$387,841 ten years later. Blue foxes, a color phase of the white fox, are found in the same Arctic areas as white foxes at a ratio of about one to one hundred.

Experience throughout Canada has shown that without conservation the beaver, which was the mainstay of the earliest fur trade, can be exterminated quickly. On the other hand, under careful management beaver numbers can be built up rapidly to a point where a good catch can be taken annually without danger of depletion. With this in mind, the trapping of beaver has been restricted since the autumn of 1945. High prices during the recent years have encouraged the trapping of mink; although an increase has been shown in the numbers caught during 1950–52, it is evident that mink numbers have declined considerably. In the period 1851–1956, the average annual marten take exceeded 60,000 pelts. Excessive catches soon decimated this valuable fur bearer and called for a ban on trapping.

The severe decline in fur prices during the decade 1945–55 may encourage more Eskimos to take up reindeer herding, something the Canadian government has been trying to stimulate for years. In 1935, a herd of 2,370 animals—from an original 6,000 that started—reached Canada from Alaska after a trek that began in December 1929. Blizzards, intense cold, straying, accidents, and the depredations of wolves delayed progress and caused serious losses in the herd. In 1952, the annual roundup on the 17,900 square mile reserve near Kittigazuit on the Arctic coast brought 7,614 animals free from serious disease. More than that number have been slaughtered for meat and skins.

Further progress in reindeer raising will depend on how many of the natives are willing to accept herding as a way of life. The introduction of a stable ranching industry among a race of nomads is an experiment; but it is an important facet of the whole Canadian effort to safeguard the Eskimo population. Results will be watched carefully.

Alaska. In Alaska, early man lived off land and sea by hunting, trapping, and fishing, occupations that feature the economy of some of his descendants, the Eskimos who now occupy Alaska's western and northern shores. These people trap and hunt walrus, seals, caribou, and fish for food, and the fox, wolverine, and other animals for furs which they dispose of at the trading post. Equipment for trapping and hunting is far different from that of their ancestors. Moreover, Eskimos now get some clothing, food, etc., from modern stores instead of depending entirely upon land and marine life directly for food, clothing, shelter, and equipment.

With the coming of modern civilization, life for Eskimo and Indian natives of Alaska has changed. Some carry on largely as before, but many work in the fishing industries, on military construction jobs, and on other tasks whose demands are far different from those made in their former primeval relationships with nature. When jobs are scarce, they suffer; they do not want to go back to their old ways of living, and yet they are not fully prepared for the new.

Near the close of the nineteenth century, the government imported reindeer from Eurasia in order to give the Eskimo a remunerative occupation of herding grazing animals. For several reasons the venture achieved little success. Most Eskimos are natural hunters, and they do not easily become interested in the exacting occupation of reindeer herding. Herds need to be guided to the better grazing areas to be protected from wild animals, and to be carefully watched to keep them from being assimilated by wild herds of North American caribou. Even if Eskimo interest were adequately developed, shipping and marketing problems are legion. They include lack of suitable docking facilities, the expense of refrigeration space, a short ice-free shipping season, the expense of shipment by aircraft, competition with the average American's preference for beef, and many other problems. Reindeer in Alaska dropped from a high of 600,000 in 1932 to a little more than 26,000 in 1952. It may be some time before a large commercial reindeer industry is developed in the Alaskan tundra.

Minerals

Canada. Large nickel, copper, and other mineral deposits are known resources on the Ungava Peninsula of Labrador. In the summer of 1957, about 50 companies combined their efforts to survey a strip of land 25 miles wide between Wakeham Bay in Hudson Strait and Cape Smith on Hudson Bay. Combined exploration by the large number of companies results from high costs of mineral exploration and development in this isolated area.

A 6,000 foot runway was built near Esker Lake and about 750 men and 1,000 tons of supplies were flown in for mineral exploration activities. One of the better grade nickel occurrences assayed 3.20 per cent nickel and one of the better copper finds assayed 2.14 per cent copper. If the Ungava nickel deposit is as good as it looks on the first exploration, Ungava may offer competition to Sudbury, in the Great Northern Forest Region.

Large occurrences of iron lie near Ungava Bay. Tentative plans have been made to process the medium grade metal near the open pit mines. After processing, it may be stockpiled on Greenland's Rype Island about 500 miles distant across Davis Straits; the Straits are free from ice only about four months of the year, but ocean shipping from Rype Island is possible in all seasons. Thus iron may be moved from Rype Island's good harbor whenever world markets demand it.

Copper was discovered near the mouth of the Coppermine River in 1771. Coal occurs near Aklavik on the Mackenzie delta and at Pond Inlet on Baffin Island. Exploration of nickel in 1950 near Rankin Inlet, on the western shores of Hudson Bay, resulted in staking a number of claims by International Nickel Company. Copper and lead have been discovered near Bathurst Inlet on Coronation Bay. Elsewhere, gold occurrences have been discovered around Hudson Bay's Chesterfield Inlet and Wager Bay. Lead occurs on the Arctic coast around Detention Harbor, and chromite is reported from the Melville Peninsula and the Coppermine River area.

Although large mineral resources have been and will be discovered in the Canadian Tundra, only those that are particularly valuable, easy to extract and refine, and close to economical transport will be developed in the near future; it is a well-known fact that the expenses incurred in bringing in labor, supplies, and equipment, in shipping out products, in heating, and in providing amenities for workers and their families are all factors that weigh heavily against profitable mineral production in the Tundra.

Alaska. Alaska possesses nearly all of the more than 30 minerals listed by the United States government as strategic or critical. The entire list may be present, because less than one per cent of the state has received detailed geological analysis, and only about half of the area has been covered by geological reconnaissance mapping. Obviously, mineral exploration and exploitation have taken place in the more accessible sites; and since the Tundra region is one of the state's most isolated sections, little exploitation of mineral and power resources has occurred.

It is known that considerable coal is present. In the area around Corwin, 34 coal beds represent an aggregate thickness of more than 135 feet. The largest has a thickness of 30 feet. Fuel from the vicinity of Corwin was used by whaling fleets many decades ago. In the Kukpowruk-Utukok section, 69 beds were measured, each at least 3 feet thick and the largest 20 feet thick. Quality of coal ranges from good grade lignite to bituminous.

The Navy has a large oil reserve along the Arctic Coast, and rich oil shales are present in the Lower Cretaceous rocks along the Etivluk River. These rocks may be the source of oil found in seepages much farther north in the same region.

In November 1957, it was announced that 20 million acres of federal lands were to be opened for mineral, oil, and gas exploitation in 1958. The area lies about 150 miles north of the Arctic Circle. There may not be a big rush to take advantage of this opening. It is true that oil corporations find rentals lower than in continental United States and royalties are also less for the first discovery upon unexplored land. On the other hand, transport costs for supplies are greater, food is more expensive, higher prices are necessary for driller's mud, and labor demands higher wages. These and other charges make Alaskan oil drilling several times more costly than that of Texas or Oklahoma.

Population

Canadian Tundra. In 1951, the Northwest Territories and the Yukon, which comprise most of the Canadian North, 1,516,726 square miles, or an area equal to half of contiguous United States, had 25,100 people. Density averaged one person for 60 square miles. Nearly 7,000 of Canada's 9,000 Eskimos live in these two territories. The remaining Yukon and Northwest Territories population includes 5,371 Indians and 12,877 others.

Settlements and trading posts on the Arctic coast of the Northwest Territories, Quebec, and Manitoba are served by the Eastern Arctic Patrol. The government wishes to maintain proper contact between the more densely settled south and the sparsely peopled north. Part of this contact is concerned with Arctic defense. For example, a radar line (Fig. 7) of bases extends across Canada's Arctic islands between Danish Greenland and United States Alaska; this line is called the DEW Line (Distant Early Warning), and lies farther north than the Mid-Canada and Pine-Tree radar barriers.

Besides the development of radar stations, attempts have been made to establish temporary meteorological bases on ice islands. The Arctic Ocean is largely covered with floating ice, loosely packed in summer and almost continuous in winter. This pack ice, about 6 to 12 feet thick, crushes when moved about by winds, tides, and currents; but ice islands, several hundred feet thick, are fractured much less by erosive agencies. These glacial relicts of 10 to 20 square miles have wavy surfaces and may have deposits of dirt, possibly acquired during glacial formation. Although

Fig. 7. Dew Line and Dew Line Station. The Dew Line extends from Alaska, across northern Canada, to Greenland. The aerial view of a typical station shows the arrangement of outbuildings, access roads, and intercommunication facilities around the dome-shaped housing of the main search antenna. Within this dome and the surrounding buildings is an electronic system capable of "seeing" an approaching aircraft or missile while it is many miles away and transmitting a warning signal to defense command centers in the United States and Canada within seconds of the initial contact. (Courtesy Western Electric Company.)

they melt a little in summer, they make up for the deficit by adding ice on the bottom in winter. They may have originated from the glacial fringe around Ellesmere Island.

Movement of the glacial islands (Fig. 8), after they enter the Arctic Ocean, is clockwise in the eddy which carries them southward toward Alaska, westward along Alaska's northern shore, and then northward to begin the cycle all over again. Landings have been made on ice islands and they may become useful temporary stations for measurements of weather, currents, magnetic fields of force, gravitational forces, and the topography of the ocean floor. One problem facing military strategists is to whom do the islands belong. If they do not get out of the Arctic into the Atlantic, they drift from United States waters to those of Canada, Denmark, and Russia and back again. If they escape from the Beaufort Drift into the warm waters of the Atlantic through the passage between Greenland and Spitzbergen, they will melt.

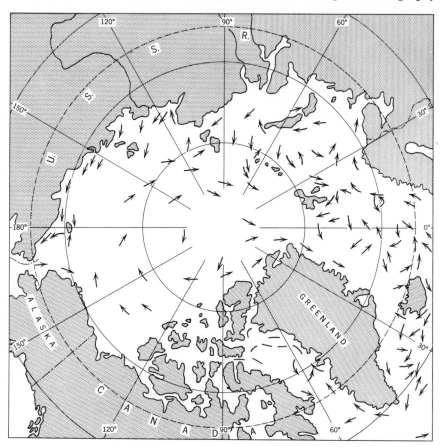

Fig. 8. Ice Drifts and Surface Currents in the Arctic Ocean. The ice islands, now moved around the Arctic by currents shown above, may be remnants of a disintegrating ice shelf formerly connected with Ellesmere Island. (After map by G. Hattersley-Smith in the *Canadian Geographer*, No. 9, 1957.)

More permanent settlements in the Canadian Tundra range in size from those on surveyed town sites to those with small groups of buildings around medical centers or trading posts. One of the latter, Arctic Bay (73° 3′ north, 85° 12′ west), is located on northern Baffin Island, Franklin District, Northwest Territories. It was established in 1926 by the Hudson's Bay Company to service the Eskimo families living in that neighborhood. The station is also useful for anchorage of the few ships reaching this high latitude. Moreover, at the head of the bay, the land rises gently in a smooth south-facing slope, which absorbs the maximum heat from the sun. Low mountains 2,000 to 4,000 feet high surround the bay and reduce the severity of the winter winds. Besides the Hudson's Bay trading post, there is a government operated radio and meteorological station in Arctic Bay.

One of the largest towns near the Tundra border is Aklavik, which until 1954 was located on low unstable ground near the mouth of the Mackenzie River. In that year scientists made a study of the Mackenzie delta to select a new site, one that would best satisfy social, economic, and physical factors favorable to a growing town. The place chosen is on relatively high ground, along a navigable river channel, and on the flanks of the delta, 33 air miles east of the old town.

Location on a navigable arm of the Mackenzie facilitates handling of river shipping during the short summer season; an air strip is available to encourage use of the town's strategic Arctic situation; road building materials are easily accessible; and domestic water supply can be secured without serious difficulty.

Another location of strategic importance is Crystal II, a military base created amid the rocks and tundra of Frobisher Bay on Baffin Island. Frobisher Bay (Fig. 9) is the midpoint on a great circle course between Los Angeles or San Francisco and London or Paris. The bay is one of the odd places that are destinations for few, but ports of call for many. Depending on the weather and the load being carried, flights between Europe and the United States West Coast may touch down on Baffin Island to fill fuel tanks.

The air station is now but a small town made up mainly of Eskimos, Air Force personnel, Canadian Department of Transport employees, Hudson's Bay Company staff, and Royal Canadian Mounted Police. Strategic location for commercial and military air activities seems about the only excuse for a town in this cold tundra situation.

The white population in the Canadian Tundra is composed mostly of government officials, Royal Canadian Mounted Police, transportation officials, missionaries, teachers, nurses, trappers, and a few others engaged in business. In the eastern Arctic, the white population is largely transitory. Here many of the government officials, missionaries, and traders spend terms of less than five years at their posts before being transferred to other locations.

Although many Canadian Eskimos continue to fish, hunt, and trap, nomadism as a characteristic economy of Arctic natives will soon be a thing of the past. Eskimos already are being trained to operate radar and weather stations; many have mechanical ability and they are better adjusted than the white man to live and work comfortably in the low temperatures. A few are becoming reindeer herders; and with increased interest in the militarily strategic Tundra, others may take up the occupation to supply meat for an enlarged local market.

In August 1953, nearly half of Canada's Eskimos voted in the nation's

Fig. 9. San Francisco-London Great Circle Route. The Canadian Tundra's Frobisher Bay lies at the midpoint of the Great Circle route from San Francisco to London and Paris. This airplane route also passes through Narssarssuaq and Sonderstrom, Greenland. Frobisher Bay lies along the southern shores of Baffin Island in Canada's Northwest Territories. (Courtesy Standard Oil Company, New Jersey and Geo-Physical Maps, Inc.)

general election. Voting equipment was taken to isolated settlements by plane, helicopter, and icebreaker. Thus the life of the Eskimo takes on modern characteristics. The old isolation is disappearing.

Alaskan Tundra. The population of the Alaskan Tundra, an area of about 100,000 square miles, numbers approximately 4,000. Density of one person to each 25 square miles is slightly greater than that of the Canadian Tundra to the east. Like the people of the Canadian section, many are Eskimos or an Eskimo-white mixture.

Life for the Alaskan Eskimo is changing, just as it is for his Canadian neighbor. Many find work on the DEW Line and on other enterprises associated with Arctic military strategy. Some find jobs on mining ventures. Several are interested in reindeer herding, and a few continue the hunting and trapping occupations of their ancestors.

The larger Eskimo villages are Barrow, Point Hope, Wainwright, and

Kotzebue, none of them connected to main highways. Travel is by plane, dogsled, or boat. United States supply ships touch these outposts during the summer to provide food, clothing, and other articles for Arctic Coast dwellers, and to deliver equipment for military installations.

A shortening of the boat route between Alaska's Arctic coast and the warmer waters of the North Atlantic was discovered during the summer of 1957. Ships of the United States Coast Guard and a Canadian icebreaker found that in Bellot Strait, a narrow but deep channel between Somerset Island and the Boothia Peninsula, the ice breaks up in the late summer months long enough to let eastbound vessels through to the east coast of North America. Thus the famous Northwest Passage has been shortened.

Summary and Conclusion

In any summary of the Tundra, several regional features stand out clearly. Its physical boundaries are fairly definite: the Arctic Ocean on the north, the Atlantic Ocean on the east, the 50° isotherm for the warmest month on the south, and the Bering Sea on the west.

The geographical environment includes a dominantly plains topography; a climate too cold for commercial agriculture; grazing land with low carrying capacity; few trees and none of large size; inadequate development of transport facilities; no manufacturing except of local raw materials; much wild life on land and in the adjoining seas; a location exposed to over-the-Pole attack by European enemies; and possibly large resources of petroleum, natural gas, and metallic minerals, many of them located in isolated areas.

Human use of the geographical environment by a sparse population has resulted in emphasis on hunting, trapping, fishing, grazing, mining, and military defense. Future changes in regional economy may be slight, but they will include greater emphasis upon the extraction of power and mineral resources and further improvements in transportation.

QUESTIONS, EXERCISES, AND PROBLEMS

1. Compare the Tundra with low and middle latitude deserts. Describe the location, boundaries, surface features, climates, vegetation, and soils. How does permafrost affect the construction of roads, bridges, buildings, plumbing, etc.?

2. Compare the mosquitoes of the Tundra with those of the wet lowland tropics. Contrast Tundra noonday-zenith-and-horizon distances of the sun with those for your latitude. Why is precipitation so low? Why are wind velocities higher than those for the forested region to the south? Why is the Tundra a good source region for air masses?

3. Of what direct importance is Arctic vegetation to man? What is the indirect importance? Describe the Arctic fauna. Tell of the present-day fur trade. What

progress has been made in the grazing industry among the Eskimos? Describe mineral production and potential. What power resources are present? What are the possibilities for agriculture? for manufacturing?

4. Tell of the number, character, and distribution of the population. Comment on the military significance of the Arctic ice islands; of radar installations. Predict future trends in Tundra economy.

5. What influences will the finding of a new Northwest Passage, have on regional development?

6. The *Arctic Manual TMI-240*, reference cited, was written to inform GI's about practical means of survival when traveling in the Arctic. Read it and indicate major points of emphasis. Read John Q. Adams, "Settlements of the Northwestern Canadian Arctic," reference cited, for relationships between Arctic settlements and the geographic environment. Glance through "Arctic Pilot Plant," and state your reactions to the description and predictions made by the author, Henry Gemmill. Write a short review of *Arctic Canada from the Air*. Note the illustrations especially.

7. Identify the following: Arctic Circle, pingo, tree line, xerophyte, DEW Line, muskeg, permafrost, Great Circle Route.

8. Look in a good atlas and learn the location of the following: the islands of Victoria, King William, Southampton, Banks, Baffin, Ellesmere, Baird, Rype, and Somerset; Cape Lisburne, Davis Straits, Aklavik, Coronation Bay, Chesterfield Inlet, Corwin, Kotzebue, Bellot Strait, Frobisher Bay, Ungava Peninsula, Point Barrow, Mackenzie River, Boothia Peninsula.

SELECTED REFERENCES

Adams, John Q., "Settlements of the Northwestern Canadian Arctic," *Geographical Review,* January 1941, pp. 112–126.

Arctic Institute of North America, *Arctic Bibliography,* 3 vols., Department of Defense, 1953 (obtainable from the Superintendent of Documents, Washington 25, D. C.).

Brown, R. J. E., J. K. Fraser, G. A. Kellaway, J. Ross Mackay, C. L. Merrill, and J. K. Stager, "The Mackenzie River Delta," *The Canadian Geographer,* No. 7, 1956.

Crary, Albert P., and R. D. Cotell, "The Ice Islands in Arctic Research," *The Scientific Monthly,* November 1952, pp. 298–302.

Department of Northern Affairs and National Resources and the National Film Board of Canada, *People of the High Arctic,* 1958.

Department of Resources and Development of Canada:
   Administration of the Northwest Territories, 1953;
   Flora, Fauna, and Geology of the Northwest Territories, 1954;
   Industries of the Northwest Territories, 1953;
   Peoples of the Northwest Territories, 1957;
   Transportation and Communications in the Northwest Territories, 1953.

Dunbar, Moira, and Keith R. Greenaway, *Arctic Canada From the Air,* Canada Defence Research Board, 1956.

Focus, "Resources of the Arctic," American Geographical Society, Vol. 2, Feb. 15, 1952.

Gemmill, Henry, "Arctic Pilot Plant: A Baffin Boom Town May Fix Patterns for Opening North Canada," *Wall Street Journal,* May 14, 1958.

Hare, F. Kenneth, "The Labrador Frontier," *Geographical Review,* July 1952, pp. 405–424.

Hogue, Donald W., *Temperatures of Northern North America,* Quartermaster Research and Engineering Center, U. S. Army, Natick, Mass., June 1956.

Hustich, Ilmari, "Notes on the Forests of the East Coast of Hudson Bay and James Bay," *Acta Geographica,* Vol. 11, 1950, pp. 1–83.

Hustich, Ilmari, "The Lichen Woodlands in Labrador and Their Importance as Winter Pastures for Domesticated Reindeer," *Acta Geographica,* Vol. 12, 1951, pp. 1–48.

Jenness, John L., "Erosive Forces in the Physiography of Western Arctic Canada," *Geographical Review,* April 1952, pp. 238–252.

Kimble, George H. T., and Dorothy Good, editors, *Geography of the Northlands,* American Geographical Society, and John Wiley and Sons, 1955.

Lantis, Margaret, "The Reindeer Industry in Alaska," *Arctic,* April 1950.

Lloyd, Trevor, "Canada's Strategic North," *International Journal,* Vol. 2, 1947.

National Geographic, "Canada Counts its Caribou," August 1952, pp. 261–268.

Nicholson, Norman L., *The Boundaries of Canada, Its Provinces and Territories,* Department of Mines and Technical Surveys, Ottawa, 1954.

Palmer, Lawrence J. and Charles H. House, "Study of the Alaska Tundra with Reference to Its Reactions to Reindeer and Other Grazing," *Research Report 10,* Fish and Wildlife Service, Washington D. C., 1945.

Porsild, A. E., "Plant Life in the Arctic," Canadian Geographical Journal, Vol. 42, 1951, pp. 121–145.

Pullen, Thomas C., and Lee Edson, "We Found a New Northwest Passage," *Saturday Evening Post,* May 10, 1958.

Reed, J. G., *Professional Paper 301,* "Exploration of Naval Petroleum Reserve No. 4, and Adjacent Areas, Northern Alaska, 1944–53, Part 1, History of the Exploration," U. S. Geological Survey, 1958.

Rowley, Diana, editor, "Arctic Research: The Current Status of Research and Some Immediate Problems in the North American Arctic and Subarctic," *Special Publication No. 2,* Arctic Institute of America, 1955.

Schiller, Ronald, "Floating Air Bases of the Arctic," *Skyways,* January 1952.

Smith, G. Hattersley, "The Ellesmere Ice Shelf and the Ice Islands," *The Canadian Geographer,* No. 9, 1957.

Stefansson, Vilhjalmur, *The Arctic in Fact and Fable,* Foreign Policy Association, March–April 1945.

U. S. Department of War, *Arctic Manual, TM1-240,* April 1, 1942.

Wilkinson, Doug, *Land of the Long Day,* Henry Holt and Co., 1956.

4 · The Taiga, or Subarctic Region of Canada

Taiga is a word meaning virgin forest, and it is a good name to apply to the great, dominantly coniferous forest, most of it untouched by man, that extends across Canadian North America from the Atlantic to the western cordillera (Fig. 1). This forest is not only one of the largest forested regions on the continent, but is also one of the most continuous forest sections in the world. The only other regions that can boast a larger acreage of trees are the Eurasian Taiga and the selva of the Amazon Basin.

The Physical Environment

Location and Boundaries. Climate is a major factor in limiting Taiga boundaries. Using temperature as a guide, the northern boundary approximates the poleward limit of tree growth, the 50° F. isotherm for the warmest month. On the south, the region borders the best area of Canadian agriculture, land that has temperatures of 50° F. or over for a period of more than three months. On the east, the Taiga reaches the Atlantic, except where it gives way to tundra along the northeast Labrador coast. On the west, the coniferous forest reaches the upper slopes of the Rocky Mountains, where altitude brings sufficient cold to limit vegetation to tundra.

Climate. The Taiga climate (Fig. 2) has several outstanding characteristics: (*a*) long cold winters; these more than (*b*) the short summers account for (*c*) the greatest temperature range of any of the world's climates. The temperature rise above zero in summer may be greater than the temperature fall below zero in winter. (*d*) Some of the coldest official temperatures on the continent occur in this climate. Summers have (*e*) long days and short nights and winters short days and long nights. (*f*) In subarctic latitudes, the summer noonday sun is never high. (*g*) Transition seasons of spring and autumn are short or almost non-existent. (*h*) Frost is a hazard every month of the year—in great contrast to the situation in subtropical climates where the danger is confined to about one month of the year. (*i*) Wide areas are characterized by permafrost. (*j*) Anticyclonic conditions dominate winter months and block the consistent movement of cyclonic storms found at lower latitudes. (*k*) Precipitation, with a summer maximum,

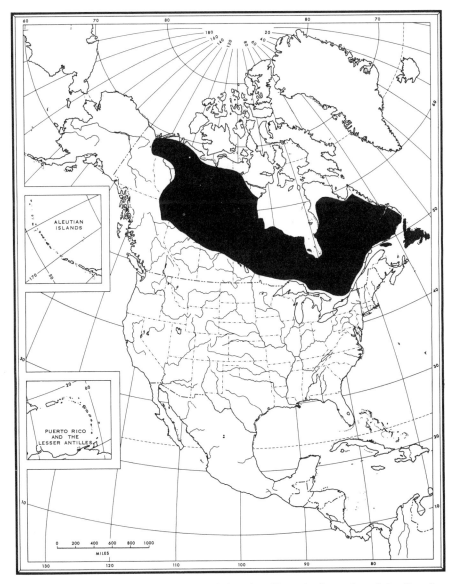

Fig. 1. The Taiga or Subarctic Region of Canada. Note the huge size of the Canadian Subarctic.

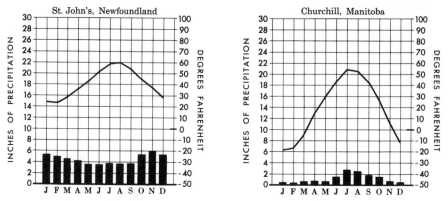

Fig. 2.   St. John's, Newfoundland (47° 32′ N., 52° 40′ W.; altitude 125 feet; mean annual temp. 41° F.; mean annual precip. 54.6 inches); Churchill, Manitoba (58° 50′ N., 94° 0′ W.; altitude 55 feet; mean annual temp. 18° F.; mean annual precip. 14.41 inches).   Churchill has a higher latitude and a more continental location than St. John's.   These conditions show their influence in Churchill's lower temperatures, greater temperature range, and lesser precipitation.

is relatively low; a few areas show an annual average of more than 20 inches. Winter precipitation in the form of snow remains a long time because of forest-cover protection from sun.   (*l*) Polar continental air, widespread in the Tundra, frequently covers the Taiga.

Surface Features (Fig. 3).   The Canadian Taiga includes all or parts of four major physiographic divisions: the Laurentian Shield, the Interior Plains, the Hudson Bay Lowland, and the Appalachian Highlands.   The Laurentian Shield underlies more than half of Canada, and includes a 2,000,000-square mile horseshoe of ancient Precambrian rock encircling Hudson Bay.   From the air it resembles a plateau broken by rounded hills, numerous lakes, and areas of muskeg.   It slopes towards Hudson Bay, and rises in the direction of Labrador.

Geologically the shield is the peneplaned remnant of Precambrian mountains.   Mountain building and later peneplanation have greatly influenced the economic life of Canada.   Valuable mineral deposits were brought nearer the surface by the folding and faulting coincident with uplift, and the higher altitudes resulting from diastrophism accelerated erosion of rocks overlying the metallic formations.   All of this made it possible for man to recover minerals at much shallower depths.   Most of Canada's gold, silver, copper, nickel, platinum, cobalt, uranium, and iron comes from the Laurentian Shield.

Peneplanation that favored mineral exploitation was not so encouraging to agriculture.   Pleistocene glaciation acted as a huge rasp, leaving widespread areas of bare rock completely stripped of soil.   Some soils were carried as far south as the United States Corn Belt.

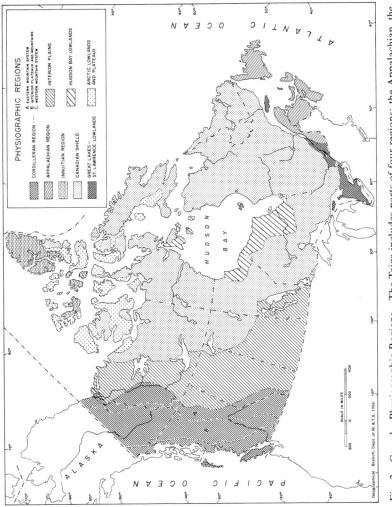

Fig. 3. Canada, Physiographic Regions. The Taiga includes parts of four regions: the Appalachian, the Canadian Shield, the Hudson Bay Lowland, and the Interior Plains. (Courtesy Department of Northern Affairs and National Resources.)

This same glacial action was responsible for the many lakes, swamps, and disarranged stream drainage that are characteristic of the Laurentian Shield; such conditions, discouraging to farming, favor hydroelectric power, so important in Canadian economy.

West of the Laurentian Shield, the Interior Plains, a poleward extension of the United States Great Plains, continue central Canada's low-lying topography to the Rocky Mountains. The Plains physiographic province includes parts of three Canadian land use regions, the Spring Wheat Region on the south, the Taiga in the center, and the Tundra on the north. In contrast to the Laurentian Shield, the Interior Plains are more nearly level and are, for the most part, underlain by sedimentary rocks little affected by folding and faulting. Here are most of the great Canadian oil fields. Land forms rise gradually from approximately 1,000 feet on the east to a few thousand feet above sea level near the base of the Rockies. Glaciation has been active over this section of the Taiga just as over the shield section; lakes, moraines, and interrupted stream patterns, although somewhat less numerous, are similar to those of the eastern peneplane.

The portion of the Taiga known physiographically as the Hudson Bay Lowland also differs from the Laurentian Shield. The nearly flat lowland, underlain by youthful sedimentary rocks, has its greatest length, approximately 800 miles, towards the southeast; the narrowest dimension, east-west, varies from 100 to 200 miles. Deposition of sediments, now forming rocks of the lowland, took place as the ice sheet receded poleward beyond the divide between the St. Lawrence and Hudson Bay drainage. Many of the sediments are lacustrine clays, laid down in waters ponded in front of the retreating continental glacier.

The Appalachian Highlands appear in Newfoundland, which is also a part of the Canadian Taiga. The island is shaped like an equilateral triangle with each side of its 43,000-square mile area approximately 320 miles in length. Inland from the 6,000-mile long subsiding shoreline, with its many coastal indentations and islands, is a rolling plateau dotted with numerous glacial lakes and hills. The surface slopes gently from about 2,000 feet in Long Range on the west to about 700 feet near the eastern coast.

Pleistocene glaciation brought both erosion and deposition to Newfoundland, and drainage patterns were badly interrupted. Metallic deposits of iron, lead, zinc, and other minerals occur in the widespread crystalline rocks, and a little coal is present in the stratified sedimentaries of the southwest.

Vegetation and Soils (Figs. 17 and 20, Chapter 1). The economic development of Canada has always been associated with forests. It was in the forest that the earliest settlers secured fur, the first commercial product of continental Canada. Forests also provided wood for fuel, timber for ships, lumber for homes, barns, and sheds, and a combination of forest products for export. However, problems of clearing the forest delayed agricultural development and forests gave shelter for Indian enemies.

Forests cover about two-fifths of Canada (Fig. 4), and most of the trees occur in the Taiga. Softwoods make up approximately three-fourths of the forest, with spruce, balsam fir, pine, and hemlock growing on most of the land; cedar, larch, and cypress appear over smaller sections (Figs. 5, 6). Poplar, birch, and maple dominate the hardwoods.

Although the Taiga is almost entirely forest, the climate is not ideal for rapid tree growth. Many trees are small; stands are not close over wide expanses of territory; and it takes many years for a tree to reach maturity. Where trees are widely spaced and penetration of light is easy, an understory bush vegetation is characteristic; where trees are closer together and only a little light reaches the ground, mosses and lichens may occur; and where stands are dense, and no light penetrates through the branches, nothing but a thick bed of leaves covers the ground.

The dominantly conifer vegetation of the Taiga contributes little in humus to the soils, much less than that contributed by deciduous forests and grasses in regions to the south. The podzol soils belong to the non-lime-accumulating pedalfer division; they are low in humus, leached, and possess unfavorable structure. Neither the thin podzol soil nor the wide-spread occurrence of bare rock scraped clean by Pleistocene ice handicaps agriculture as much as climate.

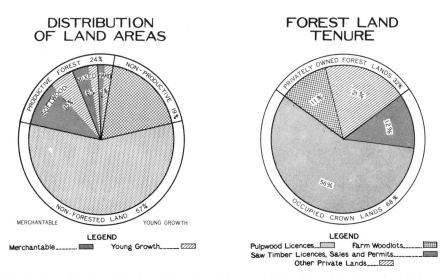

Fig. 4. Canadian Forest Land and Forest Land Tenure. Much of Canada is forested, with about one-third of the forest privately owned. (Courtesy Department of Resources and Development, Canada.)

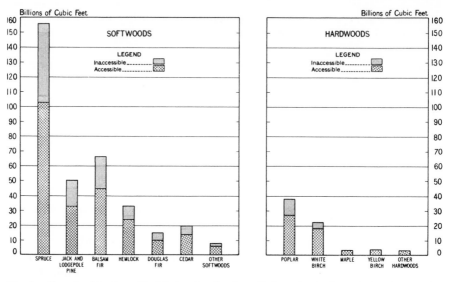

Fig. 5. Canada, Merchantable Timber by Species. Softwoods dominate Taiga forests with spruce the leading type of tree. (Courtesy Department of Resources and Development, Canada.)

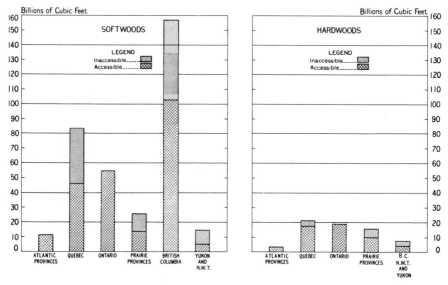

Fig. 6. Canada, Merchantable Timber by Provinces. British Columbia, Quebec, and Ontario lead among the Canadian provinces in merchantable timber. (Courtesy Department of Resources and Development, Canada.)

Land Utilization

Fishing. The Newfoundland portion of Canada's Taiga early became associated with one of America's oldest industries. When John Cabot discovered the island in 1497, he was so enthusiastic about island fishing grounds, especially to the east and south, that he called it "Baccalaos," the Indian word for codfish. Catholic Europe was also enthusiastic and hailed Cabot's discovery with joy. At that time none of the world's great grain lands had been developed, cultivated grasses were almost unknown, and domestic animals provided little meat. Newfoundland cod promised to supplement the supply coming from the North Sea banks, and to help significantly toward making the sixteenth century the golden age of fish on the European continent.

Fishing grounds (Fig. 7) were the magnet that drew ships from many nations westward in the wake of Cabot's voyage. Men cared little for the land that he discovered. In fact England, which claimed Newfoundland, actually discouraged settlement in various ways. The government levied fines upon captains of fishing boats who failed to return with full crews; warnings were issued against the use of land more than six miles from shore; and restrictions were placed upon home building and land cultivation, some of which remained in force for over three centuries after the island was discovered.

Ordinarily considered the world's greatest colonizer, England justified the bans on settlement in the belief that annual pilgrimages by the fishing fleets would provide schooling for British seamen, a training that might be diminished by permanent settlement. Furthermore, there was the thought that the settlers with nothing to do in the winter of this cold land would either starve or become idlers.

Most voyagers to the banks did not object strenuously to the British restrictions, for the land offered much less encouragement for a livelihood than the sea. A rocky plateau surface spotted with lakes and swamps; a thin veneer of soil except along the river valleys in the southwest where settlement was prohibited until 1904 because of French claims; climate characterized by long, snowy winters and cool, short, foggy summers; natural vegetation dominated by coniferous forests except in the tall grass swamp lands and lake borders; none of these features of the Newfoundland environment attracted settlement in the interior. Newcomers were interested only in the coastland and in that only as a base for fishing. For nearly four centuries their outlook was definitely seaward.

The fishing banks, a foundered portion of the North American continent made shallower by deposits of icebergs as they move equatorward from the polar ice fields, are ideal for fishing. Shallow waters allow penetration of the sunlight, so necessary for the growth of plankton, the pastures of the

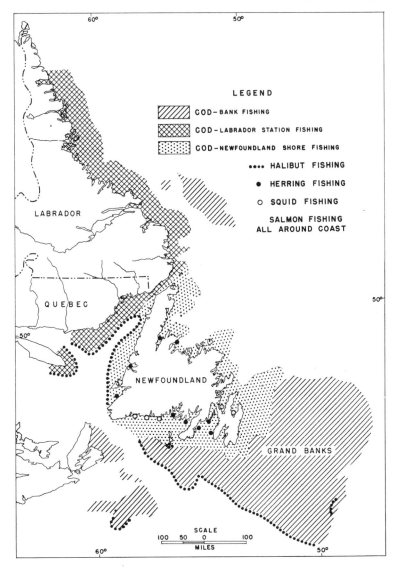

Fig. 7. Newfoundland and Coast of Labrador Fishing Areas. One of the greatest banks fisheries in the world borders Newfoundland and Labrador to the east.

sea. Cold waters coursing over the fishing grounds are also favorable for producing rich ocean meadows. Arctic currents chill the seas, already cooled by extension toward higher latitudes, and the consequent abundance of carbon dioxide encourages a rich organic growth for feeding squid, caplin, and herring, on which the cod prey. Newfoundland fishing still is an important island industry giving work to approximately one-third of the workers.

In another part of the Taiga region, Great Slave Lake, commercial fishing is a more recent development, since 1945. Whitefish and lake trout are now marketed in millions of pounds, 7,200,000 in 1952. Most of the more than $2,000,000 catch is sent to the United States. The opening of a highway from Hay River on Great Slave Lake to Grimshaw's railhead in Alberta, in 1948, has aided the industry; but iced fish reach United States markets by truck as well as by rail. Fishing is carefully regulated and catch limits are based upon sound biological information. Besides commercial fishing in Great Slave Lake and around Newfoundland, tourist fishing occurs in the numerous streams and lakes.

Furs. Furs from the forested Taiga provided the first commerce for the Canadian mainland. Moreover, for more than a century prior to 1800, the export of this commodity exceeded in value that of any other outgoing resource; and even today the output is not greatly less than 150 years ago although it is relatively far below that of other industries.

May 2, 1670 is an important date in Canadian fur history. On that day the English king Charles II signed a royal decree granting rights to sole trade and commerce within the entrance of Hudson Strait to "our dear and entirely beloved cousin, Prince Rupert, and his associates." In terms of today's geography, the grant to what is now the Hudson's Bay Company included the provinces of Ontario and Quebec, north of the Laurentian Hills and west of the Labrador boundary, the whole of Manitoba and Saskatchewan, the southern half of Alberta, and the southeast corner of the Northwest Territories. In all this vast domain, furs were almost the only resource of interest to the early traders. Although the Hudson's Bay Company does not have exclusive control over the region today, its trading posts remain not only throughout the area granted by royal decree, but also through wide expanses of adjoining land.

The Taiga has many advantages for the fur industry. (*a*) The cold climate encourages good quality furs. (*b*) Adequate feed is available for fur-bearing animals; for example beaver thrive on bark of local trees, and muskrats enjoy many aquatic plants growing in the numerous lakes and rivers. (*c*) These waterways provide trappers with an easy route to market. (*d*) Snow aids in tracking animals. (*e*) Although mining, forestry, agriculture, and other industries have invaded the quiet of Canada's forests, thousands of square miles remain to give the isolation sought by wild animals. (*f*) World standards of living are rising, a factor that encourages a broader market for furs.

Taiga trapping is carried on by Indian trappers who live a lonely and hazardous life. The Indian may work a trap line of 50 miles or more, and along the route he may build a rude cabin or two in which to store his furs.

If the trapper falls and breaks a leg, or is seriously hurt in some other way, he may never get back to camp.

Recent improvements in manufacturing have made traps lighter while retaining their original strength. Thus, the trapper can carry more of them than he did years ago. Depletion of the fur-bearing animals has forced the government to enact various conservation measures. Trapping licenses are now required and trapping is prohibited when there is danger of extinction of any fur-bearing species. Control measures are also enforced during that phase of the fur cycle when natural increase is less than average.

Today, a large share of the world's fur market is supplied by fur farms, whose number has increased throughout the Taiga and other parts of Canada. Fur traders also lease government forest lands on which the renter kills all predatory animals that threaten the ones he hopes to trap.

Forests. Tree-covered lands provide the ideal environment for fur-bearing animals whose pelts gave Canada an important commercial activity for hundreds of years; now trees furnish the nation with its first ranking manufactured commodity, forest products, especially pulp and paper.

In 1951, Canada's output of pulp and paper was valued at $1.2 billion (Fig. 8); in the same year this output accounted for more than half of the world's newsprint, 25 per cent of Canada's world exports, and one-third of her shipments to the United States. At that time, three out of five of the world's newspapers were made of Canadian newsprint. Canadian lumber also moves to all parts of the world.

Although most Taiga trees are small in size, slow growing, and weak in structure, they are low in resin content and react well to chemical and mechanical processing. Other advantages for paper making include proximity to cheap hydroelectric power and to the greatest of the world's paper and pulp markets, that of the United States. In fact, several United States corporations have moved their factories to Canada. By such a change they save on labor costs and, what is more important, they cut down transport charges. This economy comes through shipping the lighter, more compact finished product rather than the bulky heavy logs.

Availability of facilities for transport is very significant in the location of paper pulp and paper mills. Most all are located where railroads cross large streams. Thus, certain supplies may be brought in by rail and the finished product moved by the same means of transport; and with the along-stream location, the bulky logs may be floated down river to the mill. A situation near a stream also gives opportunity for hydroelectric power development; and enormous amounts of power are needed for the manufacture of wood pulp.

Kapuskasing lies well within the Taiga, near the southern edge of the Hudson Bay Clay Belt where the Canadian National crosses the north-flowing Kapuskasing River. Corner Brook, Newfoundland, has one of the

Fig. 8. Paper for Export. Only Russia and Brazil have greater forested areas than Canada. Out of a total of 3,845,144 square miles, 1,300,000 are forested, with 503,000 square miles classified as accessible and productive. Pulp and paper held many Canadian firsts in 1953; first in value of production, first in salaries and wages paid employees, first in value of exports, first in employment of transport facilities, and first in the use of electricity. (Courtesy Newfoundland Tourist Development Office.)

largest Canadian paper plants with a coastal location at the western terminus of the trans-island railroad, and at the mouth of the Humber River.

With the Canadian forests, many of them in the Taiga, accounting for one of the country's major resources, conservation should be and is practiced in every forest activity. During the last 100 years at least half of the commercial forest has been burned over. It should be stressed that fire not only destroys the trees, but it also damages the soil, and may prevent direct reforestation by the same species. Fire lessens soil fertility and good structure by burning humus; and with soil depletion, low-grade trees such as poplar and birch may crowd out pine and spruce saplings in a burned-over pine and spruce forest.

Other natural enemies of the forest appear in the form of diseases and insect pests. For example, the larch sawfly and spruce budworm have devastated thousands of trees in recent years.

One of the biggest problems for the conservationists is to maintain a balance between forest cutting and forest growth. In short, forests should be cropped, not mined; mining is a robber industry but planned cropping is not. To maintain an equilibrium between growth and forest cutting is not easy, especially when increasing demands for paper from the United States market are taxing all of the present paper pulp capacity. But it should be done regardless of market demands. Possibility of achieving equilibrium is heightened by the fact that most forest lands are government owned, and governments may be more conservation minded than private owners (Fig. 4).

Statistical proof of need for conservation comes from the United Nations publication, *Forest Resources of the World,* 1948. This report states that annual use of Canada's forests amounts to 94,660,000 cubic meters of roundwood, solid content without bark, in comparison to annual growth of 80,000,000 cubic meters roundwood, solid content without bark.

Minerals (Fig. 9). Canada is one of the world's leading producers of minerals. In 1956, the country led in the production of nickel, the platinum metals, and asbestos; ranked second in gold, zinc, cadmium, and selenium; placed third in silver, molybdenum, and barite; and was fourth in copper and lead. It may be that the nation has the world's largest iron resources. Much of Canada's mineral production is exported in the form of ores and concentrates, or in primary metallic forms, mainly to the United States. In 1956, total mineral production, including petroleum and natural gas, reached nearly $2 billion.

Although Sudbury nickel (Figs. 10, 11) was discovered in 1883, and the Yukon gold rush took place in the 1890's, Canadian mining became of age in the present century. Thus, the industry is much younger than the commercial production of fish and furs, and even younger than commerce in forest products.

Many of the minerals are located in the huge Taiga region, and more than half of the metallic deposits have been discovered in the igneous and metamorphic rocks of the Laurentian Shield. Moreover, only a small portion of the country's geology has been thoroughly mapped. With exploitation expanding constantly, any list of producing areas is quickly dated. Nevertheless, it may be useful to make a short inventory of the more important producing regions.

Beginning with the rush to the Yukon in the 1890's, gold has attracted prospectors to all parts of the nation, and many gold mines are producing today. Ontario has two important districts at Porcupine and Kirkland Lakes; one mine, the Lake Shore, has yielded about $150,000,000 of the yellow metal since operations began in 1918. A more recent gold rush took

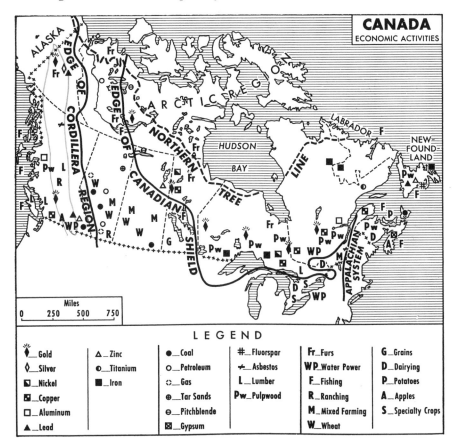

Fig. 9. Canada, Economic Activities. Note the great variety of metallic minerals in the Canadian Shield, the occurrence of petroleum and natural gas in the sedimentary rocks between the Shield and the Cordillera, and the great wheat lands in southern Alberta and Saskatchewan. (Source: Etzel Pearcy, *World Political Geography,* Thomas Y. Crowell and Co., 1957.)

place in the early 1930's on Yellowknife Bay, Great Slave Lake. Like many other Canadian mines, Yellowknife (Fig. 12) uses nearby waterfalls for power. Forests of the Taiga have also aided mining development with contributions of fuel, mine props, and building materials.

In several mining areas, gold occurs in association with copper, silver, zinc, and other metals. Two well-known places with ores of this character are Flinflon, near the boundary between Saskatchewan and Manitoba, and Rouyn and Noranda, two neighboring towns just east of the Quebec-Ontario boundary.

Practically all of the gold mining in the Laurentian Shield is found in shaft mines; discoveries may be made through placer mines, but deep mine recovery is characteristic of mother lode deposits. Once the ore reaches

Fig. 10. Sudbury Smelter. Sudbury nickel ore has a low percentage of metal; this necessitates the location of smelting operations close to the mines. (Courtesy International Nickel Company of Canada, Limited.)

the surface, separation in most cases takes place by the cyanide process; the ore is ground fine and a solution of sodium cyanide separates gold from the gangue.

One of the most famous mining discoveries was pitchblende in 1930 at Labine Point on Echo Bay, Great Bear Lake, later called the Port Radium Eldorado mine. Since the discovery of fisionable uranium, radium has become the by-product, and major emphasis is on uranium oxide.

The strategic importance of the Eldorado mine led the government to expropriate the property in 1944, and since that time the crown-operated company, known as the Eldorado Mining and Refining Ltd., has expanded mine facilities. Since 1953, three additional uranium producing areas promise to make Canada one of the world's leading producers. These are located at Beaverlodge in Northern Saskatchewan, at Blind River in northern Ontario, and in the Bancroft area of southeastern Ontario.

Taiga iron is available in large quantities in Ontario, north of the United States Mesabi region; in Labrador; and in the Bell Island Wabana mines of Newfoundland. The Schefferville (Fig. 13), Labrador ore receives the most publicity because of the richness and because of its location with ref-

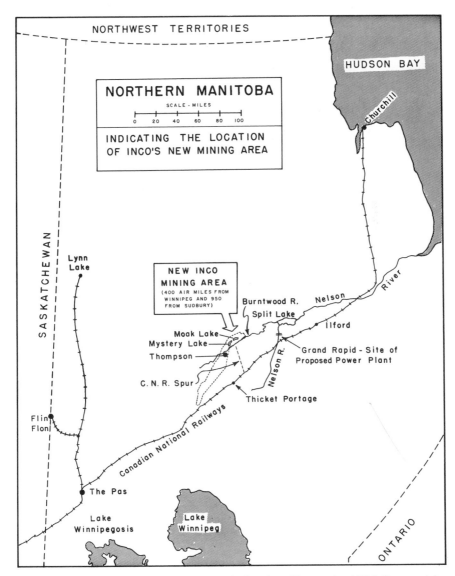

Fig. 11. Northern Manitoba. The map shows the location of International Nickel's new mining area. Nearly $200,000,000 will be invested for mining, power, and town building facilities in the world's second largest nickel producer. The ore body extends about 80 miles in length and about 10 miles in width. Note that a 30 mile spur links Thompson with the Canadian National's Hudson Bay line. (Courtesy International Nickel Company of Canada, Limited.)

Fig. 12. Yellowknife Mine. The future of Canada's Northland will be associated closely with the mining industry. The Giant Yellowknife mine was brought into production in 1948 and is now the largest producer in the Northwest Territories. (Courtesy Department of Northern Affairs and National Resources, Ottawa.)

erence to the St. Lawrence River. A railroad connects Schefferville with Seven Islands on the St. Lawrence, and iron can move easily by deep water to the North American Ruhr.

Recent developments at Sherridon and Lynn Lake stress the geographic principle that mining is a robber industry. In 1941, Sherritt Gordon Mines Ltd. was operating its rich but declining silver and copper mines of Sherridon, Manitoba. At the same time, the company, aware that mine abandonment would soon be necessary, sent prospectors to look for other metallic deposits. These were discovered in quantity at Lynn Lake, 165 miles to the north. After World War II, the company moved the entire town of Sherridon over the winter snow (Fig. 14) to Lynn Lake, where more than $40,000,000 has been invested.

Another significant recent mining development is in progress at Chibougamau, Quebec, about 320 miles north of Montreal. This copper strike serves as a good example of how actual mining development of non-precious minerals awaits the arrival of adequate transport facilities. Copper ore outcrops at Chibougamau were discovered 50 years ago, but until 1950 no road gave easy accessibility to markets. Several years later, in 1957, the Canadian National Railway completed a branch line to the copper region. With an outlet assured over both rail and road, by 1959 mining corporations had already invested more than $50,000,000 in the mines. Moreover, the mining town now has several thousand people. Another new development in copper is at Manitouwadge in northwestern Ontario, where important copper-zinc discoveries were made in 1953.

Besides possessing metallic deposits of great variety, the Taiga also has power resources with which to develop them. If all Canadian rivers were harnessed by power plants, they would supply over 50,000,000 horsepower, that is, about 3 horsepower for every man, woman, and child in the country. Up to 1950, only one-fifth of this power potential was developed.

Canada is rich in petroleum and natural gas resources, but the richest producing fields lie south of the Taiga in the Spring Wheat region. Total Canadian oil production in 1956 reached over 170,000,000 barrels.

The sedimentary rocks underlying most of Canada's Spring Wheat region extend north into the Taiga, just west of the Laurentian Shield. Here at Norman Wells on the Mackenzie River, for example, locally produced

Fig. 13. Open-Pit Mining Near Schefferville, Labrador. Millions of tons of high-grade iron ore lying at shallow depths make surface mining easy. (Courtesy Iron Ore Company of Canada.)

Fig. 14. A Miner's House on the Move. Sherritt Gordon Mines moved a 2,000-ton mining plant and concentrator and 73 houses for a distance of 165 miles cross country. Transportation was timed for the period between January and March when lakes, swamps, and muskeg become deeply frozen and covered with snow. (Courtesy Sherritt Gordon Mines, Limited.)

crude oil is used in diesel engines, power generators, and aircraft. The Canol Project, a military operation for Pacific defense, took much more oil in the 1940's. It may be that present stress on Arctic defense will expand production considerably, for expansion is possible if the market becomes available.

The story of Taiga coal is different from that of water power and petroleum. Low-grade coal occurs in southwest Newfoundland and in the sedimentary rocks of the continental interior plains, but significant amounts of high grade deposits do not occur in the Taiga.

Availability of power and mineral resources is one thing and location is another. The Canadian Taiga is large. Where local power is not present and the metallic deposit is not rich, mining probably will not develop. Transport costs, price levels for metals, and richness of the ore must all be considered with reference to exploitation in remote sections. The aeroplane has been of great assistance in developing some of the rich isolated mines.

Farming (Fig. 15). Probably 85 per cent of Canada's nearly 4,000,000 square miles is unfit for farming; more than half of this lies in the Taiga. Within the latter area, however, there are sections where opportunities for successful farming are better than those for the bulk of Canada's northern

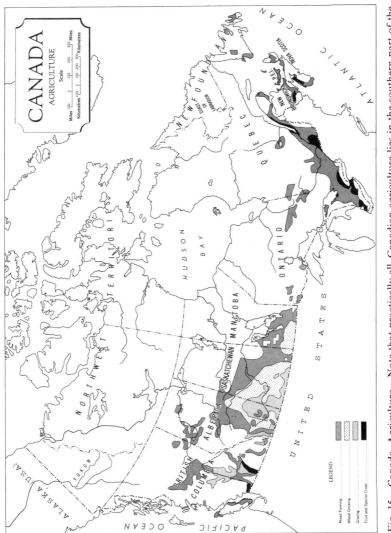

Fig. 15. Canada, Agriculture. Note that practically all Canadian agriculture lies in the southern part of the country. (Courtesy Department of Northern Affairs and National Resources.)

forest region. One of these is the section known as the Clay Belt, south of James Bay; another lies in the valley of the Mackenzie and in the valleys of some of its tributaries; and another stretches along the foothills of the Rocky Mountains, where air drainage is frequent and where winds occur that are similar to the chinook in Rocky Mountain lands of western United States.

Probably the best of these three is the Clay Belt of 40,000 square miles or more lying south of James Bay. The latitude is lower than that of the other two, and the region lies closer to market—closer to the major fraction of Canada's more than 16,000,000 people. The Clay Belt was formed by the Pleistocene glacier when it receded to James Bay and melt-water ponded between the ice front and higher land lying some distance to the south. Fine soil materials were deposited in this quiet water, and they formed a layer of moderately fertile clay lying over the resistant igneous and metamorphic rocks that make up much of the Laurentian Shield.

The natural vegetation is that of trees and a layer of moss; removal of tree cover aids drainage, and removal of moss will lessen soil dampness and increase soil warmth. Thus, in preparing ground for cultivation, trees and moss must be eliminated. The clay soils lying under the natural vegetation cover are normally colder and damper than loam or sandy soils, which contain less water. This is especially significant in a region with a short growing season; in short, the principle that water is more conservative in heating than land becomes active in a comparison of wet clay and less wet sand or loam. The removal of the moss makes it possible for the sun to impart greater heat to the soil and so to encourage faster germination of planted crops. Some farmers remove the moss by burning, but this may bring fire danger to good forest land near by. Care should be taken if fire is used for removal of moss, because the farmer must preserve his forest land to supplement earnings from the farm operations. Many Clay Belt farmers sell a crop of wood each year to the paper pulp factories.

Although farmers face danger of frost almost every month of the year, latitude is high enough to give long daylight periods in summer to encourage plant growth. With careful planting of cereal types maturing in a short season, and of root crops that complete their life cycle in similar short periods, the farmer may receive a crop in more than half the years of planting. Clay Belt farming should also include livestock raising, with cultivation of root crops and hardy cereals. Animals provide meat, milk, hides, and wool, and they furnish manures needed to add fertility to the soil and to improve soil structure. If the farm lies close to mining centers or paper towns, as some farms do, the farmer has a better market for animal products and cultivated crops.

Farms in the Canadian Taiga need people who are willing to work hard and to suffer privation to achieve success. Not many people are willing to do this; not many are willing to engage in a variety of activities to make a living. Assurance of economic success is encouraged by supplementing farming with work in the forests, in the mines, or by hunting, fishing, and trapping. Settlement has been aided in some sections by the church acting as a semicolonizing and semicooperative agent. Church organizations have been more successful in the establishment of farm settlements among the French Catholics than among other groups. Even so, probably not more than 5 per cent of the best farm land available is devoted to crops. Pressure of population upon North American land must be much greater than at present before a poleward movement of farmers to the Canadian Taiga takes place. If the present upward trend in world temperatures continues for a few more centuries and if the icecaps of Greenland, Antarctica, and the Arctic islands approach complete dissipation, Taiga farmland may attract a rush of purchasers; but these occurrences are extremely unlikely within the next few hundred years.

Transportation

(Figure 16)

Canada has two transcontinental rail lines along the southern border of the Taiga; one is the Canadian Pacific, a joint-stock corporation which commenced cross-country service in 1885; and the other is the Canadian National, a government system formed by the amalgamation of several private lines in 1923. Of the 44,476 single track miles operated in 1955, a total of 39,642 miles was operated by Canada's two major railways. Such transportation is of great help to the southern portion of the Taiga, which not only is more densely populated than the northern part, but also possesses greater agricultural and industrial development.

Another rail line runs north-south across the Taiga in its central portion; the Hudson Bay line leads from The Pas, in west-central Manitoba to Churchill, on Hudson Bay. Railroad men encountered a real problem peculiar to Taiga terrain in constructing this road. As previously indicated, large areas of muskeg and permafrost are present. A track laid during the winter on the frozen muskeg will settle the following summer when thawing takes place. It may even disappear; at least it will be so far out of line that train operation is impossible. To meet the problem, during the cold season, construction men laid down a broad, thick layer of heavy ballast on which they placed ties and rails. The ballast is so thick that the summer sun cannot penetrate to the winter-frozen muskeg, and trains run on permanently frozen ground. Still another north-south railroad was built recently across Labrador, to tap the huge iron deposits at Schefferville. Ore moves more than 300 miles to Seven Islands, on the St. Lawrence.

A cross-country highway offers competition to the transcontinental

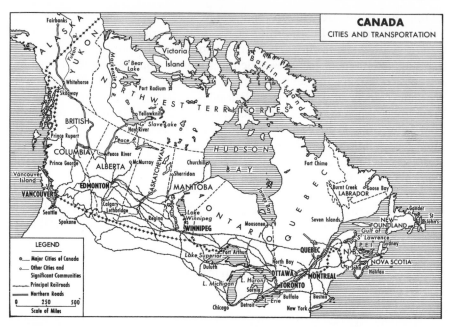

Fig. 16. Canada, Cities and Transportation. Notice the concentration of rail lines and cities in the south. Two northern roads stand out, the highway from Prince George, British Columbia, to Fairbanks, Alaska, the famous Alcan Highway, and the road from Peace River to Great Slave Lake. Other roads to the north are in the process of construction. The town of Burnt Creek, Labrador, is the site of the Schefferville iron mines. (Source: Etzel Pearcy, *World Political Geography,* Thomas Y. Crowell and Co., 1957.)

railroads, and several north-south highways branch off from the main line. One of these, built during World War II for military purposes, the Alcan route, cuts directly across the Taiga from Edmonton, Alberta, to Fairbanks, Alaska. The problem of road building over muskeg is similar to that described for building railroads. Several routes leading to mining camps are not easily passable during the short summer, and tractor trains may bring needed supplies during the long cold winter. In 1954, Canada had 192,616 miles of surfaced road and 331,439 miles of non-surfaced road. Of the surfaced road, 159,295 miles were gravel, 31,866 miles were treated with bitumin, and 1,455 were concrete. Most of these roads are in the southern part of Canada.

The Mackenzie River (Fig. 17) flows 2,514 miles from south to north across the Taiga, and carries freight about four months of the year. With a shallow, shifting channel obstructed by numerous sand bars, the paddle wheel steamer, similar to those on the Mississippi, works best. The Mackenzie area may be reached by water from the railhead at Waterways, Alberta, and by air from Edmonton, in the same province. The St. Lawrence provides a valuable water artery for the southern Taiga during the season from April to December.

Civil aviation developed in Canada after World War I. Bush pilots (Fig. 18), many of whom learned to fly during the war, pioneered in providing transportation to the new mining areas of the north, and assisted in their development. These pilots continue to play an important part in the economic life of Canada's northland. In the territories, mail, freight, and passengers travel by air. In places where there are no landing fields, planes can land on water surfaces of the many lakes in summer and on ice during the winter. The first regular freight and passenger service, into northern Quebec, was opened in 1924. During the mining boom of the 1930's Canadian airways carried a larger freight tonnage than those of any other country in the world.

The two most important scheduled air services are the Trans-Canada Airlines and the Canadian Pacific Airlines. Smaller companies traveling scheduled routes include Quebecair, Maritime Central Airways, Pacific Western Airlines, Trans-Air Ltd., etc. Canada's non-scheduled requirements, many of them occurring in the Taiga, are met by over two hundred charter and non-scheduled operations. Such services act as feeders to the scheduled airlines and provide for the transportation of personnel, equipment,

Fig. 17. Shipping on the Mackenzie River. The Mackenzie River is still an indispensable highway for the transportation of heavy freight. Here, a barge pulls away from the docks at Fort Smith for the long trip down the Mackenzie to Norman Wells. (Courtesy Department of Northern Affairs and National Resources, Ottawa.)

Fig. 18.   Transportation at Norman Wells, Northern Taiga.   In a territory with winter snows, summer muskeg, and few roads and railroads, planes are important means of transport for passengers and freight both summer and winter.   In the latter season, dogs may supplement air travel.   (Courtesy Standard Oil Co., New Jersey.)

and supplies needed in the exploration and development of the remote parts of Canada.   They have made many development projects in otherwise inaccessible areas economically sound and physically possible.

Two important international airports are located in the Taiga: Goose Bay, Labrador, and Gander, Newfoundland.   Newfoundland transport facilities also include a narrow-gauge railroad from St. John's, the capital, to Port-aux-Basques in the west; and since most of the people live along the coast, coastwise shipping has become extremely important.

All in all, no well-integrated rail, road, or air transport functions in the enormous Taiga region.   The northern Taiga has been developed but little, and mines, pulp mills, fur trading posts, and military installations are widely scattered.   Furthermore, a population density of less than five per square mile could hardly support a transportation system offering frequent service over widespread areas.

Population

Most of Canada's more than 16,000,000 people are spread over the southern part of the country, with the greatest concentration in the industrial provinces of Ontario and Quebec. Very few people live in the northern portion of the Taiga; many of these are Indians, descended from the original tribes that roamed the country before the coming of the white man. In the Newfoundland Taiga, the Indian is a minor element, with most people descended from British and French ancestors, as in continental Canada. These ancestors placed their villages along the island coast in order to be near the fishing grounds, and the interior still contains few people.

Centers of population in the continental Taiga are distinctly spotty in character. Mining developments are scattered; Hudson's Bay and other trading posts are also far apart. Pulp mills and lumbering towns are separated by long distances, but are closer together in the southern part where trees are nearer the market and where most large forest industries are centered. Farming development in the Taiga shows no dense population centers nor a dense population pattern.

Reasons for the few people and scattered towns are not hard to discover. None of the Taiga's major industries—forestry, mining, trapping, fishing, or farming—will support dense population over wide areas. Furthermore, the relatively sparse population is not likely to increase rapidly in the near future.

The Outlook

During the last few decades, many Canadian geographers have been engaged in exploring, describing, and encouraging the development of Canada's Northland—the Taiga and the Tundra; and in the 1958 election, Prime Minister John Diefenbaker pledged himself and his party to continue exploration and exploitation of the North.

However, both recent and earlier research offer little promise for great farming developing in the Taiga. Environmental difficulties, already stressed in detail, are not likely to be overcome easily.

The greatest economic opportunities exist in extracting metallic minerals from the ancient rocks of the Laurentian Shield. Rich discoveries such as Thompson's nickel, Chibougamau's copper, and Schefferville's iron have been made recently, and many more metals will be brought to light in the future. Moreover, Taiga sedimentary rocks west of the shield have yielded petroleum and natural gas, and promise to yield much more whenever market demands make further exploration and development more attractive. Many hydroelectric power sites await development, and Canada's uranium deposits may soon lead the world as bases for present and future atomic power.

The enormous forest area, better protected in the future by more careful conservation practices, will continue to provide substantially to the nation's economy with lumber, paper pulp and newsprint. Forest cover and inland water surfaces also encourage trapping, hunting, fishing, and tourism, but the great distance from dense population centers will keep many people from seeking tourist accommodations in the Taiga.

All of the previously mentioned economic opportunities are not likely to increase greatly the present relatively sparse population. That situation may develop in the far distant future if the prediction of W. H. Humphries, former director of the United States Weather Bureau, ever materializes. Some years ago, Dr. Humphries wrote an article entitled *Calamity Behind the Ice.* He stated that the melting of the polar icecaps will change world climates so that North American lands south of the Taiga will become desertlike and lands of the Taiga will experience an increase in temperature and precipitation as well. If this should prove true, the Taiga may become one of the world's bread baskets and support large numbers of people. But the world's icecaps may take thousands and thousands of years to melt away.

QUESTIONS, EXERCISES, AND PROBLEMS

1. Describe the boundaries, surface features, climate, vegetation, and soils of the Taiga. Name the physiographic subdivisions. How does the geology of the Interior Plains differ from that of the Laurentian Shield? What is the origin of the Hudson Bay Lowland?

2. Describe the Atlantic fisheries as to location, history, and markets; how are the methods of fishing related to the environment and to the habits of the fish? Tell of the fisheries on inland waterways.

3. What is the historical and present-day significance of Canadian trapping and hunting? Point out natural advantages for the fur industry. Describe seasonal activities of the trapper.

4. Outline the background for the various woodworking industries. Indicate the best location for a paper mill and give examples. Read a good reference on the manufacture of paper pulp and paper and be able to describe major steps in the process. What progress is being made in forest conservation? Comment on the significance of forestry in the Canadian economy.

5. Describe the geologic background of the Taiga for metallic minerals. What methods of mining are used? How are they related to the occurrence of the minerals? In what part of the Taiga is oil found? What is the background for the development of hydroelectric power? In general, what advantages does the Taiga possess for manufacturing? What are the disadvantages? What types of manufacturing are likely to be most successful?

6. What parts of the Taiga offer possibilities for agriculture? Describe farming in general and farm problems of the James Bay area especially. Comment on Taiga transportation, including rail, air, highway, and inland waterway. What is the character of the population? Show how the number and distribution of the population is related to the geographic environment.

7. In A. W. Currie, *Economic Geography of Canada,* read the chapter on the Canadian Shield.

8. Locate and name important economic developments associated with the following areas: Bell Island, Chibougamau, Churchill, Clay Belt, Corner Brook, Eldorado,

Flin Flon, Gander, Goose Bay, Great Slave Lake, Kapuskasing, Kirkland Lakes, Lynn Lake, Noranda, Norman Wells, North Bay, Northwest Territories, Ottawa, Pembroke, Porcupine, Port aux Basques, Rouyn, St. John's, Schefferville, Seven Islands, Sherridon, Sudbury, The Pas, Three Rivers, Yellowknife.

9. Identify the following: fur farm, lacustrine, John Cabot, banks fishing, plankton, Hudson's Bay Company, cyanide process, Canol Project, igneous, sedimentary, metamorphic.

SELECTED REFERENCES

Baum, Arthur W., "The Labrador Limited," *Saturday Evening Post,* Sept. 22, 1956.

Botts, Adelbert K., "Geographic Backgrounds of Hudson Bay History," *Social Education,* December 1947.

Brown, Eldon L., "The Sherritt Gordon Lynn Lake Project," *Canadian Mining and Metallurgical Bulletin,* June 1955.

Craig, Roland D., "The Forests of Canada," *Economic Geography,* Vol. 2, 1926, pp. 394–413.

Currie, A. W., "The Canadian Shield and The MacKenzie Valley and Hudson Bay Lowlands," *Economic Geography of Canada,* pp. 313–395, 1947, the Macmillan Co.

Debalta, Stephen L., "The Newfoundland Railroad," *Railway Progress,* March 1958.

Department of External Affairs, Information Divisions, *Fact Sheets, Canada,* 1957.

Department of Mines and Technical Surveys, *Selected Bibliography of Canadian Geography,* 1956.

Department of Resources and Development, Canada, "Forests and Forest Products Statistics," *Forestry Branch Bulletin, 106,* 1955.

Forbes, "International Nickel Company's Increase," Dec. 15, 1956, pp. 26–27.

Gerow, C., *The Story of Canada's Coal,* Canadian Coal Operator's Assoc., 1948.

Green, Thomas, "From Big Fur Empire to Chain Store Operator," *New York Times,* Jan. 8, 1958, Section C, pp. 1 and 50.

Gutsell, B. V., *An Introduction to the Geography of Newfoundland,* Department of Mines and Resources, Canada, 1949.

Hammer, Richard, "Man-Made Furs," *Barron's,* Aug. 26, 1957.

Hare, F. Kenneth, "Climate and Zonal Divisions of the Boreal Forest Formation of Eastern Canada," *Geographical Review,* October 1950, pp. 615–635.

Humphrys, Graham, "Schefferville, Quebec: A New Pioneering Town," *Geographical Review,* April 1958, pp. 151–166.

Innis, H. A., "The Hudson Bay Railway," *Geographical Review,* January 1930, pp. 1–30.

Jenness, John L., "Permafrost in Canada," *Arctic,* Vol. 2, May 1949.

McGuire, B. J., and H. E. Freeman, "Wealth from the Canadian Shield," *Canadian Geographical Journal,* Vol. 38, 1949, pp. 198–227.

Montagnes, James, "Aerial Surveys in Canada," *Barron's,* April 8, 1957.

Montagnes, James, "Rail Construction Booming in Canada's Northland," *Barron's,* Feb. 20, 1956.

New York Times, "Ontario, Heartland of Canada," April 14, 1957, Section 10, pp. 1–55.

New York Times, "Rail Plan Spurs Canadian Iron Ore Project," Feb. 15, 1959, Section 3, pp. 1 and 15.

Raisz, Erwin, *Landform Map of Canada,* Environmental Protection Section of the Office of the U. S. Quartermaster General, 1950.

Rumney, G. R., "Settlements on the Canadian Shield," *Canadian Geographical Journal,* Vol. 43, 1951, pp. 116–127.

Sanderson, Marie, "Measuring Potential Evapotranspiration at Norman Wells, 1949," *Geographical Review,* October 1950, pp. 636–645.

Shaw, Earl B., "Population Distribution in Newfoundland," *Economic Geography,* July 1938, pp. 239–254.

5 · The Middle Atlantic Coastal Plain

(Figure 1)

The Middle Atlantic Coastal Plain is a much smaller region than any of the three previously described. Moreover, in contrast to the preceding regions, two of which belong largely or entirely to Canada and the other to Denmark, the Middle Atlantic Coastal Plain lies entirely within the United States. Again, this United States region shows more intensive development than Greenland, the Tundra, or the Taiga, a development with major emphasis on intensive agriculture, manufacturing, and commerce.

Politically, the Middle Atlantic Coastal Plain is made up of parts of 5 states,[1] New Jersey, Delaware, Maryland, Virginia, and North Carolina. Latitudinally, it extends from approximately 35° north to 40° 30′ north, with a north-south extent of about 400 miles. Regional boundaries include the Atlantic on the north and east, the Fall Line on the west, and the Neuse River on the south. The Fall Line is the zone of contact between weak sedimentary rocks of the nearly level coastal plain and the more resistant igneous and metamorphic rocks of the hilly Piedmont.

The Physical Environment

Surface Features (Figs. 2, 3). Fenneman describes the region as the embayed section of the Atlantic Coastal Plain, submaturely dissected, terraced, and partly submerged. The early settlers called it the region of Sea Sand; physiographic features include offshore sand bar islands made by winds and waves, like those extending north and south of Cape Hatteras;

---

[1] Fenneman includes both Long Island and Cape Cod in the Middle Atlantic Coastal Plain. However, in this text the Cape is described in Chapter 6 with New England, to which it belongs politically, historically, and culturally; and the New York area, which lies at one entrance to the Interior Seaboard, is described in Chapter 8 with the Interior Seaboard.

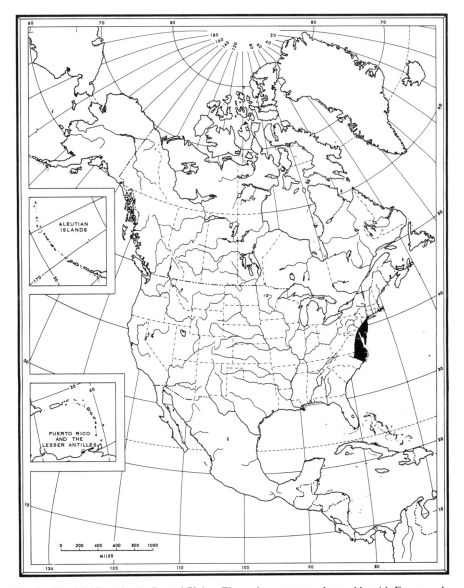

Fig. 1. The Middle Atlantic Coastal Plain. The region corresponds roughly with Fenneman's embayed section of the Atlantic Coastal Plain, minus Long Island and Cape Cod. See Nevin M. Fenneman, *Physical Divisions of the United States.*

estuaries, like Delaware Bay and Chesapeake Bay; peninsulas, such as the Delmarva Peninsula lying between the two water bodies and including parts of Delaware, Maryland, and Virginia; rivers flowing in a general east-west direction, including the Neuse, Roanoke, James, Rappahannock, and

Fig. 2.   Coastal Plain and Bordering Physical Regions.   The photograph of a portion of the Babson Model of United States land forms shows surface features of the Coastal Plain, the Piedmont, the Blue Ridge, the Great Valley, and the Ridge and Valley subregion.   Notice Richmond, Washington, and Baltimore at the western boundary of the Coastal Plain near the Fall Line; Dover, Ocean City, and Annapolis lie on the Middle Atlantic Coastal Plain.   (Courtesy Babson Institute of Business Administration.)

Potomac; low-lying coastal swamps; and water bodies such as Pamlico Sound and Albemarle Sound lying between the mainland and the offshore sand bar islands.   It is well to keep in mind that geologically the Atlantic Coastal Plain extends from Cape Cod to Panama.

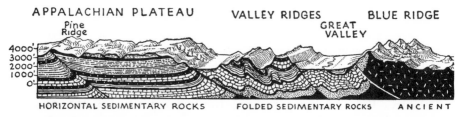

Fig. 3.   Diagrammatic Structure Section Through Virginia.   Note the contact zone between newer sediments of the coastal plain and the ancient crystalline complex rocks of the piedmont

Climate (Fig. 4). Probably the most important climatic controls are (*a*) distribution of land and water, (*b*) latitude, (*c*) prevailing winds, and (*d*) cyclonic storms. The position of the region on the leeward side of the United States gives much warmer summers and colder winters than those of coastal Oregon and Washington with their higher latitudes and marine climates. Again, the colonists who landed in Jamestown in 1607 found winters milder and summers warmer than the winters and summers of Plymouth, Massachusetts, where colonists settled a few years later. Temperature differences between the two latter locations are largely a result of differences in latitude—Plymouth 41° 55' north and Jamestown 37° north. Cyclonic storms of the westerly wind belt draw in ocean air on frequent occasions, and coastal location saves farm crops from frost when those of the interior may be damaged seriously. The southern part of the Middle Atlantic Coastal Plain has a humid subtropical climate, and the northern part a humid continental long-summer type.

Soils and Vegetation. Soils belong to the pedalfer group, with gray brown podzolics in the north, and red and yellow podzolics in the south. Within these general classes there is great variety. Sandy soils cover large areas and much of the sand is underlain with gravel. Such soils have good drainage. In the vicinity of Camden, large amounts of both clay and marl occur in the soil. In a few places, especially in the cranberry bogs of New Jersey, peat marsh lands possess a clay subsoil. Approximately 1,200 sq. mi. of the state, almost one-sixth of its total area, has been called the Pine Barrens; this section has remained undeveloped, largely because the soils are too sandy or gravelly to encourage field agriculture—especially with better soils in abundance not far away (Fig. 5).

The natural vegetation includes marsh grass along coastal swampy sections, and forests of pine, oak, tupelo, and gum on the better drained lands. Oak and pine trees dominate forests north of Chesapeake Bay, and tupelo and gum are widespread in the south. Today approximately half of the area remains in cut-over forest and brush, in spite of 350 years of European settlement, and the nearness to great urban centers such as New York and Philadelphia.

P I E D M O N T

COASTAL PLAIN
FALL BELT (T i d e w a t e r)

OCEAN

CRYSTALLINE COMPLEX ROCKS   NEWER SEDIMENTS

in the Fall Belt. (After Wallace W. Atwood, *The Physiographic Provinces of North America*, Ginn and Co.)

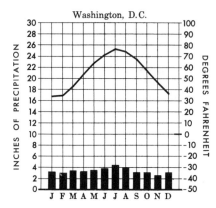

Fig. 4. Washington, D. C. (38° 55′ N., 77° 0′ W.; altitude 75 feet; mean annual temp. 55° F.; mean annual precip. 40.7 inches). Washington climate belongs to the humid subtropical type (Ca) with hot summers and relatively mild winters. July and August heat, together with high relative humidity, not shown on the chart, makes summers unpleasant and air conditioned homes and offices almost a *must*. However, this coastal plain climate encourages rapid plant growth.

Colonial Agriculture

Tobacco was the money crop of colonial days. A few quotations from colonial laws may emphasize its importance at that time.

Every person who refuses to have his child baptised by a lawful minister shall be amerced 2,000 pounds of tobacco; half to the parish, half to the informer. . . . In actions of slander occasioned by a man's wife, after judgment passed for damages, the woman shall be punished by ducking, and if the slander be such as the damage shall be adjudged at above 500 pounds of tobacco, then the woman shall have a ducking for every 500 pounds of tobacco judged against her husband, if he refuses to pay the tobacco. . . . Enacted that the Lord's Day be kept holy, and no journeys be made on that day, unless upon necessity. And all persons inhabiting in this country having no lawful excuse, shall every Sunday resort to the parish church or chapel, and there abide orderly during the common prayer, preaching, and divine service, upon the penalty of being fined 50 pounds of tobacco in the county court.[2]

Besides being used for payment of fines, tobacco was used in Maryland and Virginia as payment for wages, debts, and taxes; and during the Revolution, Virginia leaf was used to pay interest on loans from France and to pay for war materials.

Since tobacco is a soil robber, Coastal Plain soils were soon depleted of their fertility through overemphasis upon tobacco; and many parts of the region went through the cycle of clearing forest lands, planting tobacco on the clearings, soil depletion, and reversion to second-growth forest.

Agriculture Today

Production of tobacco on the coastal plain is no longer so important as it was in the days of early settlement. Only in southern Maryland, west

[2] See G. T. Surface, "Geography of Virginia," *Bulletin of the Philadelphia Geographical Society,* Vol. 5, 1907, pp. 1–60.

of Chesapeake Bay, and in northeastern North Carolina can it be considered a cash crop of any significance.   Now the region is best known for its truck crops, that is, vegetables such as potatoes, tomatoes, sweet potatoes, beans, peas, and cabbage, and fruits such as strawberries, blueberries, and cranberries.   Tree fruits, including peaches and apples, are also grown (Figs. 6, 7, 8, 9).

Edward Higbee has described well the vegetable production on the Atlantic Coastal Plain in his story of "A Delmarva Vegetable Farm," *American Agriculture,* John Wiley and Sons, 1958, pp. 362–366.   Most of this geographic study follows below:

The southern tip of the Delmarva Peninsula, sometimes called Virginia's Eastern Shore, is one of the most important vegetable crop centers on the Atlantic seaboard. There the tempo of the truck market is such that all men cannot take it.   It divides them, as they say, into two classes: the "plungers" and the "stayers."   The plungers are the gamblers.   They buy land or rent it at high prices, and they don't hedge themselves by preseason contracts with dealers.   Such contracts assure the grower the mini-

Fig. 5.   New Jersey "Pine Barrens."   A large part of New Jersey is in forest, much of which lies in the southern part of the state, where trees cover over 1,200,000 acres.   The above view shows "the Plains," a stunted portion of the "Pine Barrens"; the photo was taken from a fire tower on Route S-40.   Note the fringe of taller trees along the left edge of the highway, due in part to less severe burning the last time the area was swept by fire.   Note also the broad expanse of level land, so typical of Middle Atlantic Coastal Plain topography.   (Courtesy Dr. Del Botts and New Jersey Department of Conservation and Economic Development.)

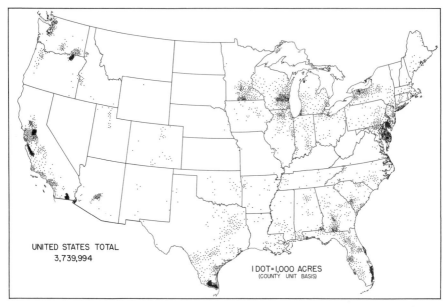

UNITED STATES TOTAL
3,739,994

I DOT=1,000 ACRES
(COUNTY UNIT BASIS)

Fig. 6. Vegetables Harvested for Sale. Other Than Irish and Sweet Potatoes. Note the heavy concentration of dots along the Middle Atlantic Coastal Plain. (Courtesy U. S. Department of Commerce, Bureau of the Census.)

Fig. 7. Ensilage Cutter and Loader on New Jersey Dairy Farm. This is a typical scene of cutting corn for silage in New Jersey. The chopped-up corn will be taken to a silo and blown in. New Jersey dairy farms produce 500,000 tons of corn silage a year. Proximity to a large urban market makes dairying as profitable to New Jersey farmers as raising vegetables and poultry. Notice the forest in the background; nearly half of New Jersey is still in forest. (Courtesy Dr. Del Botts and New Jersey Department of Agriculture.)

Fig. 8. White Leghorns on the George R. Parker Poultry Farm, Plainsboro, New Jersey. The feeders in the foreground are automatic and operate on a continuous belt running through the poultry house. The arrangement is a push button operation. New Jersey's location in the heart of a huge urban district gives a strong market boost to the poultry industry. (Courtesy Dr. Del Botts and New Jersey Department of Agriculture.)

mum price, but they also tie him up so that if the market should be high he cannot take advantage of it. The stayers are the conservatives; the ones with long memories and some with land titles in their families dating back to the King's Grants. They are the ones who rent lands to the plungers or play it safe by contracting their crops to dealers at low but guaranteed prices. They never have bonanza years, but neither do they lose their farms as long as they remain cautious.

Nearly every city of any size has market gardeners on its periphery who supply perishables in season; but, as every housewife knows, some fresh vegetables are on the counters of grocery stores and supermarkets every day of the year. To supply these truck crops in a steady flow there must be crops to harvest somewhere at all times. . . . [Figure 6] shows the distribution of commercial vegetable farming. Certain areas stand out prominently, and it will be noted that with few exceptions the most important ones are either near the sea or on the shores of the Great Lakes. Other features of the distribution pattern are the areas of concentrated production extending from subtropical Florida to the Canadian border. These two factors of location and spread are both intimately tied in with the gambling aspects of vegetable farming.

We may use the example of green beans to illustrate the tight schedule by which a vegetable crop comes on the market. The green bean season begins with the harvest

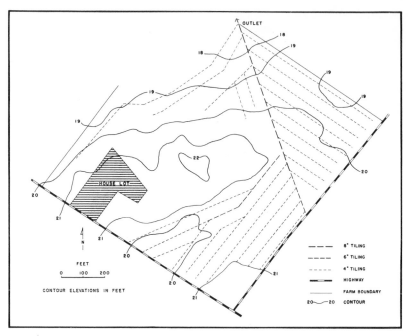

Fig. 9.   Drainage Systems on a Virginia Eastern Shore Truck Farm. (Source: Edward Higbee, *American Agriculture,* John Wiley and Sons, 1958.)

in southern Florida in February or early March.   By the middle of March central Florida and the Rio Grande Valley of Texas are already in competition, and by the first of May there are harvests in California and along the Gulf coast.   As more localities contribute to the supply, prices may decline.   The first growers to harvest are generally, but not always, the ones who receive the best prices.   From the end of May to early July so many areas are producing green beans that proximity to the biggest market is more of an advantage than timing.   It is then that the growers of New Jersey, Long Island, and the Lake Ontario area compete with one another for the nearby metropolitan markets.   After the middle of July the growing season is generally too warm for successful production, except at high altitudes in the West, along the shores of Lake Ontario, or near the coasts of Maine, Oregon, and Washington.

Such a schedule as that outlined is a general one which is certain to vary with changes in the weather.   Because temperature variation is reduced near oceans and lake shores these locations are preferred by the growers of many specialty crops.   Also the sea tends to warm the air over coastal lands during the early spring months and thus hastens the season.   In summer the sea and the Great Lakes tend to cool the air along their shores, thus extending the season where high temperatures might otherwise do damage.

It may be noted that the most important centers of production in the humid East are:

1. Peninsular Florida which is bounded by the Gulf and the Atlantic.

2. The Delmarva Peninsula bounded by Delaware Bay, the Atlantic, and Chesapeake Bay.

3. Southern New Jersey, bounded by the Atlantic and Delaware Bay.
4. Long Island in the Atlantic.
5. The shore of Lake Ontario.

The terrain of these areas is level to gently rolling. This permits intensive cultivation with little prospect of soil erosion. Of particular advantage is the sandy loam texture of coastal plain soils from Long Island southward. These light-textured soils drain more easily and warm more quickly in the early spring than heavier textured soils which are common farther inland. The matter of getting a crop to market just a few days early may mean the difference between a substantial profit and a small one. The farm with the best-drained soil, nearest the sea, at the right latitude, may be worth two or three times as much per acre as another farm only a few miles or a few degrees distant but not so well situated.

As we know, drainage is one of the common problems on the coastal plain. . . . [Figure 9] shows the design of a tile drainage system on a truck farm in Accomack County, Virginia, which is on the Delmarva Peninsula, or "Eastern Shore." The one-foot contour lines reveal the nearly level character of this land, and the figures on the contour lines indicate the slight elevation above sea level. In Accomack County, as elsewhere on the coastal plain, the possibilities for irrigation are often excellent. Rainfall is approximately 43 inches annually, and there are many fresh-water swamps and brackish estuaries. By placing dams across the estuaries, the tides can be repulsed and the waters kept fresh. Some swamps may be converted into reservoirs by damming the streams which drain them. Supplementary irrigation is now becoming common on the Eastern Shore, just as it is in Florida, the Carolinas, in New Jersey, and on Long Island. In fact, irrigation is rapidly becoming essential to vegetable farming everywhere because the investment risk is too great to trust to natural rainfall. Some farmers are discovering that they may bring crops to market a week or two ahead of normal schedule by planting early in spring before the danger of frost is past. By using sprinkler irrigation systems on frosty nights they keep the plants from being nipped.

The preceding study by Dr. Higbee shows that man must take advantage of every favorable feature of the physical environment and of the market to make a success of vegetable farming, an industry of great importance on the Middle Atlantic Coastal Plain.

Other steps that man is taking to expand Coastal Plain vegetable and fruit production and to make this type of farming more profitable include improved methods in canning, in freezing, in transport refrigeration, and in dietary education, especially in making people vitamin conscious.

However, in spite of man's ingenuity and a relatively favorable physical environment, large amounts of Middle Atlantic Coast land remain out of production because of surpluses in both fruit and vegetable crops; in fact, overproduction is a major problem in this region, just as it is throughout most of the commercial crop producing areas of the nation. The presence of large numbers of mosquitoes is another factor discouraging agricultural expansion. Mosquitoes find ideal breeding grounds in the enormous area of poorly drained lands. It may be as easy and as cheap to expand crop lands by correcting United States drainage conditions as to keep building so many dams in dry regions to expand irrigation agriculture.

Manufacturing and Commerce

Nearness to the great United States market, ocean accessibility to world-wide raw materials and markets, proximity to Appalachian coal and hydroelectric power, climate, labor, and capital—these and other factors have attracted manufacturing to the Middle Atlantic Coastal Plain.

Market is probably the most important of many factors in industrial localization. Within and near the region is the country's greatest concentration of population with high living standards. Moreover, seaside location not only gives easy opportunity for sales in port cities of other countries, but also provides opportunity for purchasing raw materials not easily available in the United States. Foreign raw materials and exports of manufactured goods move over the world's cheapest highway, the ocean.

United States Steel's Fairless plant (Fig. 10) on the Delaware River and Bethlehem Steel's Sparrows Point works at tidewater near Baltimore may be cited to emphasize the influence of market and coastal situation upon industrial location. Coastal plants of Bethlehem and United States Steel draw iron ore from Venezuela, Cuba, Chile, Liberia, Labrador, and other well known iron resource areas. Almost 5,000,000 tons of iron ore entered Delaware River ports in 1954. Coal is obtained largely from nearby interior mines of West Virginia, but it can be brought like iron from one of several foreign market resources. Limestone is easily available from Pennsylvania.

The Delaware and Potomac rivers supply quantities of fresh water needed in the manufacture of iron and steel. Many steel mills use as much as 65,000 gallons of water in manufacturing one ton of steel. Humid continental and subtropical climates, especially their coastal portions, are characterized by 40 to 60 inches of mean annual precipitation, rather evenly distributed through the year. Such a rainfall assures relatively adequate and constant stream flow in both the Delaware and the Potomac.

River mouths like those of the Delaware and Potomac, together with estuaries and bays at their seaward extremities, offer ideal locations for ship building (Fig. 11). Factors of the physical environment are as favorable as those on Scotland's Clyde River, but labor costs are somewhat higher in America.

Besides market and seaboard location, the availability of large areas of flat land gives further advantage for steel plants as well as for other factories. The Fairless steel works covers 2,000 level acres, most of which were formerly planted to spinach; and the original land purchase includes nearly as many more acres for possible future expansion.

Local raw materials of surplus fruits and vegetables probably provide the most important influence upon the Middle Atlantic Coastal Plain's high rank in fruit and vegetable processing. More canning and freezing

Fig. 10. Aerial View of U. S. Steel Corporation's Fairless Works. In the foreground is the water-filled slip where ocean going carriers bring ore from foreign countries. Back of the slip, center, are unloading docks, ore storage yard, ore bridge, and blast furnaces. Location with reference to world and local markets was a significant factor in the building of the Fairless Works at Morrisville, Pennsylvania. (Courtesy United States Steel Corporation.)

occur in the southern portion of the region than in the north, probably because the south lies at a greater distance from the big market for fresh produce.

Market and coastal locations encourage sugar refining, just as they do oil refineries and chemical plants; but availability of skilled labor is of more than average importance in the location of several aircraft plants. Funds for industrial expansion may be secured for any sound manufacturing enterprise. Of all factors affecting industry, capital and labor are the most mobile. Both will move to any place that offers good profits and wages.

Falls and rapids along the western boundary of the Coastal Plain influenced choice of location for many early colonial settlements. Here a change of transport was necessary and here it was possible to utilize water power for colonial manufacturing. Colonists started the town of Philadelphia at a place where the Schuylkill River passes from the hard old rocks

Fig. 11. Tankers under Construction at Sparrows Point, Maryland. Nearby iron and steel, tidewater location, proximity to markets, and ample supplies of capital and labor encourage shipbuilding. The Sparrows Point plant is one of the major shipbuilding yards in the United States. It led the world on a tonnage basis in 1953. (Courtesy of Bethlehem Steel Company.)

of the bordering uplands to the weaker younger sediments of the Coastal Plain (Fig. 3). Early development of Baltimore was also influenced by the same Fall Line boundary.

Baltimore's leading industries with their percentages of the nearly 200,000 industrial employees in June 1956 were: primary metal industries, 20.7 per cent; transportation equipment 19.5 per cent; food and kindred products 10.4 per cent; apparel and other fabric products 7.7 per cent; fabricated metal products 6.9 per cent; chemicals and allied products 5.0 per cent; printing and publishing 4.7 per cent; non-electrical machinery 4.4 per cent; and electrical machinery 4.0 per cent.

The city's early commerce was based upon trade between the Chesapeake Bay area and England, the West Indies, and New England. Today, its interior location has an advantage over other Atlantic ports by its nearness to the Middle West, but the route to Europe is lengthened by the interior position, and a location west of the Delmarva Peninsula. This situation necessitates a long southward movement before any ship may turn northeast towards Europe. The north-south path is an advantage, however, in trade with the West Indies.

Philadelphia, like Baltimore, possesses diversified manufactures; and fully 87 per cent of all the country's manufacturing industries listed in the United States census "blue book" are represented in the former city. But unlike Baltimore, Philadelphia is surrounded by satellite cities and towns, also busily engaged in manufacturing and commerce.[3]

The foreign commerce of Philadelphia and its satellites is not well balanced as to exports and imports. In 1950, imports of the Greater Philadelphia area amounted to 94 per cent of the total, and three-fourths of the import tonnage was crude oil for riverside refineries. In 1950, foreign imports and exports made up 37 per cent of the total commerce—69,000,000 tons; 44 per cent was coastwise trade; and 19 per cent was local trade.

Several cities, including Norfolk, Newport News, and Portsmouth, have grown up around Hampton Roads near the mouth of the James River. Excellent harbor facilities favor the use of the area by the U. S. Navy, and trains moving downgrade from interior coal fields find excellent port facilities for shipment of high-grade bituminous coal. Commerce and naval affairs are more important than manufacturing around Hampton Roads.

Megalopolis

Because of the manufacturing, commerce, and other conditions, many parts of the Middle Atlantic Coastal Plain form an almost continuous urban district. Thus, Jean Gottman has included several sections (Fig. 12) in the Megalopolis described in the July 1957 issue of *Economic Geography*. A few excerpts from this useful article appear below.

[Megalopolis extends] from a little north of Boston to a little south of Washington, more precisely from Hillsborough County in New Hampshire to Fairfax County in Virginia. . . . The super-metropolitan character of this vast area, the greatest such growth ever observed, called for a special name. We chose the word *Megalopolis,* of Greek origin, and listed in Webster's dictionary as meaning "a very large city."

---

[3] For example Morrisville, Pennsylvania, is the home of United States Steel's Fairless plant. Across the Delaware River is Trenton, New Jersey, which manufactures a long list of articles in its more than 300 industrial plants—articles ranging from structural steel to Lenox china. Between Trenton and Philadelphia are Burlington, with cast iron pipe mills; Bristol, with chemical factories; Florence, with pipe mills; and Roebling, with wire plants. Across the Delaware from Philadelphia are Camden, New Jersey, with rows of shipways from which newly built ships slide down into the Delaware, and Gloucester, a busy port of call for ships bringing specialized products such as licorice and cork. A little downstream from Philadelphia is Paulsboro, where tankers heavy with crude oil make frequent calls; across the river is Eddystone, Pennsylvania, which should be renamed Baldwin for all the locomotives built there; a short distance downstream lies Chester, Pennsylvania, where many oil tankers are constructed; nearby is Marcus Hook, Pennsylvania, famous for petroleum and rayon; a few miles across the Pennsylvania-Delaware border is Claymont, Delaware, noted for chemicals and steel; and a little to the south lies Wilmington, Delaware, one of the nation's most famous chemical towns. In the Philadelphia Metropolitan area, major industries employing most of the 600,000 workers in 1952 included apparel, chemicals, food, machinery, printing and publishing, textiles, and transportation equipment.

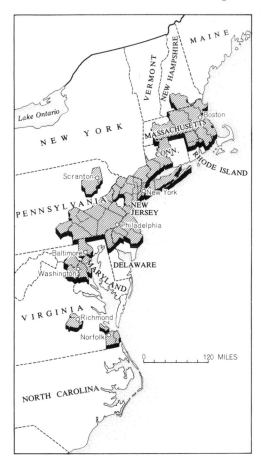

Fig. 12. Megalopolis, 1950. The
northern portion of the Middle Atlantic Coastal Plain and a small part of
the southern section may be noted on
the above map. (Courtesy Jean Gottman and *Economic Geography*.)

. . . Megalopolis grew up from the network provided by the early mushrooming
of sea-trading towns along the coast from Boston to New York and then, along the
Fall Line, from New York to Washington. James Madison defined New Jersey as a
"Barrel tapped at both ends"; that this state's function was essentially to link the area
of New York and Philadelphia was apparently understood by such a clever observer
at the end of the eighteenth century. . . .

Megalopolis' growth in the past sums up a good part of the economic history of
the United States. Although it is, in area, only a small section of the Northeast,
Megalopolis had a crucial part in determining national trends; on the other hand, the
main swings of its own history were usually the consequence of shifts in national
policies.

Why was Megalopolis' growth throughout its history more rapid and continuous
than that of many other urban areas in the world? This question leads to an examination of the factors motivating or determining urban expansion in a given area. . . .
The two major ones among these factors appear to be on the one hand, the polynu-
clear origin and the part played by the series of northeastern seaboard cities as a *hinge*
of the American economy. The federal organization of government and the division
of the Atlantic seaboard into so many states (each with access to Tidewater) that en-

gaged in a fruitful rivalry made all nuclei compete one with another until their growth joined them together.

The role of the "hinge" is more difficult to perceive, but is easily demonstrated by the material accumulated in regional economic history. This seaboard had from the inception of the United States the opportunity and the responsibility of serving both as an oceanic façade for relations abroad and as a springboard for the settlement and development of the continent inland. At different periods the main weight of the northeastern interests oscillated from sea trade to continental development and back again; in New England one of these oscillations in the beginning of the nineteenth century was defined as the period when the main interest shifted "from the wharf to the waterfall." In many towns which, on the Fall Line, were later integrated with the area of Megalopolis, wharf and waterfall were very close to one another. Whether the general trends of the American economy threw the door open towards the outside or closed it to turn the main endeavors inland, the hinge remained fixed at the series of eastern cities, extending from Boston to Washington, which alone had the geographical position, the authority, the capital, and the skill to elaborate such policies and put them into application.

The inheritance of the past still influences heavily present situations and trends. Whether the eastern seaboard will keep the monopoly of the "hinge" advantages after the St. Lawrence Seaway is completed remains a burning question. However, the faculty of direct access to the sea was only one of many factors which favored Megalopolis, and the others may still operate in the future.

Prominent among the other factors listed and discussed by Gottman in his article are the manufacturing function, the commercial and financial functions, and the functions of cultural leadership.

Fishing

Fishing is of some importance along the coast. As is the case in most fishing areas, the commercial fish belong to two main types, demersal, or bottom feeders, and pelagic, or surface swimmers. The oyster, a shell fish, has many demersal characteristics. For a few days after birth, until oysters settle and anchor on rocks, brush, or bits of shell on shallow bottoms, the fish are free-swimming larvae. But they spend most of their lives feeding on the sea bottom. Most of the mature oysters are captured with tongs or by dragging weighted dredges behind oyster boats (Fig. 13), primarily in the Chesapeake and Delaware bays.[4]

[4] For a long while, Maryland's oyster fishing grounds were known the world over; between 1880 and 1890 the annual catch amounted to 12,500,000 bushels, more than half of the world's total. In a recent year, 1950, only 100,000 bushels were taken from the same Chesapeake Bay waters where temperature, salinity, and freedom from most enemies except man are relatively ideal. Overfishing is the reason for the decline, and how to control fishing and win back a formerly flourishing industry is a conservation problem that Maryland would like to solve. New Jersey would also like to solve the problem of declining oyster production. In 1901, the oyster take was approximately 20,000,000 pounds; a half century later, only about 5,000,000 pounds were taken from nearby waters. Besides overfishing, New Jersey's conservation problems include control of the starfish and other natural enemies of the oyster. The Bivalve Experimental Station of Rutgers University has been active in conservation research connected with commercial fisheries.

Fig. 13.   Oyster Boat in Chesapeake Bay.   Maryland's conservation regulations forbid the use of power boats in dredging oysters; so the dredgers use the bugeye—a sailing boat big enough to weather rough water in the open bay.   Two conspicuous hawse holes for anchor chains, one on each bow, give the bugeye its name.   (Courtesy Standard Oil Company, New Jersey.)

Although menhaden range from Louisiana to Maine, they are important pelagic fish caught along the Middle Atlantic Coastal Plain.   In fact, this fish leads in total annual tonnage marketed by United States fishermen.[5]   Menhaden, about a foot in length and weighing approximately a

[5] When menhaden schools are spotted by airplane or other means, fleets of tuglike vessels, approximately 100 feet long, carrying purse seines travel out to trap these pelagic fish.   Such ships return with their cargo to shore bases from Louisiana to New York, for menhaden migrate as far as Maine in the summer to seek ocean temperatures of approximately 50°F.   In short, they follow the summer sun poleward to gain the temperatures they like.

pound at maturity, are so bony that they are seldom used for human food, but they supply millions of gallons of oil for steel-plating purposes, for leather currying, for linoleum making, and as a general substitute for linseed oil. They also supply thousands of tons of nitrate-rich fertilizer as well as thousands of bags of meal for feeding poultry and livestock. Other fish caught by Middle Atlantic coastal fishermen include blue crab, shad, flounder, sea trout, butterfish, and alewives.

The Tourist Industry

One of the most important factors attracting tourists to any locality is nearness to a dense population with relatively high standards of living. Potential tourist resorts may have the most beautiful scenery in the world, but if they are far removed from population centers, development is likely to be delayed or unlikely to take place. The Middle Atlantic Coastal Plain has not the breath-taking scenery of the Alaskan Panhandle or of southern Chile, but it does have long stretches of barrier beaches making up its coast line, most of which are suitable for bathing; and the sea that borders them contains water much warmer than that of the New England coast; furthermore, there are opportunities for boating and fishing, which may also prove interesting to tourists. Such tourists may come from New York State, containing more than 15,000,000 people, from Pennsylvania with about 10,000,-000 people, and from other densely populated areas lying east of the Mississippi River.

Atlantic City (Fig. 14), one of America's most famous resorts, has been built on a barrier beach in the northern part of the region; and Virginia Beach, near historic Kitty Hawk flying field of Wright brothers' fame, has become a famous resort on the southern part of the plain.

Beaches are not the only regional attraction for tourists. The nation's capital, Washington, D. C., probably attracts as many visitors as any other city in the United States. Here they may view historical as well as present government institutions. Famous historical restorations such as Williamsburg, Virginia, also attract thousands of tourists annually.

Regional Unity and Regional Future

In retrospect we may ask what sets apart the Middle Atlantic portion of North America's Coastal Plain as a geographic region. On three sides, the east, the north, and the west, the Atlantic and the Fall Line make definite physical boundaries. On the south, there is no rock or water boundary, but an agricultural one, largely based upon climate; here is the approximate northern boundary of cotton growing.

From an economic standpoint several features contribute to regional

Fig. 14. Boardwalk, Atlantic City, New Jersey. Location on a barrier beach near large population centers contributes important advantages for the tourist industry. (Courtesy Standard
Oil Company, New Jersey.)

unity: (*a*) truck crops are significant in agriculture; (*b*) activities associated
with the sea, the nation's capital,[6] and historical centers dominate the tourist industry; (*c*) several coastal indentations, good harbors, and the bordering sea have long encouraged commercial enterprises; (*d*) ocean proximity
beckoned man to harvest fish from the sea; and (*e*) the nation's two great
tidewater steel plants, Sparrows Point and the Fairless works strengthen
regional manufacturing.

Agricultural possibilities of the region are attractive. Climate and
terrain are generally encouraging; soils have relatively good structure, and
what is lacking in fertility may be improved by commercial fertilizer, easily
accessible. A large market is close by and land prices have not boomed
so wildly as in some parts of the United States. Yet farming has many
problems: much land needs drainage; mosquitoes discourage land purchase
and operation; and crop surpluses may eliminate profits.

Both physical and man-made factors encourage expansion in manufacturing, commerce, recreational industries, fishing, and other occupations.

[6] Its central location among the early colonies encouraged site selection of the nation's capital—a location that is far from the center today, and one that may be extremely vulnerable to
enemy attack, just as it was in the past.

QUESTIONS, EXERCISES, AND PROBLEMS

1. Indicate the states that contain parts of the Middle Atlantic Coastal Plain. Describe its boundaries, surface features, climates, soils, and natural vegetation.

2. Point out the geography of the Jamestown settlement. Show relationships between early tobacco production and colonial life.

3. Give the geographic background for the region's agriculture. How do sandy soils influence the early marketing of vegetables? Irrigation has increased rapidly in eastern United States since 1950. Explain the significance of irrigation in the Middle Atlantic Coastal Plain. How successful has cooperative marketing of farm products become?

4. Analyze the regional advantages for manufacturing—iron and steel, processing of fruits and vegetables, ship building, etc. Scrap iron has become an extremely important factor in iron and steel manufacturing. Consult the *Bethlehem Review*, reference cited, or some other source and explain the advantages of scrap iron for manufacturing. Point out the materials used, where they are procured, and the processes involved in the manufacture of iron and steel. The region is known for its production of commercial fertilizers. What materials are used and what processes are employed in this type of manufacturing?

5. Describe the various activities involved in oyster farming.

6. Compare the background of the tourist industry with that of New England. Tell of the urban geography, using such examples as Atlantic City, Baltimore, Camden, Chester, Newport News, Norfolk, Philadelphia, Portsmouth, Richmond, Trenton, and Washington, D. C. What is the meaning of Megalopolis? Account for its development in northeastern United States.

7. What characteristics favor regional unity? Comment on future economic trends.

8. Identify the following: Fall Line, Delmarva, the coastal plain geologic region, Sparrows Point, Fairless, the American Clyde, menhaden, starfish.

SELECTED REFERENCES

American Tobacco Co., *The First Fifty Years,* 1954.

Angell, Orson, "The Eastern Shore," *The Lamp,* Spring-Summer, 1958, pp. 10–15.

Baltimore Chamber of Commerce, *Baltimore: Its Supporting Economy,* 1957.

Bethlehem Steel Corporation, "Shipbreaking Feeds Scrap to Bethlehem's Furnaces," *Bethlehem Review,* June 1958.

Federal Reserve Bank of Philadelphia, *Industry on the Delaware,* 1952.

Gottman, Jean, "Megalopolis or the Urbanization of the Northeastern Seaboard," *Economic Geography,* July 1957, pp. 189–200.

Gottman, Jean, *Virginia at Mid-Century,* Henry Holt and Co., 1955.

Green, Paul, "The Epic of Jamestown," *The New York Times Magazine,* March 31, 1957.

Higbee, Edward, *American Agriculture,* John Wiley and Sons, 1958.

Miller, Scott A., "Irrigation Moves East," *Better Crops With Plant Food,* June–July 1958.

Mullaney, Thomas E., "Fairless Works is Still Growing," *New York Times,* March 4, 1956.

New Jersey State Promotion Section, *Know Your State,* 1953.

New York Times, "Old Oyster War in a New Phase," March 10, 1957, p. 84.

New York Times, "2 States Observe Truce on Oysters," Feb. 8, 1959, Section 2, p. 54.

Philadelphia Chamber of Commerce, *Greater Philadelphia Facts,* 1958.

Shalett, Sidney, "Look What they're Doing to the Delaware," *Saturday Evening Post,* Sept. 30, 1950.

Surface, G. T., "Geography of Virginia," *Bulletin of the Philadelphia Geographical Society,* Vol. 5, 1907, pp. 1–60.

Thruelsen, Richard, "The Secrets of Jamestown," *Saturday Evening Post,* Feb. 9, 1957.

6 · The Northeast

(Figure 1)

The Northeast is bigger than the Middle Atlantic Coastal Plain, although it is not one of the larger regions of the continent. In an area smaller than Texas, it contains New Brunswick, Nova Scotia, Prince Edward Island, part of the province of Quebec that lies south of the St. Lawrence, New England, and northeastern New York.

Regional boundaries are almost entirely of water; on the north are the St. Lawrence River and Gulf; the Atlantic forms the eastern border, and with Long Island Sound makes up the southern fringe; on the west, the boundary follows (a) the Hudson Lowland north to Albany, (b) the Mohawk and Ontario Lowland west to Lake Ontario, and (c) Lake Ontario's eastern shore as far north as the St. Lawrence Lowland.

Besides boundaries composed mostly of water, large areas of the Northeast are covered by water. Look at the map of northern Maine and note the large number of glacial lakes. All this watery landscape gives a certain regional unity. The nearby ocean and inland lakes and rivers encourage fishing in both Maritime Canada and in New England. Again, in both Canadian and United States portions, water falls, some glacially caused and others resulting from differential erosion, provide bases for hydroelectric power. Waterfalls, lakes, and sea also contribute tourist attractions for the entire region. Regional forests are partly a result of the water surfaces and partly a response to large land areas too rugged for successful agriculture. The nearby sea aids tree cover by furnishing ample, well-distributed precipitation for the conifers of the north and the mixed forest of the south. Tree cover, the bordering ocean, lakes, streams, and water falls, the dominantly rugged terrain, and location within the continent all contribute a high degree of unity in the physical landscape.

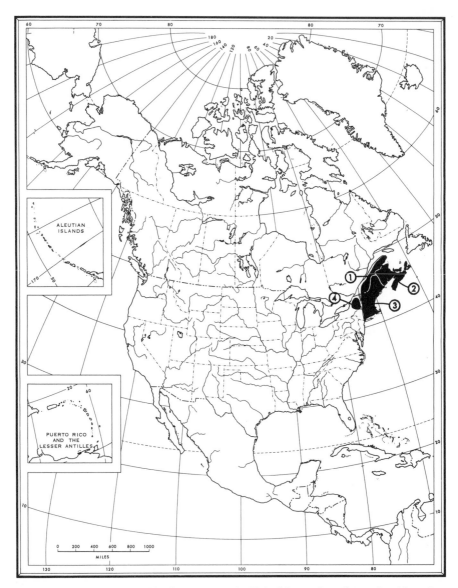

Fig. 1.   The Northeast.   The Northeast crosses the United States-Canadian national boundary
to include (1) part of the Canadian province of Quebec, lying south of the St. Lawrence; (2) the
Canadian Maritime Provinces of New Brunswick, Nova Scotia, and Prince Edward Island; (3)
New England; and (4) the Adirondacks in the United States.

Man's response to the physical environment is not unified throughout the entire region. There is no unity of history, no unity of government, and no unity in land use. In spite of many differences in man's adjustment to the geographic environment, we may consider the Northeast as a major geographic region.

The Physical Environment

Surface Features. Land forms are dominated by the poleward extension of the Appalachian Mountains. The old worn-down ranges with their gentle slopes and rounded summits show contrast to the higher, steeper, and more youthful Rockies in the western part of the continent. Highlands include the Green Mountains of Vermont, the Adirondacks of New York, the Caledonia, Boundary, Notre Dame, and Schickshock ranges of Canada, and the Berkshire Hills of Massachusetts. West of the Berkshires and the Green Mountains are the very old Taconics. East of the Green Mountains are the White Mountains, the highest in the Northeast, with New Hampshire's Mount Washington rising to 6,293 feet; in Maine, Katahdin reaches 5,273 feet, but altitudes become progressively lower in northern Maine and New Brunswick.

Scattered among the old worn down mountains are lowlands such as the Connecticut Valley, the Annapolis-Cornwallis Valley of Nova Scotia, Maine's Aroostook Valley, and Cape Cod, which geologically belongs to the North Atlantic Coastal Plain, but is included in the Northeast, because culturally it is a part of New England. Along the coast narrow marine terraces occur in places, and coastal lowlands extend a short distance toward the interior around the Maritime Provinces and the Gaspé Peninsula.

In addition to the worn-down mountains and scattered lowlands, there are plateaus, conspicuous in northern Maine and in parts of the Maritime Provinces. A hilly belt fringes the coast in many areas; average height is a few hundred feet above sea level, but it rises to over 1,500 feet on Maine's Mount Desert Island. Lowland, hill, plateau, and mountain, all show many evidences of glaciation, and glacial lakes may be counted by the thousand.

Climate (Fig. 2). With the exception of the Gaspé Peninsula, the climate belongs to the humid, continental, cool summer type. Winter is the dominant season and the long period of snow cover is a factor favorable to winter sports. Summers are shorter and cooler than those of the Middle Atlantic Coast, and coastal waters are colder. Thus, swimming generally is not so attractive at Northeast shore resorts. The colder waters offshore are caused by the cold Labrador current and higher latitude. Cyclonic storms are active and the Northeast is a major continental outlet for low pressure areas moving towards the Icelandic Low. Location on the leeward side of the continent and near the Atlantic contributes both

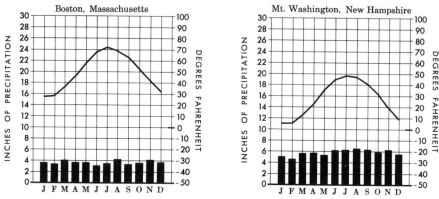

Fig. 2. Mount Washington, New Hampshire (44° 16′ N., 71° 18′ W.; altitude 6,262 feet; mean annual temp. 26.9° F.; mean annual precip. 70.66 inches); Boston, Massachusetts (42° 15′ N., 71° 7′ W.; altitude 124 feet; mean annual temp. 49° F.; mean annual precip. 44.6 inches). Considerable contrast occurs between the climate of Mt. Washington, over 6,000 feet above sea level, and the climate of Boston, approximately sea level. With no month showing an average temperature above 50° F., the top of Mt. Washington rises above the tree line.

continental and marine influences. Altitude provides an important climatic control on high mountain areas. Length of growing season ranges from 200 days in the south to about 100 days in the north, and precipitation is ample and well-distributed throughout the year.

Vegetation and Soils. Climax forest includes the oak and tulip of southern New England, the spruce and fir in northern Maine, the Gaspé, and the Adirondacks, and mixtures of conifer and broadleaf in the intermediate latitudes. Mountain vegetation of New England may range from broadleaf at the bottom to mixed conifer and deciduous at medium heights, and conifers at the top. Vegetation of this character shows extremely attractive color in the autumn. Most all of the area has been cut over since early settlement, and little virgin forest remains. However, the region has become conservation conscious, and tree farms are widespread.

Pedalfer soils are characteristic of the region, the gray-brown podzolics in the south, and the podzols in the north. The podzols of the conifer forests are leached, have poor structure, and contain little humus. Fortunately most of these are located in the poleward sections where growing seasons are short and other climatic hazards lend little encouragement to farming. In the south, where a longer frost-free period occurs, and natural vegetation is that of broadleaf deciduous trees, gray-brown podzolics develop. These soils have a better structure than the podzol, are not badly leached, and accumulate more humus than soils occurring under coniferous forests. Well-drained lowland soils, like those of the Connecticut Valley, are the most favorable for agriculture.

New England

Probably the most important economic subregion of the Northeast is New England, a political area of approximately 65,000 square miles, a little smaller than Missouri, with a population of 9,500,000, about a half million more than Illinois.

New England is not set apart from other areas by clearly marked boundaries. On the east and south, the sea does provide a definite physical border; on the west, the Taconics, Lake Champlain, and the Hudson give an approximate physical separation from other political units; on the north, New England merges with Canada by physical boundaries of rivers like the St. Croix, and St. John, which separate Canada and the United States for short distances only. There is no sharp regional separation on the basis of climate, glacial history, land forms, soils, or vegetation.

In spite of the lack of definite physical boundaries, most people think of New England as a separate region. Many government studies treat it as a unit; banks separate this area of six states, Connecticut, Maine, Massachusetts, New Hampshire, Rhode Island, and Vermont, from surrounding lands in making regional financial reports; the press reports on happenings in New England; tourist advertisements feature New England; and history sets the region, named by John Smith centuries ago, apart for special study. Thus, New England may not be a physical unit, but it is often considered a region because of many similar cultural characteristics.

Manufacturing. The manufacturing industry of the United States began in New England. Much of the land was not well suited for agriculture. Rolling topography suffered from soil erosion when row crops were planted. Podzol and gray-brown podzolic soils are of mediocre quality. Forests had to be removed to plant crops, and cutting forested land with colonial tools was a laborious process. However, the rolling topography that discouraged farming included many abrupt interruptions of stream courses; and adequate, well-distributed precipitation gave a relatively even stream flow throughout the year. Proper surface features and sufficient precipitation—two most important physical factors in water power development—were available throughout most of New England; and water power was utilized by scores of colonial grist mills.

Among the textiles, wool manufacture started first, largely as a home industry, but it was cotton that gave New England its factory leadership. Although water power sites, ample water supply, humid air, and an energizing climate all encouraged New England manufacturing, perhaps availability of labor and capital contributed the early critical advantage the region held over the South. Immigrant labor was easily available in southern New England after the cotton industry became well established, and whaling as well as trade provided capital for the early New England cotton industry.[1]

New England held the leadership in cotton manufacturing for many years, but lost the lead to the South about 1920. Labor laws, or the absence of them, limited unionization of workers, government concessions in taxes to textile corporations, gifts of factory sites, etc., encouraged a movement of many New England factories to southern United States. Geographically, cheaper labor rests upon the South's advantages of low costs for shelter, fuel, and clothing in a warm climate, and low prices for food in an area with a long growing season.

Hard times have hit other industries in New England; in the early 1950's, the region's shoe factories turned out less than one-third of the nation's footwear, although the area long contributed one-half, or more, of national production. Some of New England's urban areas have been hard hit by the decline in cotton textiles and shoes, especially the one-industry centers. In the 20 years, ending 1939, New England lost 158,000 textile jobs, and 38,000 jobs in the shoe and leather industry. Unemployment areas include Fall River, New Bedford, Lowell, and Lawrence, cities whose names are synonomous with textiles; and Brockton, Haverhill, Lynn, and Marlboro,[2] urban centers whose economy has been closely tied to shoes for years. In July 1953, New England had 18.8 per cent of the nation's substantial labor surplus areas.

If conditions are discouraging in textiles and shoes, they are not so difficult in certain other industries. In 1950, over one-half of the nation's woolen mills were in New England, a location encouraged by skilled labor, nearness to market for finished goods, and proximity to Boston, the importer of over half of the country's foreign raw wool.

Furthermore, the expansion in metalworking since World War II has been more than sufficient to offset contraction in the still important textile industry. In 1950, metal goods factories employed twice as many workers as the textile mills. In that year General Electric was New England's largest single employer; but Bethlehem Steel and United Aircraft employ many skilled workers in ship building and airplane manufacture. In 1958, employment in New England's electronics industry reached 75,000 and the value of electronic end products was $1,150,000,000. Skilled labor and other local advantages still attract specialized industries even if these industrial factors show less attraction for textile and shoe factories.

---

[1] For further information on the influences of labor and capital see Ellsworth Huntington, *Principles of Economic Geography,* John Wiley and Sons, 1940, pp. 570–571 (out of print).

[2] In 1954, out of a total of 22,816 factory workers in Fall River, 15,242 were employed in textile and clothing industries; in the same year, 5,124 out of Brockton's total of 7,980 factory workers were making boots and shoes; and at the same time, 7,210 out of the total 9,715 factory workers in Haverhill were on the pay roll of boots and shoe and leather plants.

The transition of New England manufacturing from the non-durable goods (Fig. 3) to durable goods carries with it a threat of even greater vulnerability to business fluctuations. Metalworking centers such as Bridgeport, Hartford, Waterbury, and New Haven should be as ardent supporters of diversification as the shoe cities. Manufacturing areas like Worcester, Massachusetts, noted for its diversified industries, are hurt less seriously by a down swing in the business cycle. In 1954, Worcester's 32,000 workers were distributed as follows, in round numbers: fabricated metal products, 6,000; machine tools, 3,000; foundry products, 2,000; woolen textiles, 1,000; textile machinery, 1,000; printing and publishing, 1,000; men's and women's clothing, 1,000; boots and shoes, 2,000; paper industries, 1,000; electrical machinery, 1,000; plastic products, 1,000; all other widely diversified industries, 12,000. Worcester weathered the depression of the 1930's relatively well, and also suffered minor financial damage from weak textile markets in the early 1950's.

Today, New England is as poor in some of the basic resources of industry as it once was favored. Without coal or petroleum, and with little hydroelectric power and practically none of the minerals essential in this age, the region would be sore pressed to maintain a growing population

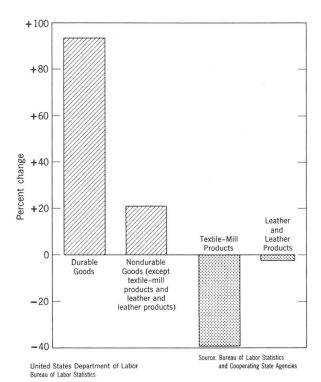

Fig. 3. Industry Shifts in Manufacturing Employment, New England, 1939–1956. Notice that the gain in the manufacture of durable goods more than makes up for the loss in textile and leather products. (After drawing in *Monthly Labor Review,* March 1957.)

United States Department of Labor
Bureau of Labor Statistics

Source: Bureau of Labor Statistics
and Cooperating State Agencies

were it not for its geographic position. The fact that half of its boundary is still the sea means that oil, coal, and some steel can be brought by economical ocean transport to its ports. The principal purchasers of its factory products are only a relatively short distance overland in New York, Pennsylvania, New Jersey, and Ohio. Location, more than mineral resources, land, or ingenuity, is today New England's primary advantage, and this is likely to be accentuated rather than diminished as the resources of the United States are depleted and foreign supplies grow more necessary to the national economy.

Agriculture (Figs. 4, 5). New Englanders have practiced agriculture since the Mayflower sailed into Plymouth harbor, where colonists learned much about subsistence farming from their Indian neighbors. Of the many changes that have occurred since early colonial days, one of the greatest came about 1870, when farming in New England became relatively less important with the rapid development of agriculture on the more fertile midwestern lands.

Not only has New England farming lost its leading place among regional occupations, but it also has changed from an extensive type of land use to one with intensive characteristics. Prior to the middle of the nineteenth century, production of such commodities as wool, beef, and wheat was significant but during the latter part of the century, farming emphasis changed to intensively grown crops, such as potatoes, cranberries, blueberries, tobacco, and apples.

The change from extensive to intensive agriculture was accompanied by changes in farm acreage, number of farms, and value of crops per acre. In 1880, New England's extensive agriculture occupied 22,000,000 acres on 207,000 farms, with 5,000,000 acres in crops. In 1950, corresponding figures were 12,546,000 acres on 103,000 farms, and 2,805,000 acres in crops. Although the region has but 1.1 per cent of the nation's farm land it contributed 2.5 per cent of the value of the nation's farm products [3] in 1950.

Agriculturally there are important differences between northern New England (Maine, New Hampshire, Vermont) and southern New England (Connecticut, Massachusetts, Rhode Island). The 1950 census shows that about 35 per cent of the land area of southern New England is in farms compared to 30 per cent in northern New England; and more of the southern New England farm land is in crops. But the largest difference is in the value of farm products per acre. Farming is much more intensive in the southern part than in the northern; more labor is employed per acre and more feed and fertilizers are purchased. Vermont has a little more of its

---

[3] The 1950 census shows that three of the five leading states in value of crops per acre harvested are in New England. These states and the average value for each are Connecticut, $201.53; Rhode Island, $179.40; Florida, $178.56; Arizona, $172.35; and Massachusetts, $169.06.

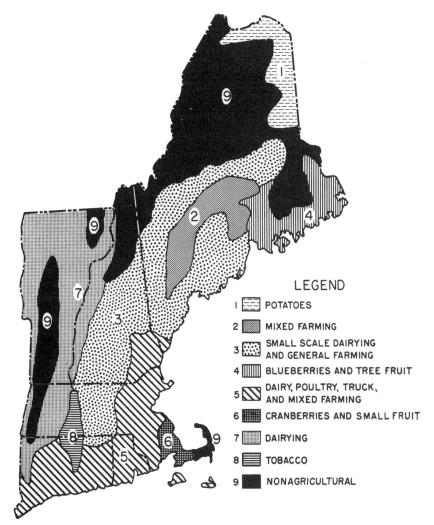

Fig. 4. Farming Areas in New England. Note the influence of rugged relief on land use in the large area of non-agricultural land; dairying also occupies land, most of which is unsuited for crop cultivation. (Courtesy U. S. Department of Agriculture.)

land in farms and in crops than Connecticut, but the value of Connecticut's agricultural products per acre is about four times that of Vermont.

Dairy farms (Fig. 6) are found throughout New England. Adequate amounts of well-distributed precipitation assure good drinking water for dairy animals and encourage heavy yields of hay for feed. Cool summers also hasten hay growth and are more favorable for milk production than the warmer summers of the South. Proximity to large markets enables sale

Fig. 5. Farm Building Unit in the Northeast. Connecting barns and farm houses are quite prevalent in southern Quebec and Vermont, and some may be seen in southern New England. With this arrangement it is unnecessary for the farmer to brave winter snow and cold in getting wood for his fires and in caring for his livestock.

of a large percentage of the milk in liquid form, a practice generally more profitable than sales of concentrates such as dried milk, cheese, and butter. Man himself has done much to improve New England's dairy industry. Since 1880, the number of dairy cattle in Massachusetts has declined, but milk production has increased three-fold; also no more land is in hay than in the 1880's, yet hay production has doubled and the quality is superior to that of early types.

Apple farms are widespread, especially in the Connecticut Valley, north-central Massachusetts, southern New Hampshire, and western and central Maine. Rolling topography, so characteristic of New England, favors apple orchards; these slope lands encourage air drainage which may be helpful in saving budding trees from damage in a later than usual spring frost.

Farms specializing in poultry are numerous. The poultry farmer raises little of his feed and keeps no other animals. Nearness to market is his big advantage. His flock may number thousands of birds and he may stress the sale of market eggs, hatching eggs, or broilers, or all of these. Market eggs move freely and promptly to nearby urban centers. Hatching eggs may be used on the farm or sold to the broiler industries along the Atlantic seaboard. The local broiler industry has grown remarkably in the last few years with a New England production of 60,000,000 in 1951.

On the poorer, rougher, or smaller farms of southern New England, part-time farming may be practiced. In northern New England, far from cities, small, rough, or isolated farms, or those with poor soil, have either become summer homes or, as is perhaps fully as common, have been abandoned.

Other types of farming should be mentioned. In the coastal region from Rockland to Eastport, Maine, blue berries become a major crop on

Fig. 6. New England Dairy Scene. New England has stony pastures; but well-distributed rainfall, of about 40 inches annually, assures good growth of grass and hay and provides ample supplies of fresh drinking water. The silo is useful for storing winter feed, and the dairy barn gives shelter from winter cold and snow. (Courtesy Worcester *Telegram and Evening Gazette*.)

large and small farms. Proper management of a wild crop by pruning (burning) together with disease, insect, and weed control usually results in a profit for the farmer.

Southeastern Massachusetts accounts for nearly two-thirds of United States cranberry production in Barnstable and Plymouth counties and on the islands of Nantucket and Martha's Vineyard. There are many large holdings and numerous small bogs of an acre or more. Cultivation requires intensive preparation of the soil, including sanding, and making available and controlling water supply to assure flooding during critical periods of frost. Investment per acre is high and much labor is needed to produce the crop.

Potato growing in Aroostook County, Maine, extends from Houlton to Fort Kent, with the center of production near Presque Isle and Caribou. Several conditions encourage localization of northern Maine potato growing. Loose loam soils allow easy root expansion; heavy fertilization, with as much as 2,500 pounds per acre, assures high yields; cool moist climate, too cool for corn grown for animal feed, is good for potatoes; the building of the Bangor-Aroostook railroad in 1895 stimulated increased plantings. During the ten-year period, 1942–51, Maine had slightly less than 8 per cent of the nation's potato acreage, and raised 15 per cent of United States potatoes. Prior to 1890, New England yields averaged 100 bushels per acre. In 1950, Maine's average was 480 bushels per acre with a total value of $48,000,000.

One of the largest areas of specialized agriculture occurs in the Connecticut Valley (Fig. 7) between the northern border of Massachusetts and New Haven, Connecticut. Here, weak red sandstones and shales have weathered into reddish soils with good texture and structure, and all that is needed to produce large crops of tobacco, vegetables, and fruit, which feature Connecticut Valley agriculture, is large additions of commercial fertilizer.

Tobacco farms are both large and small. Shade tobacco, produced mainly for cigar wrappers, is grown on large holdings, and broadleaf and Havana seed tobacco feature smaller fields. A serious problem appeared in 1956 for Connecticut Valley tobacco growers. With a new process, cigar makers can get the same amount of binder material from one acre's production as was formerly required from three acres. The Connecticut Valley has been the source of two-thirds of the cigar binders used in the United States, mostly from the broadleaf and Havana seed tobacco.

The typical Connecticut Valley vegetable farm is a small family-size farm, growing a succession and variety of crops from early spring until late fall, which are sold on the market from day to day. A few farms have large acreages and employ many workers during planting, weeding, and harvesting. Crops include onions, potatoes, sweet corn, asparagus, tomatoes, cauliflower, brussels sprouts, strawberries, and other vegetables and fruits.

Fig. 7. The Connecticut Valley, South Deerfield, Massachusetts. Notice the tobacco barns on the intensively cultivated flood plain. Mountains in the background are covered with forest. (Courtesy Standard Oil Company, New Jersey.)

Forestry. More than three-fourths of the land area of New England is forested. Although the region contains only 2.1 per cent of the nation's land, it has 6.7 per cent of the commercial forest. Maine and New Hampshire, with 84.5 and 83.9 per cent of their land in forests, rank well above any other state in the country. All the New England states are more than 60 per cent forested. Only three other states in the country have such a high percentage.

Two groups of New England industries are in various degrees supported by forests. The first group includes all logging (Fig. 8) and manufacturing of lumber and lumber products, wooden containers, pulp, paper, paperboard, wooden furniture, veneer, and plywood, and numerous other wood processing industries. These industries give direct employment to between 135,000 and 145,000 workers in an average year, almost 10 per cent of the region's industrial labor force. Indirectly, they provide employment for many more. In 1950, the wood-consuming industries paid almost $300,000,000 in wages, and the total value of manufacture exceeded $640,000,000. Annual shipments of finished products have a value in excess of a billion dollars.

Fig. 8.   Maine Log Jam.   There was a total of 1,500,000 feet of logs tied up in this drive on the Machias river. Man himself still contributes power in a few phases of modern forestry.   Most of the work is highly mechanized. (Courtesy U. S. Forest Service.)

The second group of forest-based industries includes all the activities that depend in whole or in part on standing forests. The region's vacation business, for example, relies heavily on the New England forests to attract tourists, because forests improve the outdoor environment in a number of ways. New England agriculture needs the forests to help prevent erosion and floods by slowing and stabilizing stream flow. The forests are similarly important to many other industries dependent on a steady supply of water power or process water.

For more than two centuries New England looked upon the forest either as an obstacle to farming, something to be removed the quickest way possible, or as an inexhaustible source of local building materials and export. Thousands of clearings were made for farms, thousands of acres of virgin forest were utilized for houses and other buildings, and thousands of ships left ports of northern Massachusetts and southern Maine with cargoes of forest products. New England used the same ruthless forest exploitation that has been followed by regions and nations many times.   In the

United States, for example, the best trees were depleted in New England; the foresters moved on next to the Lake states and continued *mining* the forests there; with Lake forests carelessly exhausted, woodmen attacked forests in the South; careless cutting continued there; and not until rapid depletion of western forests started did the nation finally practice real forest conservation. Today, tree farming and not tree mining is a national philosophy. New England has fallen in line with the trend.[4]

A unique New England forest gathering industry, much of it in Vermont, is the spring tapping of sugar maple trees for sap—sap that may be processed into maple syrup and maple sugar (Fig. 9). Ideal weather for sap flow comes when winter changes slowly into spring, bringing to the snow-covered region warm sunny days with frosty nights.

Although much of New England is unfavorable for agriculture, the environment contributes many advantages for forestry. Among these are (*a*) ample well-distributed precipitation; (*b*) relatively long growing season; (*c*) many streams on which logs may be moved to saw mills or to pulp mills; (*d*) well-developed roads and railroads; (*e*) a large nearby market, a very important factor; and (*f*) sufficient capital and labor to implement the industry. With proper conservation practices, New England may again become the large forest reserve that the Pilgrims saw more than three centuries ago.

Fishing (Fig. 10). Fishing is not so important to New England economy as it was when the Pilgrims founded Plymouth, or when the *sacred cod* was placed in the Massachusetts statehouse in 1784; but the industry still makes a significant contribution. Fish of many kinds may be obtained by alongshore fishing and from the distant banks. Market fish include cod, flounder, haddock, hake, halibut, herring, mackerel, pollock, and shell fish such as clams, lobsters, quahaugs, and scallops.

Relationships between fishing and the geographic environment are not hard to discover. Adjoining seas abound with fish, and nearby forests give timber for boats in which man can travel to and from the fishing grounds. The deeply indented subsiding shoreline gives good harbors for safe anchor-

---

[4] Tree farming works something like this. On many small farms, especially in northern New England, the farmer may keep a few cows and a few chickens and maintain a woodlot of 100 or 200 acres. When he is not milking and tending to his cows or feeding and caring for poultry, he may be busy thinning, pruning, and harvesting selected trees for the market. The annual harvest may include several thousand board feet of saw logs, a few cords of pulp wood, and more cords of fuel wood; these items may add $500 or more to the yearly income. By serious attention to farm wood lots, many farmers in rugged New England are practicing one of the best types of forest conservation and are providing the market with a dependable source of forest products. Tree farming is not confined to the small farmer. In New England, big corporations like Great Northern Paper Company strive to maintain a constant forest growth. Over the nation as a whole millions of acres of forests and woodlands have been designated as tree farms. These range from farm woodlands of 10 acres to industrial operations of 500,000 acres and more.

Fig. 9. Plastic Tubes Provide a New Method for Collecting Maple Sap. Trees build up 20 to 25 pounds pressure, and force the sap through collecting tubes direct to storage tanks. Pipelines save labor and eliminate wading through the snow with big buckets. Maple products provide an interesting but minor money crop throughout the Northeast. See *Farm Journal,* February 1959, p. 72C.

age. The meeting of the warm North Atlantic Drift and the cold Labrador Current in the vicinity of the Newfoundland banks encourages fogs, which provide a hazard for ships at sea; but this same meeting of warm and cold currents probably stimulates the growth of plankton, the pastures of the sea. Waters above the banks may have been shallowed and the bottom made relatively smooth by deposition from millions of icebergs; bergs moved from high to low latitudes and melting forced them to deposit their load of earth. Shallow waters allow the sun's rays to penetrate far enough to encourage plankton growth. Furthermore, plant nutrients such as nitrates and phosphorus are more easily available in sea water of slight depth because of the greater possibility of their being carried upward from the sea floor by vertical currents. Some of these nutrients may be returned to the surface after organisms in which they are contained have disintegrated on the bottom or in deeper water. Rivers from the Northeast also contribute soluble salts upon which plankton and fish feed. These and other influences make the Northeast's offshore banks one of the world's most productive fishing area.

Trawling for the bottom feeding cod, a demersal fish, is made easier by the relatively smooth surface of the shallow bottom. Obviously, to drag the modern trawl (a meshed bag about 150 feet long) over extremely rugged sea bottom would ruin the equipment. In contrast to the cod, mackerel are surface feeders, pelagic fish, and are caught with purse seines differing from the trawls used for cod. The purse seine is an expanding and contracting device employed to surround the surface swimming fish on all sides as well as above and below. Thus, the catching of mackerel and cod illustrates a basic principle of the fishing industry. Methods of fishing are influenced by the habits of the fish and by the environment in which the fish are found.

Since New Englanders are farther from the banks region than Canadians, it takes longer for the former to make each trip, fewer trips can be made in the same amount of time, and these conditions add to expense of the catch. Furthermore, labor costs are lower in Canada, a fact that also lessens Canadian fishing costs; but New England has a market advantage through tariff-free entrance into the biggest North American market, that of the United States.

For centuries cod fish were sold in dried and salted form; now, however, frozen fillets are of growing importance on the market. Gloucester and Boston are the greatest New England fishing ports and account for a large percentage of the catch. Thirty per cent of the entire labor force in Gloucester is employed in catching, processing, and distributing fish. New Bedford and Portland stand third and fourth among New England fishing cities.

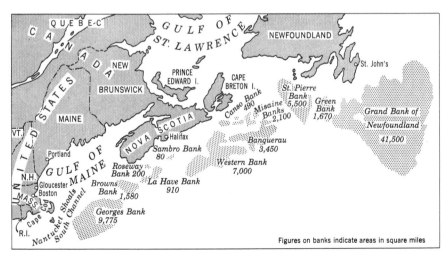

Fig. 10. Fishing Banks of the Northeast. The fishing banks northeast of Cape Cod provide one of the world's great fishing grounds. (Courtesy U. S. Fish and Wildlife Service.)

Nearly 75 per cent of the Massachusetts[5] catch is taken by otter trawl, and 91 per cent by otter trawl, lines, dredges, and purse seines. Other equipment used includes traps and pound nets, rakes, tongs, pots, gill nets, dip nets, haul seines, and harpoons.

Mineral and Power Resources. No section of the United States of similar size has smaller mineral and power resources than New England, with the exception of water power. In 1949, New England's mineral production in value, amounted to $0.40 for every $100 produced by the entire United States. Vermont's share of New England production amounted to $0.17 of the $0.40 total.

One of the leading minerals is asbestos, accounting for 80 per cent of United States production, yet only 5 per cent of United States consumption. Other minerals include berryllium, 36 per cent of United States production; slate, 32 per cent; marble, 26 per cent; feldspar, 23 per cent; granite, 22 per cent; quartz, 21 per cent; graphite, 21 per cent; basalt, 14 per cent; peat, 12 per cent; talc, 10 per cent; and sheet mica, 5 per cent.[6]

New England's position with reference to mineral fuels can be summarized simply. There are no commercial deposits within its borders to supply the enormous fuel needs for heating, generating electric power, and motive force. Thus, New England is singularly well suited for substituting nuclear for combustion fuels.

New England does have both potential and actual development of hydroelectric power. Falls and rapids show that surface features are suitable for water power, and ample, well-distributed precipitation insures little fluctuation in stream flow. As previously indicated, Pleistocene ice disarranged stream courses to such an extent that few pre-Pleistocene streams occupied in entirety their former valleys in post-Pleistocene time. The situation caused many small water falls, which gave power for New England's early widespread manufacturing development. Today, the use of water power has declined. Major causes for the decline include (*a*) increase in size of factories; and (*b*) nearness of all New England to the sea, which makes coal and oil easily available by cheap water transport.

Commerce. A few years ago, a New England newspaper, the *Worcester*

[5]   FISH AND SHELLFISH LANDINGS BY THE NEW ENGLAND STATES, 1951

State	Pounds Landed	Value	Per Cent of Catch	Per Cent of Value
Massachusetts	633,188,900	$46,814,722	69.0	70.0
Maine	223,051,000	15,606,047	24.0	24.0
Rhode Island	48,795,300	3,496,174	5.3	4.4
Connecticut	11,184,900	1,299,248	1.1	1.3
New Hampshire	587,500	215,477	0.6	0.3
Total	916,807,600	$67,431,668	100.0	100.0

[6] All mineral statistics are from A. A. Bright, Jr., *Economic State of New England,* Yale University Press, 1954.

Telegram, carried a full page advertisement for the New York, New Haven, and Hartford Railroad about Boston commerce. The advertisement includes several of the following facts.

In 1708, Boston's deep sea ships outnumbered those of New York 194 to 124. Some of the most resourceful privateers sailed from the Massachusetts harbor. One of the greatest ships of our wooden navy, "Old Ironsides," proved to the world that Bostonians could fight as well as bargain. Ships from Boston pioneered in the China trade during the early 1800's, and Boston merchant vessels continued their leadership through the entire period of sailing ship commerce. With the increasing use of steamers on the high seas, and the routing of trunk line railroads to other ports, Boston began to lose some of her former prestige.

The natural advantages of Boston harbor are many. It may be well to cite several of these:

1. It is well protected from storm winds and waves. Aiding in this protection are peninsulas such as Lynn Beach and Nantasket Beach, together with numerous islands—Deer, Long, Lovell, Peddocks, Calf, Georges, Gallups, and others.

2. Boston is located closer to Europe than other large American ports; it is 110 miles closer to Liverpool than Montreal, 194 miles closer than New York, 337 miles closer than Philadelphia, and 493 miles closer than Baltimore.

3. Boston lies close to the open sea; Boston light is only an hour's journey by ship from the steamship piers. By comparison, Sandy Hook is two hours away from New York piers, Philadelphia is 90 miles up the Delaware River, and Baltimore is almost a day's journey up Chesapeake Bay.

4. Boston's harbor is deep enough for most ocean ships. Since 1956, a 40-foot depth is maintained from President Roads to Commonwealth Pier Number One. However, deep draft vessels must use caution in entering the harbor, because of the rocky bottom.

5. Ice is no serious problem. Occasionally during severe winters the greater part of the harbor may be frozen, but tow boats and steamers have little trouble in keeping the main channels open.

6. Fogs are relatively infrequent. Average frequency is approximately 500 hours a year with one-sixth of the total occurring during the month of July.

7. Tidal range is moderate. It averages 8.9 feet at the Boston lighthouse and 9.6 feet in the interior harbor.

8. Boston may be called a river mouth harbor, but deposition from the Charles and Mystic rivers is not excessive.

9. Many indentations are available for anchorage on the subsiding coast.

10. Flat land for building warehouses is easily available.

Although Boston is now accessible to a productive hinterland by train and truck, New York gained a great advantage over all eastern ports with the building of the Erie Canal. A water level route gave New York easy contact with the interior by way of the Hudson River, Mohawk Valley, and the Ontario plain. Boston and other ports had no such break through the Appalachians to the West. Boston, Philadelphia, and Baltimore have never overcome New York's early accessibility to the midwestern hinterland.

Another handicap to progress has been the failure to modernize Boston port facilities (Fig. 11) as rapidly and extensively as those of other large Eastern ports. Again, Boston has been unable to attract iron and steel works like the ones in the Baltimore and Philadelphia areas. Each of these steel plants will account for several million tons of cargo annually. Boston's chamber of commerce believes that other cities have been granted better rail rates than those given to Boston. The chamber is trying to gain a better equalization of these differentials.

Like Philadelphia, Boston's imports far exceed exports. Imports in 1953 totaled 4,972,908 short tons, with exports for the same year only 309,851 short tons. Commodities totaling more than 100,000 tons were petroleum products, accounting for three-fifths of Boston's total trade, sugar, gypsum, wood pulp, and wool. Others among the first 20 items were lum-

Fig. 11. Longshoremen Carry Individual Cartons by Hand at East Boston. Old-fashioned hand labor methods of moving cargo, pictured above, have been one of the most serious drawbacks to progress at the Port of Boston. The use of pallets—prohibited by ILA restrictions— would cheapen such handling. (Courtesy Worcester *Telegram and Evening Gazette,* and Wide World Photos, Inc.)

ber, molasses, iron and steel, coal, rubber, coffee, sisal, and cacao. Grain and grain products made up half of the total exports; smaller shipments of steel scrap as well as textiles, machinery, and many other manufactured items appeared on the export list.

The Tourist Industry (Figs. 12, 13). One of New England's most promising and most rapidly growing industries is tourism, which annually grosses about a billion dollars. Basic reasons associated with this growth involve the character of New England's tourist attractions. From the scenic standpoint, the region has about everything. The sea touches the area around half of its boundary, a sea which strikes the deeply indented rock bound coast of Maine as well as the flat sandy beaches of Cape Cod. Even though parts of the six states do not border the sea, such sections are not more than two or three hours away by motor over many good modern highways. Scenic inland attractions include several streams and thousands of glacial lakes. Mountain types range from erosional elevations like Monadnock, which gave its name to mountains of its class all over the world, to those of plutonic origin such as the Holyoke range. Trees are of many varieties, the evergreen conifers, and the deciduous which change color with the seasons. Changing seasons also bring relatively cool summers and snowy winters. It is only within the last few decades that New England has awakened to the tourist possibilities of many snowy hillsides. Ski resorts are now attracting winter visitors, especially places in highland Massachusetts, New Hampshire, and Vermont. Added to winter snows, cool summers, diversified forests, mountains with gently rounded contours, lakes and streams, and long stretches of sea coast are many features of great historical interest.

The above list of scenic advantages, however, would be of little use in attracting tourist dollars if New England were not located close to a dense population with high standards of living. In short, this geographic principle of the tourist industry is vital in developing a large successful business.

Besides scenic attractions and a location close to a dense population New England trys hard to make visitors comfortable; a good system of modern highways favors motor travel; rail and bus service is available; and ski trains leave large population centers for New England hills during the ski season. Forecasts on ski weather are given at regular intervals during the winter season. Hotels, motels, and restaurants by the hundreds dot the New England landscape. Pages and pages of tourist propaganda appear in the metropolitan papers and national magazines. New Englanders all are aware that tourism is one of their most valuable industries.

Somewhat related to tourism is the out-of-state attendance at many New England colleges and universities. In the early 1950's more than 50,000 students from outside the six state area contributed about $85,000,000 annually to the regional economy.

Fig. 12.   The Lake with a Long Indian Name.   New England tourists find lakes with unique names.   One interpretation of the above name is "You fish on your side; I fish on my side; nobody fish in middle."

The Canadian Northeast

Comparison with New England. The Canadian subregion of the Northeast includes the three Maritime Provinces, Nova Scotia, New Brunswick, and Prince Edward Island, and southeastern Quebec, of which the Gaspé peninsula makes up a part. The Maritime Provinces have an area of approximately 50,000 square miles and a population of 1,200,000. The area approximates that of North Carolina, but population is less than one-third that of the Southern state.

The Canadian subregion resembles New England in many ways. Geologically both subregions belong to the Appalachian highlands; rocks are similar in structure and age; land forms show resemblance in the dominance of mountain, plateau, and hill land, with minor sections in lowland; both coasts are bold and rocky with many indentations.

Canadian and United States subregions show similarity in soils, all podzols in the former, and in the latter podzol and gray-brown podzolic. Both areas are heavily forested; New England's forest is mixed or deciduous in the south and coniferous in the north, whereas the Maritime Provinces are dominated by conifers. Climatically the subregions display but little difference; the Canadian Northeast, at a little higher latitude, has cooler, shorter summers, slightly colder and longer winters, and somewhat heavier snowfall; but both are included in North America's humid continental, cool summer climate.

The sea forms a large portion of the boundary for both, and no part is far from the ocean. Neither subregion has significant petroleum or natural gas resources, but both have a good base for hydroelectric power. The Canadian Northeast does have coal and several metallic minerals which will be described later.

Occupations north and south of the Canadian border show much similarity. In agriculture, emphasis is placed upon pasture, hay, oats, root crops, hardy fruits, and dairying; fishing is important along Canadian and New England coasts; in forestry, the manufacture of wood pulp is signifi-

Fig. 13. Old Man of the Mountain. Weathering has weakened some of the rocks in the famed tourist attraction in the White Mountains. During the summer of 1958 helicopters carried many tons of steel rods and other repair materials to the Franconia, New Hampshire, mountain. (Courtesy Associated Press and Worcester *Telegram and Gazette.*)

cant in both subregions. New England leads in the tourist industry, but tourism is increasing in the Canadian Northeast. It is in the lesser development of manufacturing that the northern subregion differs sharply from New England. It might be said that the Maritime Provinces could be taken for New England with the factory towns left out. In fact, in the Canadian subregion there are fewer than a dozen cities of more than 20,000 people, whereas New England has many times that number; and whereas the two subregions are similar in size, New England has seven times as many people as the Canadian subregion.

Nova Scotia. Nova Scotia or New Scotland is part peninsula, part isthmus, and part island (Cape Breton). In area, 21,000 square miles, it is a little larger than New Hampshire and Vermont combined, 19,000 square miles. In population (1950), however, 650,000, it has about two-thirds as many people as the two states, 910,000. Before Newfoundland became a part of Canada in 1947, Nova Scotia was known as Canada's Sunrise Province and the Eastern Doorstep. Today, Newfoundland deserves those names because it lies to the east of Nova Scotia.

Permanent settlement preceded that of Massachusetts and Virginia. In 1604, 16 years before the Pilgrims landed at Plymouth, French settlers disembarked at Port Royal, now Annapolis. Here along the Bay of Fundy shores, Acadians drained marshlands and established farms for the growing of hay, small grains, and hardy fruits. The settlement prospered and grew in numbers until 1755, when the British forcibly removed thousands at the time of the Seven Years War. The English evidently considered such a large concentration of French in this east coast Canadian location a menace to British control. Later, some of the Acadians drifted back to the Maritime Provinces. The Scotch, who gave the Canadian province its name, did not arrive in Nova Scotia until after the American Revolution, as did many British Loyalists who left the thirteen United States colonies.

Today, the Annapolis Cornwallis Valley, where the Acadians settled, is one of the richest farming regions of the Maritime Provinces (Fig. 14). On this valley, about 80 miles long and 10 to 15 miles wide, agricultural specialization is practiced just as it is in New England. Millions of barrels of apples have been produced on an area whose physical environment is generally favorable. Geologically, the soils are residual from the soft Triassic sandstone which floors the valley; they possess better than average fertility for podzols. An elevated ridge of volcanic trap rock to the north protects the fruit from cold air masses. A resistant gray granite ridge parallels the valley to the south. Autumn winds over the Bay of Fundy lengthen the maturing season for fruit; and in the spring, breezes moving over the same bay may delay budding until danger from late frosts has passed.

Besides apples, which have made the valley famous, root crops, oats, and hay are grown. Pasture, hay, and oats are fed to dairy cattle, which appear not only on valley farms, but also on many others throughout the Canadian Northeast. Dairy products include a greater proportion of butter, cheese, and dried milk than in New England. As previously mentioned, the Canadian Northeast does not have a large urban population demanding liquid dairy products; hence concentrates are prepared for sale overseas as well as for the home market.

Nova Scotia towns which specialize in lumber, wood pulp, and paper are located at the mouths of streams where they enter the sea. At such locations cheap ocean transport is easily available for the finished product; and floating logs downstream is cheaper than hauling them from the interior by train or truck. Falls and rapids, plus adequate, well-distributed precipitation, provide suitable conditions for hydroelectric power needed in the forest industries. Large amounts of water, available in this well-

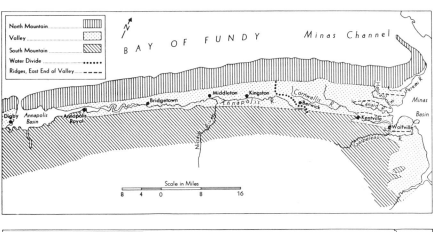

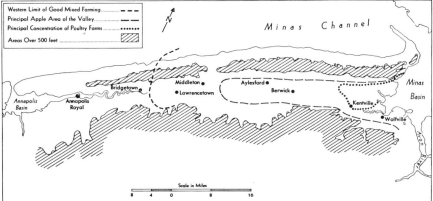

Fig. 14. Physiography and Agriculture of the Cornwallis-Annapolis Area. Note the influence of relief on the location and character of the agriculture. (After Brooke Cornwall.)

watered region, also favor wood pulp manufacturing. Conifers, especially spruce, characteristic of the Maritime Provinces, provide high-grade materials for wood pulp.

In colonial days forests provided timber for building boats useful in the fishing industry. Nova Scotia fishermen go to the Newfoundland banks for cod and other fish just as the New Englanders do. Nova Scotians also utilize alongshore fishing grounds. Pictou, on the north coast, is famous for its lobsters. Fish may be marketed fresh or frozen. A few go over the United States tariff walls to urban markets in eastern United States; dried and salted products are exported in quantity to Latin America and to Mediterranean countries.

Halifax, a British naval base, is the major exporting port for fish, apples, and forest products; and during the winter months when ice blocks Montreal shipping, exports from interior Canada may reach Halifax by train for overseas carriage.

Sydney (Fig. 15) is another important port, located on the northern

Fig. 15. Sydney Steel Plant. The iron and limestone from the Canadian province of Newfoundland meet the coal mined in Cape Breton at Sydney and eventually there emerges a long list of iron and steel products. The steel plant covers 467 acres and employs 5,000 workers. (Courtesy Dominion Steel and Coal Corporation, Limited.)

shores of Cape Breton Island, with a large well-protected harbor. Underlying these shores are large quantities of good quality coking coal as well as limestone. A few miles overseas to the northeast, at Bell Isle, Newfoundland, the Wabana mines tap one of the richest iron deposits in the British Empire. Wabana iron moves to Sydney coal and limestone; these three items provide the base for Sydney's well known iron and steel industry. Market, however, is largely limited to Canada, because United States tariff barriers are difficult to surmount, and Sydney steel would meet strong competition on the European market.

Besides possessing one of the good coal deposits of Canada, Nova Scotia has a little natural gas near Moncton; millions of tons of gypsum on Cape Breton Island shores, enough to account for the bulk of Canadian production; enormous supplies of building stone also along the coast; and salt deposits on the Malagash Peninsula that are useful in the fishing industry.

New Brunswick. Physically, New Brunswick may be called a northeast extension of Maine, for the entire length of the southwest boundary touches that state. Its 27,085 square miles are only slightly less than Maine's 33,215. In population density, Maine has 27 people per square mile and New Brunswick but 18.

Land use is similar to that of the rest of the Canadian Northeast. Potatoes are an important crop; dairying is based on good hay, small grains, and pasture; fishing practices are similar to those of the other Maritime Provinces; forests are widespread, and they probably cover a larger percentage of New Brunswick than they do of Nova Scotia. The manufacture of wood pulp is an important forest industry and paper mills and lumber camps may be seen in several places. Forests also provide a good environment for fur farms.

Shipping is influenced by the great tidal range on the funnel-shaped Bay of Fundy (Fig. 16), a bay with a wide opening to the south and a narrowing to the north. At high tide ships may float easily in the harbor, whereas at low tide they may rest on mud bottoms with deep water far away. Ship owners take advantage of this situation and repair boat sides during low water; again, boats may be moved easily into dry docks with tidal range of 40 feet or more. A unique result of tidal range appears at the falls of the St. John River, not far from the city of St. John. When the tide is out, fresh water moves seaward over falls and rapids; at high tide the falls are completely covered.

St. John in New Brunswick, like Halifax in Nova Scotia, is an important city for Canadian foreign trade. Exports are likely to be heavy during winter when Montreal is closed by the icy St. Lawrence. The fact that St. John is the eastern terminus of the Canadian National railroad gives it certain advantages in obtaining cargo.

Fig. 16. Bay of Fundy Harbor at Low Tide. This photograph shows the seriousness of shipping problems brought about by great tidal range.

Prince Edward Island. Prince Edward Island is the smallest Canadian province, with an area of 2,184 square miles; this is a little larger than Rhode Island, 1,214 square miles, the smallest state in the United States.

An examination of the names applied to this Canadian province, which include "Garden of the Gulf," "Emerald Isle of America," and "Great Potato Land," gives a good idea of the agricultural environment. Land forms lack the ruggedness of most of the Northeast; reddish soils on the gently rolling topography contain few stones and are deep and relatively fertile; abundant limestone to add fertility may be obtained by digging oyster-mussel mud resulting from old shell heaps; climatic factors give mild summers with plentiful rainfall. All these conditions are good for grass, oats, and hay, three good bases for dairying; the physical environment also favors root crops, especially seed potatoes, which yield several million bushels annually.

The island has no mineral wealth and manufacturing is almost nil. Many people look to the harvests of the sea as well as to those of the land. Besides fishing for cod, herring, and other fish, some islanders have developed oyster farms. Oyster farmers drop oyster shells and shells of other fish in shallow alongshore waters. Oysters attach themselves to these shells and gather feed from moving sea water. After two to five years, oysters reach maturity and are removed from the oyster farm for market.

In 1914, Prince Edward Island Scotsmen started Canadian fur farming with silver black foxes. Prime furs continue to be produced upon local fur farms and the activity adds diversity to island economy.

The "Garden of the Gulf" is the most densely populated Maritime

Province, with a density of 47 per square mile, but the island's rich geographic environment could support more people.

Southeast Quebec. On the Gaspé Peninsula, which makes up a major portion of southeastern Quebec, the Shickshock range rises to more than 4,000 feet, leaving only a narrow belt of lowland along the coast. Until recently there was no continuous road around the Gaspé, and a sparse population of French made a poor living by fishing and subsistence farming. However, tourists discovered the beauty of the landscape and the interesting population, and now a motor route extends through the coastal villages entirely around the peninsula. This improvement has made for more accessibility and has placed tourism first among uses of the land. One of the most propagandized bits of scenery is Percé Rock, off the southeast coast. It is a long narrow limestone island, bounded by cliffs 150 to 300 feet high and pierced by an opening large enough for small boats to pass through. A tall chimney rock rises at the seaward end, and a sand bar, uncovered at low tide, unites the island to the mainland.

Many of the people on the Gaspé are active in fishing, farming, or forestry, or a combination of the three. These occupations follow in sequence from the coast to the interior. Several fishing villages dot the shoreline. Long narrow fields extend inland from the coast, many of them enclosed by rail fences. Inland from the fields, forest monopolizes the geographic landscape. Gaspé farmers grow hay, oats, and grass to feed their dairy cattle, and potatoes and other root crops for their own use. Everyone speaks French, and numerous Catholic churches and shrines border the roads.

South of the Gaspé, near the Vermont border, is one of the world's largest asbestos deposits. Thetford is an important producing center. Both open pits and shafts are employed in mining.

The Adirondacks

A third subregion of the Northeast, the Adirondacks, lies in northeastern New York. This rugged upland, with its igneous and metamorphic rocks, uplifted fault blocks, a dissected dome with radial stream drainage, several conspicuous monadnocks rising as high as 5,344 feet, Mt. Marcy, and hundreds of glacial lakes, is completely surrounded by lowlands. On the west is Lake Ontario; on the north and west, the St. Lawrence Lowland; on the east the Lake Champlain trough; and on the south the Mohawk Valley. The Adirondacks belong to the Northeast on the basis of physical features and land use.

The tourist industry is emphasized throughout the region. Physical features such as Lake Placid are scenic; the Adirondacks lie close to dense population areas; the State of New York has set aside a state park in the mountain section; and interested groups have provided many facilities for the accommodation of both summer and winter tourists.

Agriculture receives little attention, although some dairy farms may be noted. However, wood pulp and lumber industries have a strong basis with the widespread occurrence of deciduous and coniferous forests. Unlike the uplands of New England, the Adirondacks show some mineralization with magnetic iron, the most important metal (Fig. 17). Concentration of the metal is necessary and several ores lie deep enough for shaft mines on the flanks of the mountains. Both factors contribute to high-cost production. When ample supplies of rich ore were available in the Lake Superior region, the Adirondack mines were largely neglected. With approaching depletion of the best Mesabi ores near, and World War II in progress, mining activities in the New York mountains were stressed. Now, with rich Labrador ores available in quantity, Adirondack mining may slow down. In short,

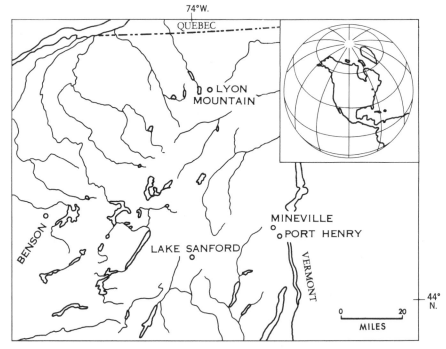

Fig. 17. Adirondack Iron Mines. Mines at the four places shown above—Lyon Mountain, Benson, Lake Sanford, and Mineville—Port Henry—are active or have been active in recent years. Each deposit is estimated to contain over 10,000,000 tons of ore. Ores occur in steeply inclined tabular to lenticular masses, whose shape and orientation are controlled by foliation and fold structures of the enclosing pre-Cambrian gneiss. (Data from United Nations, *Survey of World Iron Resources, 1955.*) Note that the drainage pattern gives a clue to the location of the Adirondacks.

Adirondack iron mines are marginal producers. When iron prices are high and ore is badly needed the mines may be operated at full capacity; but with good ore more easily accessible and more cheaply produced, activity is likely to diminish.

The Outlook

Some years ago, Ellsworth Huntington gave a lecture on New England's economic prospects. The gist of this talk can be summed up in one short sentence: Don't sell New England short.

In the 1880's, many New England farmers migrated west to North America's great grain lands. But that did not stop New England farming. New Englanders changed from general farming to highly specialized agriculture and three of New England's states are among the leaders in value of crops per acre. Again, in the 1920's, New England lost the leadership in cotton textiles to the South. But that loss has not stopped New England manufacturing. The shortage in textiles and leather goods has been more than balanced by an increase in durable goods.

It took New England a long time to realize the great potential for tourism. But now that the region is awake to its tourist advantages, expansion will probably continue. New England supplies two of the basic needs of tourism—beautiful scenery of great diversity, possibly the most beautiful in the world, and proximity to dense population with high standards of living. Many regions have one of these requirements, but few have both.

New England's humid continental climate cannot produce forests as rapidly as the humid subtropical of the South. But with careful conservation, and the selection of rapidly growing tree types, New England forests promise more profitable yields in the future than in the past. Furthermore, New England may awake some day to its possibilities in summer grazing for beef cattle.

Fishing and commerce can be increased with the same use of Yankee ingenuity that has been applied to farming, manufacturing, tourism, and forestry. Ellsworth Huntington believed that New England's climate and the challenge of a difficult but rewarding environment gave economic encouragement to New Englanders. He may be correct. Whatever the cause, New England will probably remain a valuable geographic subregion to the nation's economy, and the same can be said for the entire Northeastern region, of which New England forms a major part.

QUESTIONS, EXERCISES, AND PROBLEMS

1. How does the physical environment contribute to regional unity? Describe the physical environment in considerable detail.

2. Describe geographic relationships occurring in New England colonial settle-

ment. What early advantages for manufacturing did New England possess over those of the South? Why did New England lose its leadership in cotton textile manufacturing? Point out the main areas of manufacturing, and the character of manufacturing in each New England area. Why has New England no basic iron and steel manufacturing? Why has manufacturing failed to develop in the Canadian portion of the Northeast as much as it has in New England? What relation exists between (1) the attitudes of New England legislators on federal aid to schools and (2) the migration of New England industries to the South? Study one of the issues of the Federal Reserve Bank's *New England Business Review.* Do the same for the March 1957 issue of the *Monthly Labor Review.*

3. Comment on New England agriculture. What advantages does the region possess for dairying, poultry, truck crops and apple growing? Describe the forest industries of New England. Show relationships between the fishing industry and the geographical environment. Describe New England's power and mineral resources. Trace the history, development, and present position of New England commerce. Describe the background for the tourist industry. Describe the new method of collecting maple sap in the Northeast.

4. Compare and contrast the Canadian Maritime Provinces and southeastern Quebec with New England as to physical environment and economic activities. Describe the main features of Nova Scotia economy. How does New Brunswick resemble Maine? Comment on agricultural crops, the Bay of Fundy tides, and the significance of St. John. Describe the economy of Prince Edward Island and that of southeastern Quebec. What economic activities are important in the Adirondacks?

5. Each of the following cities has about 100,000 people or more: Boston, Bridgeport, Cambridge, Fall River, Hartford, Lawrence, Lowell, New Bedford, New Haven, Providence, Somerville, Springfield, Waterbury, and Worcester. Name major activities accounting for each urban development. To begin your study examine the latest editions of *Webster's Geographical Dictionary* and *The Columbia Lippincott Gazetteer of the World.*

6. Locate and identify the following cities and towns and emphasize important economic and historic features for each: Augusta, Concord, Brockton, Frederickton, Halifax, Holyoke, Lynn, Manchester, Moncton, New London, Pawtucket, Portland, Quincy, Rimouski, Rutland, Sydney, Thetford, and Woonsocket.

7. Identify the following: tree farming, Icelandic Low, maize culture complex, salt tanks, intensive agriculture, trawling, Acadians, Garden of the Gulf, Monadnock, Mt. Marcy, Percé, Schickshock.

8. Describe the distribution of population in the Northeast. Where are the empty areas and why do they remain empty?

SELECTED REFERENCES

Alexander, Lewis M., "The Impact of Tourism on the Economy of Cape Cod, Massachusetts," *Economic Geography,* July 1955, pp. 265–271.
Anderson, Sven A., and Augustus Jones, "Iron in the Adirondacks," *Economic Geography,* Vol. 21, 1945, pp. 276–285.
Ashley, Clifford, *The Yankee Whaler,* Houghton-Mifflin Co., 1938.
Bird, J. Brian, "Settlement Patterns in Maritime Canada," *Geographical Review,* July 1955, pp. 385–404.

Bird, Will R., "Nova Scotia's Highland Cape Breton," *Canadian Geographical Journal,* Vol. 38, 1949, pp. 78–91.

Black, John D., *The Rural Economy of New England,* Harvard University Press, 1950.

Bright, A. A., Jr., *Economic State of New England,* Yale University Press, 1954.

Burpee, L. J., "Prince Edward Island," *Canadian Geographical Journal,* November 1946, pp. 192–217.

Commonwealth of Massachusetts, Department of Labor and Industries, Division of Statistics, *Principal Data Relative to Manufactures in Worcester, by Industries,* 1956.

Commonwealth of Massachusetts, "Report of the Port of Boston Commission," *Public Document Number 164,* January 1955.

Cornwall, Brooke, "A Land Use Reconnaissance of the Annapolis-Cornwallis Valley, Nova Scotia," *Geographical Bulletin* 9, 1957.

Corps of Engineers, U. S. Army and U. S. Maritime Commission, *Port Series No. 3,* 1946.

Department of Natural Resources, Division of Marine Fisheries, *Massachusetts' Oldest Industry: The Ocean Fishery,* 1953.

Federal Reserve Bank, *New England Business Review:*
"Agriculture Reorganizes," November 1957;
"Forest Land as an Investment in New England," October 1956;
"Industrial Fuel Costs in New England," August 1957;
"Manufacturing in New England," September 1957;
"Ocean Steamship Service and New England," August 1957;
"The Port of Boston: 1957," July 1957.

Gentilcore, R. Louis, "The Agricultural Background of Settlement in Eastern Nova Scotia," *Annals of the Association of American Geographers,* December 1956, pp. 378–404.

Geographical Record, "The Bay of Fundy Salt Marshes," *Geographical Review,* April 1956, pp. 263–264.

Harris, Seymour E., *The Economics of New England,* Harvard University Press, 1952.

Higbee, E. C., "The Three Earths of New England," *Geographical Review,* July 1952, pp. 425–438.

Isard, Walter, and John H. Cumberland, "New England as a Possible Location for an Integrated Iron and Steel Works," *Economic Geography,* October 1950, pp. 245–259.

Klimm, Lester E., "The Empty Areas of the Northeastern United States," *Geographical Review,* July 1954, pp. 325–345.

Laing, Jean, "The Pattern of Population Trends in Massachusetts," *Economic Geography,* July 1955, pp. 265–271.

Manchester, Lorne, "Science in Fisheries," *Canadian Geographical Journal,* Vol. 41, 1950, pp. 189–209.

Morrow, Robert R., "Pipeline Milkers for Maples," *Farm Journal,* March 1958.

New York Times, "Massachusetts" (advertisement, 56 pp.), May 18, 1958.

Phillips, Fred H., "New Brunswick: Varied Vacationland of the Maritimes," *Canadian Geographical Journal,* Vol. 40, 1950, pp. 12–43.

U. S. Department of Agriculture, "The Changing Fertility of New England Soils," *Agriculture Information Bulletin 133,* December 1954.

U. S. Department of Labor, Bureau of Labor Statistics, "New England Labor and Labor Problems," *Monthly Labor Review,* March 1957.

U. S. Weather Bureau, "Weather on Mount Washington," *Daily Weather Map,* April 22, 1955, Washington, D. C.

Vandusen, Albert E., "Colonial Connecticut's Trade with the West Indies," *New England Social Studies Bulletin,* Vol. 13, March 1956.

Wall Street Journal, "Electronics Help Bolster Activity of New England's Industries," Feb. 11, 1959.

7 · The Southwest Appalachians

(Figures 1, 2, 3)

The Southwest Appalachians [1] comprise a large region, one extending from the Mohawk Valley to the Gulf Coastal Plain and from the Atlantic Coastal Plain to the Central Lowland. The highest elevations of the entire Appalachian system are here, with Mt. Mitchell reaching 6,711 feet; ridges notched by wind gaps and water gaps extend for long distances in a general northeast-southwest direction; fast-moving streams interrupted by rapids and falls have cut gorges hundreds of feet deep; valleys of all kinds, narrow, broad, enclosed, and those with wide openings diversify the general mountainous landscape. Land forms are not uniform, but the topography as a whole may be considered an upland, an upland with sufficient unity to be classified as a geographic region.

Several differences exist between the Southwest Appalachians and those of the Northeast. (*a*) The mountains of the Southwest are higher and more rugged than their northeastern neighbors; (*b*) all the northeastern highlands were glaciated by Pleistocene ice, whereas the glacier touched only the poleward border of the southwestern uplands; (*c*) the Southwest Appalachians have a greater east-west extent and a greater total area than that of the mountains of the northeast.

Boundaries of the Southwest Appalachians are clearly marked on the east, south, and west; on the east is the Atlantic Coastal Plain, separated from the upland by the Fall Line; on the south lies the Gulf Coastal Plain; and on the west is the Central Lowland. For a land use study the northern

[1] The region, sometimes called the Appalachian Highlands, has been named the Southwest Appalachians because (1) of the similarity in area and location to the "Appalachian Highlands: The Southwestern Division" described by W. W. Atwood, *The Physiographic Provinces of North America,* Ginn and Co., 1940; and (2) because the name distinguishes the region from the Northeast, much of which also belongs to the Appalachian Mountain system.

boundary may be taken as the Hudson-Mohawk Valley and the Lake Ontario Lowland. From east to west, subregions include the Piedmont, the Blue Ridge, the Ridge and Valley, the Appalachian Plateau, and the outlying Ozark Highlands.

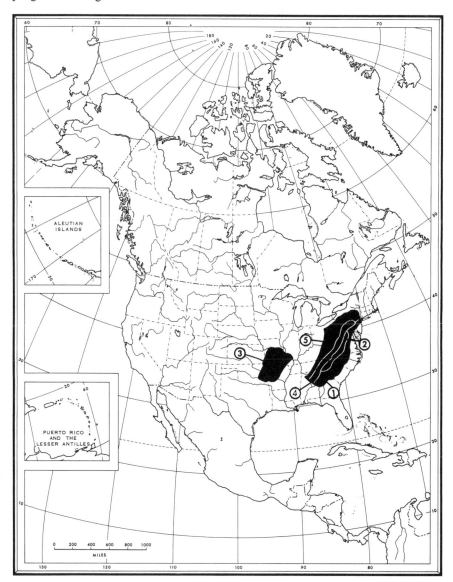

Fig. 1. The Southwest Appalachians. The Southwest Appalachians include several subdivisions: (1) the Piedmont; (2) the Blue Ridge; (3) the Ozarks; (4) the Ridge and Valley province; and (5) the Appalachian Plateau.

Fig. 2.   Geologic Structure Section Across Tennessee, East-West.   Note the many

The Piedmont Plateau

Location and Surface Features.   The Piedmont Plateau borders the Middle Atlantic Coastal Plain, described in Chapter 5, on the west and extends about a thousand miles in a northeast-southwest direction from northern New Jersey to Alabama's Gulf Coastal Plain.   The plateau is not so broad as it is long.   In Maryland it is only about fifty miles wide, but its east-west extent reaches approximately 125 miles in North Carolina.

The Piedmont received its name from its location at the foot of the Blue Ridge Mountains bordering on the west; and it is a plateau only when contrasted with the low and relatively flat coastal plain to the east.   This upland is a region of rolling hills whose summits at the western margin average 1,000 to 1,200 feet above sea level; elevations decline gradually from west to east until hills are no more than 400 to 500 feet high at the eastern Fall Line boundary.

Peneplanation has been active on the highly folded gneisses and schists making up much of the plateau; further erosion may be seen in the deep narrow valleys which streams are cutting into the broadly undulating surface.

Climate.   An interior location provides a certain uniformity in the continental aspect of Piedmont climates, but the great latitudinal extent gives two major climatic types; the north possesses a humid continental warm summer variety and the central and southern Piedmont has a humid subtropical type.   Because of a 10° difference in latitude between north and south, growing seasons range from 160 days in the former to 240 days in the latter.   Differences in location with reference to the Gulf of Mexico bring contrast in regional precipitation.   The southern Piedmont, lying closer to tropical maritime air masses, receives more rainfall, about 60 inches in the south compared with about 40 inches in the north.

Vegetation and Soils.   Before the period of European colonization, the entire Piedmont was covered with forests, dominantly hardwood in the north and a mixture of hardwood and conifer in the south.   European settlers stripped the land of its original forest cover to make way for field crops, pasture, and orchards.   But after a time many of these farms were abandoned to second growth forest and bush—vegetation that covers broad areas today.   Most trees on cutover land of the north belong to either the oak or

physiographic regions included in the state of Tennessee. (Drawn after E. Raisz.)

tulip species, while those of the south include oak, pine, tupelo, gum, and bald cypress.

The pedalfer soils include gray-brown podzolic in the north and red and yellow earths in the south. The former show better structure and fertility than the latter and also suffer less leaching.

Rolling topography and 40 to 60 inches of rainfall will cause soils to erode unless conservation practices are employed. Among the Piedmont's red clay soils are some derived from coarse granite which have weathered into a gravelly loam. An important characteristic of these soils is their lack of tenacity both at the surface and in the subsoil. Such soils are especially susceptible to erosion.

Tobacco and cotton, money crops of the middle and southern Piedmont, are soil robbers, and they demand heavy fertilization. Probably as much fertilizer is applied per unit of area in the southern Piedmont as in any place in the United States. Proximity to natural fertilizer, however, helps this situation. Large phosphate beds, which can be exploited by open pit mining, occur in nearby Florida; and thousands of menhaden, caught in offshore waters, are processed for commercial fertilizer. Geologically speaking, clay soils are the rule on the Piedmont, in contrast to the wide occurrence of sandy soils on the adjoining coastal plain.

Subregions. Largely on the basis of agricultural differences, the Piedmont may be divided into three major parts, the north, the central, and the south. The north includes southeastern New York, north-central New Jersey, southeast Pennsylvania, central Maryland, and north-central Virginia; the central Piedmont comprises parts of south-central Virginia and north-central North Carolina; the south includes south-central North Carolina, western South Carolina, most of northern Georgia, and a portion of east-central Alabama.

The North. Lancaster County, Pennsylvania, one of the richest farming counties of the United States forms part of the northern Piedmont. Many of the people belong to the Amish religious sect; and besides their deep religious feeling, they believe in hard work, in careful attention to crops and livestock, and in well-built barns (Fig. 4) and sheds for protecting livestock, crops, and machinery. The combination of hard work; farming know-how; and a physical environment of gently rolling land; of

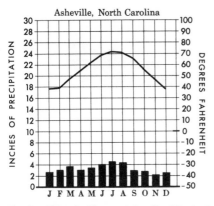 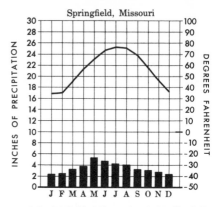

Fig. 3. Climatic Charts, Asheville, North Carolina, and Springfield, Missouri. Asheville (35° 35' N., 82° 34' W.; altitude 2,253 feet; mean annual temp. 55.1° F.; mean annual precip. 40.37 inches); Springfield (37° 14' N., 93° 17' W.; altitude 1,302 feet; mean annual temp. 55.6° F.; mean annual precip. 42.17 inches). Asheville, at a higher elevation and closer to the coast, has a lesser range in temperature, a higher minimum temperature, and a lower maximum temperature than Springfield. Explain.

productive soils, kept productive by commercial fertilization; proper crop rotation; and animal manures; and of humid continental climate—all this results in a farm landscape that is a joy to the eye. Field crops include tobacco, wheat, corn, potatoes, hay, oats, and pasture. Many cattle are kept for fattening, and large numbers of feeders are brought in from the rugged parts of Virginia and West Virginia and even from the West. Locally produced grains provide feed for the cattle as well as for hogs and poultry.

Major money crops in this diversified farming land are wheat and tobacco. Climate permits the planting of winter wheat on acreages larger than those used for tobacco. The latter commodity, not so dominant in the northern Piedmont as in the central section, is farmed more intensively than wheat. Both crops possess the advantage of proximity to large markets. This factor is especially advantageous for growing another crop, potatoes, a minor money crop. The potato does not have the keeping qualities of tobacco and wheat. Thus, the northern Piedmont potato grower can take advantage of the geographic principle that bulky commercial crops with poor keeping qualities and low value per unit of weight should be grown near market.

Although diversified farming is widespread, there are many specialized dairy farms in the north. Nearness to market is an encouraging influence for dairy farmers. With such a densely settled area so close to the northern Piedmont, market conditions relieve the necessity of selling dairy products in a concentrated form.

The northern Piedmont is well known for its apples, and several large orchards are located near the boundary between the Maryland and Virginia Piedmont and the adjoining Blue Ridge. Apples, a tree crop, need no cultivation, and thus the problem of soil erosion is not serious. Slope lands also provide air drainage, a deterrent to frost on nights with critical temperatures for budding trees or a maturing apple crop.

The Central Piedmont. The central Piedmont is one of the leading tobacco producers in the United States, and it may be informative to describe tobacco farming activities throughout a typical season.

In North Carolina, America's biggest tobacco growing state with about a billion pounds annual production, tobacco seeds are hand sown in small seed beds during the early part of the year. Thousands of such beds, canopied with white cloth for frost protection, dot the farm landscape. In about two weeks, pale green shoots push up through the soil. Meanwhile, fields, where these plants are to be transplanted, have been plowed, fertilized, and dampened by early spring showers and are ready for planting.

Transplanting begins toward the end of April. In May and June, fields must be weeded constantly and worms plucked by hand from the tender leaves. About the last week in June, flowering tops are pulled off. Snake-like tendrils called suckers spring out of the stalk at the leaf joints. For the best tobacco these too must be removed.

Fig. 4. Amish Barn Raising in Lancaster County, Pennsylvania. Amish farmers are some of the best in the United States; they cooperate on many of their agricultural activities. (Courtesy Charles S. Rice.)

Harvesting begins in July, and five to six weekly pickings are needed to gather the entire crop. Leaves near the ground ripen first, but the best come from the middle of the stalk and are plucked on the second or third picking. Yields correspond closely to the amount of fertilizer applied. Application has increased from 800 pounds per acre to 1,200 pounds.

After the tobacco has been taken from the fields in July, a cover crop of rye or vetch may be planted to add fertility to the soil in preparation for next spring planting; then the same annual sequence of tobacco activities will follow again.

As leaves are picked they are stacked on one-mule sleds or carts built to fit the narrow space between two rows, and are then hauled to the tobacco barn, typically a sixteen-foot hollow cube of logs or planks surmounted by a peaked shingle roof. There the leaves are looped with string into bunches called hands—three leaves to a hand—and tied on sticks four and one-half feet long and tiered seven feet high (Fig. 5).

Much of the tobacco is cured by oil or wood fires for a period of four or five days. After flue curing, which makes the tobacco dry and brittle, it is left in the open barn without artificial heat overnight so as to absorb moisture from the dew and night air. Then, left on the original sticks, it is taken to a storehouse. At market time, in late August, tobacco is taken off the sticks and sorted into a dozen or more grades. It is tied into bundles, each bound with a tobacco leaf, and the aromatic packets are stacked high in cart, wagon, or truck. Then for days, road and highway are thronged with every manner of vehicle, all converging on the huge warehouses in the 40 or more marketing towns of North Carolina.

Into the warehouses crowd growers, buyers, and auctioneers, because all tobacco is sold at auction. Packed according to grade in shallow withe baskets holding up to 250 pounds, it goes under the hammer. At the end of each clamorous day, all tobacco is cleared from the warehouse and started to the factories.

Although tobacco is the leading cash crop in the central Piedmont, considerable agricultural diversity is present. Corn occupies a larger acreage than tobacco and provides both human food and feed for a growing number of livestock. As in the northern Piedmont, dairy farming is concentrated on farms near urban centers. On the other hand, farms raising beef cattle are well distributed throughout the subregion. Many of these farms specialize in raising Black Aberdeen Angus, a breed of cattle that originated in the hill lands of Scotland. The Piedmont possesses much of rolling land similar to that of Scotland, but the humid subtropical climate is hardly the same as the Scottish west coast marine type.

The Southern Piedmont. The southern Piedmont is one of the problem areas of American agriculture, and one of the country's oldest producers of cotton and corn. Probably there is some relation between these two state-

Fig. 5. Curing Tobacco. The farmer is lighting an oil burner in one of the curing barns. The green tobacco hangs in the barn at a controlled temperature for about five days, during which it gradually dries out and becomes golden in color. (Courtesy Standard Oil Company, New Jersey.)

ments. Both cotton and corn are row crops, encouraging soil erosion, and both take more fertility from the soil than they put back in. Corn is grown for human food and for animal feed, but cotton is the money crop.

Climate is generally favorable for short staple cotton, a type that competes on world markets with the low-grade cotton from Brazil, China, and India. Growing season is 200 days or more, a requisite for successful cotton maturity, and rainfall is sufficient to assure a crop. In fact, humidity is too high for the growth of long staple cotton, which brings the highest prices.

Like the rest of the South, the southern Piedmont needs more diversified farming and a greater stress on soil conservation. Crop plans should include more contour plowing, strip farming, terracing, and the use of close cover crops like lespedeza and kudzu, which will discourage soil erosion and add fertility.

The climate is ideal neither for dairying nor for the North European beef breeds like the Shorthorn, Hereford, or Angus; but an increase in dairy animals as well as beef cattle offers several advantages. More land can be left in grass and hay, which will limit erosion and enrich the soil, and animal manures also add soil fertility. The Piedmont has a longer pasture season than northern latitudes and less shedding is necessary because of fewer severe winter storms. Breeders of beef cattle are turning to crossbred animals; the cross between the Indian Zebu or Brahman and the North European breeds seems better adapted to the environment than either the North European or Brahman type.

Tree crops of various kinds offer possibilities for further diversity. Piedmont land in the Carolinas and Georgia already has millions of peach trees. Trees eliminate soil erosion and may bolster the economy in many years.

Piedmont Manufacturing. Much of the Piedmont lies south of the major manufacturing belt, the Eastern Quadrilateral,[2] but several industries, including chemicals, furniture, paper, pulp, textiles, and tobacco, are of national as well as of local importance.

Fifty years ago, most United States cotton was manufactured in New England. The South has now taken over the leadership with many of the spindles located in the Piedmont. In 1953, South Carolina had over 50,000 more textile workers than Massachusetts, and the former state's textile factories exceeded those of the Bay State in value added by manufacturing. There are several reasons for cotton textile movement from New England to the South. The southern location assures availability of raw materials with a minimum of transportation from local or nearby production. Southern laborers work for lower[3] wages than those demanded by labor in the North. Labor comes from workers unable to find employment in local agriculture, or from large families in nearby mountain regions lacking enough farm land to provide farm work in the isolated environment. Since the manufacture of low-grade cotton goods does not necessitate highly

---

[2] The greatest United States industrial concentration lies in a quadrilateral with an eastern boundary extending from Baltimore to Portland, Maine; the northern boundary extends from the latter city to Minnesota's twin cities; on the west, the border joins Minneapolis and St. Paul to Kansas City; and on the south, the boundary follows a line from Kansas City to St. Louis, then along the Ohio River to Cincinnati, and continues east to Baltimore.

[3] The cost of labor differential is lessening. Unionization of workers is slowly increasing in the South.

skilled labor, workers from the mountain country can do a satisfactory job.

People of the North are inclined to complain of the southern advantage in cheap labor. But the South would be deprived of certain geographic advantages if a unified labor law were applied throughout the nation. Climate gives the South warm temperatures, permitting lower costs for clothing, housing, and fuel. A longer growing season makes food production cheaper also. The same climate that lowers the cost for basic necessities may not encourage as much efficiency among Southern workers as does the more energizing climate of New England.

Hydroelectric power has been an important advantage of Piedmont manufacturing throughout American history. It has already been noted that (*a*) 40 to 60 inches of well-distributed rainfall and (*b*) weak and resistant rocks in close contact along the Fall line provide basic conditions for water falls. Other power resources include coal from the Appalachian Plateau coal fields a few miles to the west, and oil and gas by way of pipeline, tank car, or ocean steamer from Gulf Coastal fields of the South.

Mention has been made of local raw materials in Piedmont cotton textile plants. A similar advantage exists in the tobacco factories, especially in North Carolina and Virginia. Cotton and rayon textiles bring in more money for Alabama, Georgia, South Carolina, and Tennessee than any other commodity. In North Carolina and Virginia, however, textiles rank second to tobacco products in value.

Large acreages of forests on the Piedmont and other subregions of the Southwest Appalachians encourage investment in lumber, paper, and pulp mills, and in furniture factories. Southern Piedmont forests have a growth advantage over those of the Northeast. Higher temperatures and more rainfall bring trees to early maturity.

An important influence upon the increase in Piedmont manufacturing has been the favorable attitude of state and local governments towards factory expansion. This influence may be fully as important as the availability of local raw materials, cheaper labor supply, and other conditions that can encourage factory growth. Government officials have limited tax rates, granted factory sites, and done many other things to stimulate manufacturing.

Although Piedmont factories are not located in the center of the United States market, they are not far distant, and transport facilities on rail, road, and even on the ocean are good. Richmond, a great manufacturing city, with tobacco factories, sugar refineries, pulp mills, etc., is a railroad center and an ocean port as well. Depths of 25 feet are maintained along Richmond's James River piers. Another Piedmont commercial and factory city is Atlanta, Georgia, one of the best known rail centers in the United States. In 1954, 16 main railway lines, 60 truck lines, and 10 major air routes functioned in Atlanta; and Lockheed Aircraft Corporation paid out nearly $75,000,000 to over 15,000 workers. However, Atlanta has no ocean shipping service like Richmond.

The Blue Ridge

Location and Surface Features. The Blue Ridge physiographic province extends in a northeast-southwest direction from south-central Pennsylvania to northern Georgia, occupying parts of Maryland, Virginia, the Carolinas, and Tennessee, as well as Pennsylvania and Georgia. The Piedmont lies to the east and south, and the Ridge and Valley region to the west and north. Between the northern boundary and Roanoke, Virginia, the Blue Ridge east-west extent is no more than a few miles; south of Roanoke it broadens to more than 100 miles. It is in this widest part that elevations rise to more than 6,500 feet; and here the several ranges making up the wide extent have received local names such as Unaka, Great Smoky, etc.

The southern Blue Ridge is featured by an irregular escarpment facing the Piedmont on the east, an escarpment over which streams drop as much as 2,000 feet within a distance of three miles. These streams have been extending their headwaters rapidly westward in a labyrinth of hills, and long spurs that enclose coves where many of the mountain people live. The coves, hills, and spurs result from strong differential erosion of a mass of highly irregular rock. Most of the rock belongs to two major classes, metamorphic, such as gneisses, schists, and slates; and igneous, including granites and diorites.

Climate, Vegetation, and Soils. A relatively high altitude and a location close to the Atlantic are the two most important influences upon Blue Ridge climates. Altitude lowers temperatures, and proximity to the sea encourages milder winters and cooler summers. Both influences are active in stimulating heavier precipitation than that for any other portion of the Southwest Appalachians.

During early settlement days, the Blue Ridge possessed heavy forests, mainly hardwoods with a few conifers at the higher elevations. The woodsman's axe has removed virgin trees and now only cutover lands remain.

The significant relief is probably the most important factor affecting soil development. The most productive soils occur in the stream valleys, for on the steep slopes there is little opportunity for the development of a mature soil profile. The term *undifferentiated soils* might well be applied to the various classes of pedalfers occurring in the region.

Agriculture. Commercial apple orchards feature land use in the Blue Ridge near the Piedmont boundary and also near the Ridge and Valley subregion. Slope land is no handicap to tree crops, for cultivation is unnecessary and air drainage minimizes frost danger during periods of critical temperatures in the spring and autumn.

Such fruit raising belongs to commercial farming, but much agriculture is of a subsistence type. Small farms are found on hill slopes where disastrous soil erosion results from the planting of row crops.

In the more isolated areas, surplus corn is still sold in the form of liquor. Marketing the crop in bulk would show little profit, but bulk can be reduced about 97 per cent by distilling the corn into whiskey (Fig. 6). Whiskey poured into jugs can be carried easily by man or slung across a horse's back to move over winding trails to market. Making corn whiskey in mountain areas is a good illustration of a well-known geographic principle. A money crop in isolated country must be of high value per unit of weight and must possess good keeping qualities. Whiskey not only keeps long periods of time, but improves with age.

Forest Products. The growing of tree crops is suggested by almost every authority in planning the economic future of mountainous regions. Blue Ridge precipitation is relatively heavy and the growing season is long. These conditions encourage rapid growth; moreover, when trees have

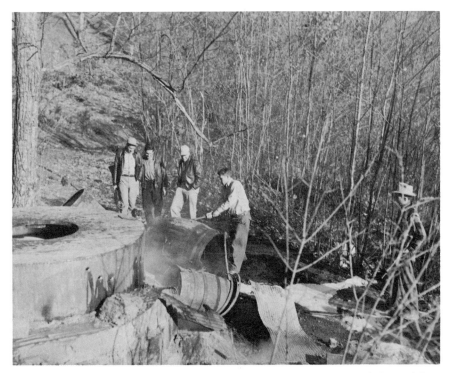

Fig. 6. Hillside Still in the Tennessee Mountains. All materials must be carried to and from the still, whose chief locational advantage is seclusion. During much of the year, dense foliage of broadleaf deciduous trees effectively screens operations from the ground and from the air; but from November to April, when trees are almost bare of leaves, chances of discovery are greater. (Courtesy Tennessee Alcohol Tax Division.)

reached maturity, they lie but a short distance from the big Eastern market.

Blue Ridge trees supply materials for railroad ties, mine props, barrel staves, fuel, furniture, lumber, paper, and other products.   Recently pulp mills have begun to use a hardwood-conifer mixture for making paper.   In the early part of the twentieth century, Blue Ridge forests were widely used as feeding grounds for swine.   Mast feeding has become less important here just as it has throughout most of the world.

It should be pointed out that if farming is to give way to forestry, the latter will not support as dense a population as farming.   Thus, people will have to leave mountain lands for industrial pursuits, as they have started to do already.

Mining.   Mining is not a dominant industry in the Blue Ridge.   In 1953, 7,829 short tons of copper were mined in Ducktown, Tennessee, a rather low figure in comparison to the Bingham, Utah, production of 268,571 tons for the same year.   More zinc is produced in eastern Tennessee than copper.   In 1953, Tennessee's eastern district yielded 38,465 tons.

North Carolina's Blue Ridge area contains a number of minerals, including feldspar, mica, kaolin, vermiculite, olivine, limestone, marble, asbestos, chromite, sand, gravel, iron, ilmenite, copper, and rutile.   For a number of years, about 45 per cent of the feldspar mined in the United States has come from the Blue Ridge; during the same period, approximately 70 per cent of the mica and 75 per cent of the primary kaolin have come from the region.   Important deposits of talc are also present; and in 1953, commercial deposits of tungsten, most of it from the Blue Ridge section, provided the state with a total of 2,000 tons.

Tourism.   Tourism is important and growing more so in the Blue Ridge.   Scenic attractions include the highest mountains east of the Mississippi, heavy forest growth with a great variety of vegetation types, streams with attractive water falls and rapids, a cool summer climate, and a location not far from the Atlantic Coast.

Road building has been actively pursued and many good roads are available for the numerous tourists living in nearby densely populated eastern United States.

The Ridge and Valley Region

Location and Surface Features.   The Ridge and Valley region [4] extends in a northeast-southwest direction from the Hudson River to central Alabama.   Parts of nine states are included: southeastern New York,

---

[4] Study carefully pp. 298–306, Edward Higbee, *American Agriculture: Geography, Resources, Conservation,* John Wiley and Sons, 1958.   Note the illustrations of specific farms and be able to describe agriculture at Glade Creek, Virginia, and in the Shenandoah Valley.

northwestern New Jersey, east-central Pennsylvania, the central part of Maryland's Panhandle, eastern West Virginia, western Virginia, eastern Tennessee, northwestern Georgia, and northeastern Alabama. The eastern and western boundaries are sharply defined, the Blue Ridge on the east and the Appalachian Plateau on the west. The Gulf Coastal plain forms the southern boundary.

The Ridge and Valley, sometimes called the newer Appalachians, includes rather regularly folded strata and long narrow valleys separated by nearly parallel ridges. A great lowland extends with minor interruptions from end to end of the long physiographic province; this is not a single valley but a composite of many valleys. It is frequently called the Great Valley.

In the broad view, the Ridge and Valley region consists largely of valleys and valley lowlands in the south, such as the Coosa Valley in Georgia and Alabama and the Tennessee Valley in Tennessee. In contrast, there are more mountains than valleys in the north.

The distinctive features of Ridge and Valley topography in Pennsylvania, Maryland, and Virginia are long, parallel, sharp-crested ridges, often with zigzag pattern, and with narrow valleys intervening. Adjoining ridges are often markedly parallel. In places they are developed upon anticlines that expose resistant strata, in some places upon synclines, and in other places upon strata with a more complex internal structure. All the larger valleys have their positions and directions determined by weak rocks and have been developed subsequent to both the deformation of the strata and the base-leveling that is responsible for the even-topped character of the ridges.

The most striking features of the valleys within the zigzag ridges, whether of one structure or another, are their linear extent and shut-in or covelike character. Bald, Eagle, and Black Log valleys, Pennsylvania, are typical. Kishicoquillis Valley, between Stone and Jacks Mountains in Mifflin County, 53 miles long and 4 miles wide, is completely isolated except for the single outlet of Logan's Gap, near Lewiston. Tuscarora Valley is 50 miles long and 5 miles wide. Path and Nittany valleys are both over 30 miles long and from 2 to 5 miles wide, with no easy outlets except through an occasional water gap or over a higher wind gap. The sharp contrast between the linear extent and the width of the valleys is a direct result of the attitude of the strata, giving broader valleys where the strata are gently inclined and narrower valleys where steeply inclined.

No less striking than the topographic features of the zigzag ridges of the northern section of the Ridge and Valley region are the drainage features. The master streams flow roughly at right angles to the trends of the ridges and cut across them through water gaps of notable depth and often of pronounced beauty. The course of the Delaware through the Delaware water gap, the Susequehanna through the gaps of the central Pennsylvania ridges above Harrisburg, and the prominent gaps of the Potomac through the same or similar ridges farther south are illustrations of this feature. Where they cross the ridges in the gorgelike water gaps, the main streams are swift, often descending in short rapids, whereas across the intervening valleys they often flow lazily in regularly meandering courses.

Climate, Vegetation, and Soils. Much of the Ridge and Valley country has a humid subtropical climate, although the northern portion may be classed as humid continental. Growing season ranges from 160 days in the north to 240 in the south. Mountains as barriers, the Blue Ridge on the east and the Appalachian Plateau on the west, give an enclosed location, which in general, lessens precipitation.

Various sections display different vegetation and soils. The limestone valleys, which form so large a portion of the southern district, were originally covered with a heavy growth of hardwoods, interspersed with open parks or natural prairies where the limestone is most fissured and porous and therefore most dry. At present, the limestone valleys are extensively cleared, owing to the fertility of their soils and the abundant supply of timber available on the uncultivated ridges. The zigzag ridges of the north, on the other hand, are, for the most part, still covered with trees. Their bordering slopes are too steep and their summit areas too small to tempt the farmer. They constitute forest land of value when kept in trees, and are of little value, even as sheep or goat pastures, when cleared of their timber. The drier, sandier ridges formed on resistant sandstone, such as the Pocono, are marked by stunted growths of scrub pine and red and black oak; the more fertile valleys underlain with limestone have a native growth of walnut, blue ash, etc. The best growth occurs on the highest ridges of eastern West Virginia, where the rainfall is greater than elsewhere in the province. All soils are pedalfers, those in the southern part red and yellow earths, and those in the northern section gray-brown podzolics.

The Influences of Limestone (Fig. 7). Most valleys are floored with limestone and this parent soil material has broken down into clay soils with better than average structure and fertility; these qualities are ideal for pasture, hay, wheat, corn, apples, and other crops. Wheat and corn are money crops, but pasture and hay are bulky crops best marketed when fed to cattle. In a land devoid of many large cities, the dairy breeds are not so numerous as the beef breeds. Sheep become important on ridge farms; they can thrive on poorer pastures and are more nimble than cattle in grazing rugged uplands. Also, valley slopes provide a useful environment for apples.

Valley agriculture aided by the limestone soils adds an attraction for tourism in the Southwest Appalachians. No observing person who has driven south over the Skyline Drive on the crest of the Blue Ridge can fail

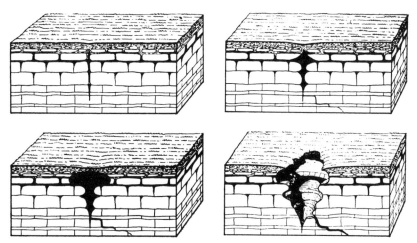

Fig. 7. Sinkhole Formation in the Appalachians. The length of the block, in front, is about 150 feet. It represents the development of a funnel-shaped sink in compact, jointed, limestone overlain by a thin residual mantle of unsoluble weathered material covered by sod. Sinkholes are common in the Appalachian and Ozark plateaus where many limestone rocks occur. (Source: C. R. Longwell, A. Knopf, and R. F. Flint, *Physical Geology,* 2nd ed., John Wiley and Sons, 1939.)

to be impressed as he looks down on the Shenandoah Valley. The Shenandoah's attractiveness is enhanced by the fields, livestock, barns, and houses that are all included in a beautiful farming landscape (Fig. 8).

At Birmingham, Alabama, coal, iron, and limestone are present in large amounts. Few steel centers of the world possess this advantage. Water is also available in adequate supply in the humid subtropical climate characteristic of Birmingham. Capital and labor can be obtained at costs as low as those of most any competitive area. One major factor is lacking in the steel-making complex; the city is too far removed from the largest United States market for steel; this market lies close to the southern shores of the Great Lakes.

Limestone is an important resource for the manufacture of cement. Cement may be composed of limestone and slate or limestone shale. These rocks are burned in a furnace and then ground to powder. In several places, slate quarries and limestone quarries lie close to one another, and they provide basic materials for cement plants. One of the largest producing sections is the Lehigh Valley (Fig. 9) near Allentown and Bethlehem, Pennsylvania. Philadelphia and New York are only about 100 miles distant and they provide good local and export markets.[5]

[5] For further information, especially on routes of travel, see J. Russell Smith, "The Great Valley, A Function of Limestone," *Journal of Geography,* September 1921, pp. 234–238.

Fig. 8. Farm Land and Wooded Hill Slopes in Virginia Valley. This distribution of farm land and forests is typical of the Ridge and Valley region—farm land in the valleys and timber on the ridges. (Courtesy U. S. Department of Agriculture.)

The Ridge Country. The ridges that separate the numerous small valleys and sometimes enclose them have an economy influenced by their topography and the resistant rocks of which the land is composed. Ridges have much more land in pasture and hay than have valleys; and if cultivation is attempted, contour plowing, strip cropping, terracing, and other conservation practices are necessary to prevent soil erosion. Less commercial and more subsistence agriculture is practiced on hill farms than in the valleys, and among the livestock, sheep are numerous.

In the highly folded strata of ridges in northeastern Pennsylvania, coal that was formerly bituminous has been changed to anthracite by extreme pressure. Because of the contorted coal beds, mining anthracite may be more difficult and costly than extracting bituminous coal in the horizontal strata of the Appalachian Plateau to the west. Supplies of anthracite are adequate for the declining market.

Tree farms are starting in some areas. Forestry is a logical land use for the ridges just as it is for rugged topography throughout all the Appalachians. Forests will provide not only timber, wood pulp, etc., but they will also provide a regional attraction for tourists.

The Appalachian Plateau

Location and Surface Features. The Helderberg Mountains, with a steep northern escarpment facing New York's Mohawk Valley, form the northern border of the Appalachian Plateau. This boundary crosses New York and Ohio and extends as far west as Cleveland; there the boundary turns south and passes through Ohio, Kentucky, and Tennessee, meeting the Gulf Coastal Plain in Alabama. The Central Lowland lies to the west, and the Ridge and Valley region lies to the east.

In contrast to the highly folded strata of the Ridge and Valley, the Blue Ridge, and the Piedmont, rock layers in the plateau are nearly horizontal. Plateau strata consist almost entirely of sedimentary rocks, including sandstone, limestone, shale, and bituminous coal.

Local names have been applied to different sections of the plateau, just as in the Great Valley. In the north, New York's Catskills, and the plateau section west of the Catskills, have been maturely dissected by stream action and Pleistocene glaciation. South of the Catskills, the terms Alle-

Fig. 9. Portland Cement Plant, Sandt's Eddy, Pennsylvania. The Ridge and Valley region has many large cement plants. (Courtesy Lehigh Portland Cement Company.)

gheny and Kanawha Mountains have been applied to the plateau in Pennsylvania, West Virginia, and Kentucky, as far south as the Cumberland River; the area south of that stream, extending through Kentucky, Tennessee, and northern Alabama, is known locally as the Cumberland Mountains.

Each of the above names includes the word *mountains* rather than *plateau,* which gives an idea as to the ruggedness of most land forms. There are sections, however, that conform closely to the definition of a plateau—a significant elevation with a maximum amount of summit level; and when the adjective *dissected* precedes *plateau,* the two names seem entirely proper. Geological unity may be noted in the horizontal strata characteristic of rocks in the entire region.

Climate, Vegetation, and Soils. Altitude influences climate in some sections—Catskill elevations rise above 4,000 feet, as do plateau sections of West Virginia and Kentucky. The long north-south extent influences length of growing season, which is several days longer in the south than in the north. The long latitudinal extent also necessitates subdivision into humid continental climate in the north and humid subtropical in the south. Cyclonic storms bring heavier precipitation to high elevations.

Deciduous forest, including oak, maple, walnut, poplar, tulip, beech, hickory, ash, and other varieties, dominates tree cover, although conifers may be found on high elevations and upon thin soils. For example, thin forests of pine and oak occur on the infertile sandstone and shale soils of the Tennessee "Barrens," but, in coves and hollows where soils are deeper and more fertile, hickory and oak trees show dense stands and great size.

Deciduous trees contribute more to soil structure and fertility than conifers, but not so much as middle latitude grasses contribute. However, the rugged topography of much of the plateau gives little opportunity for mature soil profile development.

Geologic history and parent rock material have had much to do with soil character. Pleistocene glaciation contributed favorably to soils of the northern plateau border by spreading a generally fertile veneer of glacial till over the uplands. On the other hand, parts of the Cumberland Plateau are covered with thin infertile soils derived from sandstone. Soils formed from beds of pure limestone which occupies level or gently rolling areas are productive as a rule. Floods due to spring rains and the melting of late winter snows are common and rise to great heights, washing away valley soils or covering up the soils of narrow flats or flood plains with heavy deposits of coarse waste. All soils are pedalfers with gray-brown podzolics in the north and red and yellow earths in the south.

Coal (Figs. 10, 11). This highland region might well be called the Plateau of Vulcan because it possesses one of the largest resources of easily exploited good quality bituminous coal in the world.

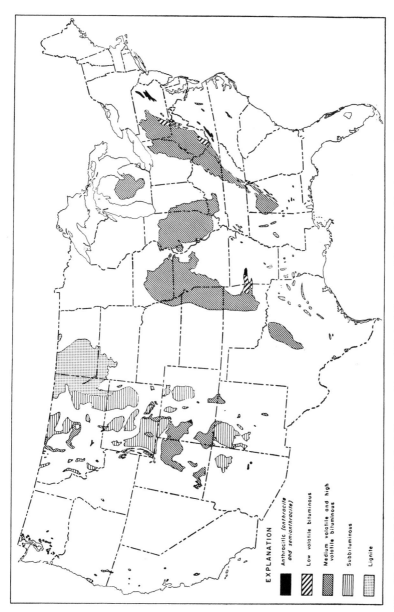

Fig. 10. Coal Fields of the United States. Most of United States coal is produced in the Appalachian Plateau. (Courtesy U. S. Geological Survey.)

Fig. 11. Drift Mining for Coal in the Appalachian Plateau. The coal-bearing strata, with thick seams in many Appalachian fields, were little disturbed by uplift of the plateau. After uplift, stream action dissected the highland and produced numerous valleys. Now man makes horizontal shafts into the valley walls to extract high-grade bituminous coal. Note that the coal moves downgrade to coal trains, using valleys as the best routes of transport through the plateau. In some places, navigable valley streams make barge transport possible. (Courtesy General Electric Company.)

Appalachian coal formation took place on lowland swamp topography millions of years ago. After the coal beds were formed, uplift of many hundreds of feet took place with a minimum of folding and faulting. Following uplift, stream erosion cut deep valleys, making it easy for man to extract thick horizontal beds of coal from the valley by drift mining. Thus coal can be brought to the edge of the valley by underground transport moving horizontally or nearly horizontally, and from there the fuel moves downgrade to the bottom of the stream valley, where it may be moved by barge or rail through an easy valley route to market. Of course, stream erosion, which made mining and transport of the product easy, removed some coal during the dissection of the plateau.

The large resources of good coal in the plateau have encouraged the growth of valley towns; one of the largest and best known is Pittsburgh. The confluence site where the Monongahela, flowing north, meets the Allegheny, flowing south, to form the Ohio was sure to be chosen for a city location (Fig. 12). In the early days, pioneers were anxious to reach the Ohio which would take them from the Appalachian Plateau by easy downgrade route to the Central Lowlands. Fort Pitt became an outfitting point for these early travelers. With the coming of the railroads, Pittsburgh's growth received further stimulus. But the greatest expansion came with the use of local resources for iron and steel manufacture. The Connellsville coal seam, near Pittsburgh, was one of the plateau's richest deposits, and coal could be moved from this seam to Pittsburgh by barge. Manmade factors, the discovery of the Bessemer and open hearth steel-making processes, aided the physical environment in stimulating growth. After local iron deposits were depleted, Lake Superior ores moving east by way of the Great Lakes more than made up for local metal deficiencies.

Fig. 12. The Golden Triangle. Pittsburgh, located where the Monongahela and Allegheny join to form the Ohio, has a very strategic location. Note the numerous bridges, the close utilization of the narrow flood plain, and the Appalachian Plateau in the background. (Courtesy American Iron and Steel Institute.)

Pittsburgh became so important in making steel that local steel men maintained their strong position by the man-made monopoly factor, Pittsburgh-Plus. Pittsburgh-Plus involved sales tactics that forced rival steel companies to add freight charges from Pittsburgh to point of sale for any steel sold. With this advantage, Pittsburgh plants could force competitors out of business or keep them from starting iron and steel plants even in locations with extremely favorable geographic environment.

After a while, the United States government stopped the monopoly advantage. Today, Pittsburgh is still one of the leading steel producers, but among its many advantages it has a few environmental weaknesses. First, the Ohio, Monongahela, and Allegheny valleys, where steel mills are located, are too narrow to allow easy plant expansion. Second, Lake Superior ore must be transferred from lake boats to rail cars for movement from the lake shore to Pittsburgh district steel plants. Sometime in the future an endless belt or a canal may eliminate the necessity for rail transport.

For several years the Appalachian coal industry, and that of the entire country, suffered a serious depression; and United States coal production dropped to 392,000,000 tons in 1954, approximately that for the U.S.S.R. in the same year. Reasons for the decline are not hard to discover. Two stand out. The railroads have changed almost entirely to diesel oil-burning locomotives, and most householders find automatic heat from oil and gas much more convenient than non-automatic coal. In 1944, railroads used 132,000,000 tons of coal; in 1952, 38,000,000 tons. In 1944, retailers supplying home owners with coal bought 125,000,000 tons; in 1952, they purchased 68,000,000 tons.

But all is not bad with the coal market. Steel is still almost completely dependent upon coal for fuel. In 1952, mills used 104,000,000 tons. Utilities, which took only 27,000,000 tons in the early 1930's used 103,000,000 tons in 1952. In 1955, the United States exported 37,000,000 tons and there are good prospects for a continuing overseas trade. In the early 1950's one company alone spent $11,000,000 in research to find new uses for coal in the chemical industry; possibly with further advances in coal chemistry all slack in the market will be removed. Should the market get tight, an expanding production will be easy; Appalachian resources are enormous and with 90 per cent of United States coal mechanically mined, and mechanization increasing, the output per man per day, already high, may be increased.

Forest Industries. Appalachian forests were first used by the pioneers who pushed through mountain and plateau country to the Ohio Valley. As time went on, many settled in the bottom lands, cut down the trees, built homes, and reared families there. Some of these small settlements grew into towns and townspeople also built houses and stores with wood from the virgin forest. Before the 1860's, timber was used mainly for local construction, and only the trees accessible to mountain water courses were rafted to distant sawmills.

After the Civil War, railroads began to tie together the little villages originally built with wood from local forests; and the railroads not only connected villages, but they also made it possible for big saw mills to exploit the forests successfully. Mills came slowly at first, but later became more numerous; they even built logging railroads. In fact, many ugly, temporary sawmill towns sprang up, thrived for a time, and then vanished as the forest was depleted. Sawmills large and small moved across the Appalachian forests and big timber disappeared.

Because of early indiscriminate cutting and fire, the present volume of timber is light; much of the area is in young timber in the sapling stage or pole size; and marketable trees are scattered and often consist of forest remnants inaccessible to logging jobs of the past. However, the future of Appalachian forests is more promising than present returns. Between 1911 and the late 1940's, the federal government purchased more than 6,000,000 acres of Appalachian timber land and set it aside in national parks. Here the forest is treated as a crop. Dozens of forest rangers are guided by the concept that trees which have the best chance of rapid growth and high value shall be allowed to develop fully by removing those that are defective, of poor form, or have undesirable qualities. Moreover, they believe that a productive forest is a growing forest and one in which trees should be used as they reach maturity.

Mature trees and those of undesirable quality are sold in small quantities to local people with limited resources—to people who prefer to become timber operators without leaving home and working for someone else. Many, who live on their native acres, farm during the growing season and remove timber from the forests after the crops are planted. Consequently, the federal government has a growing clientele of farmer-loggers who readily augment their cash income by timber work and still stay near their own firesides.

The local small operator in the national forest is not always a farmer. Many are in the wood processing business as their major occupation. Some small lumber producers operate one or more small sawmills. Others log railroad ties and mine timbers or cord wood for local markets on a year round basis. Throughout the Appalachian national forests, thousands of small sales of timber to be cut by local people are made annually; and local residents get much of their fuel wood from dead material free of charge.

The federal government is not the only forest agency employing proper conservation methods in the Appalachian forests. The New York and Pennsylvania Company, Inc., manufacturers of pulp and paper, and its subsidiary, the Armstrong Forest Company, for more than 50 years have managed their timberlands in Pennsylvania for continued growth of pulp-

wood. The West Virginia Pulp and Paper Company employs forest conservation methods and obtains the bulk of the wood used at its mills in New
York, Pennsylvania, Maryland, and Virginia from farmers and other sup-
pliers over wide areas. Even some of the mining companies are following
a conservation program on their holdings of land purchased for mineral
rights. One West Virginia company leases timber separately from the coal.
Diameter limits for cutting are specified and are varied to favor the species
that are best for mine props and lumber. The company forester estimates
that the program under way will double the yield of timber on lands to
which it applies.

It is possible that cropping the forests may revive one of the earliest
forest industries, that of mast feeding. Another unique forest industry of
the Appalachians is that of gathering forest products for medicine, food,
drinks, etc. Although not of great economic importance, forest gathering
may add a useful money crop or contribute to a subsistence farm economy.

Agriculture. In a subregion as large as the Appalachian Plateau, the
largest in the Southwest Appalachians, farms, crops, practices, etc., are
sure to show significant differences. Money crops range from the dairy
products of the New York section to the corn whiskey of isolated areas on
the Cumberland Mountains. Yet some farm problems are similar throughout the plateau. A large part of the land is rugged; soils generally do not
rank high in fertility; and forests must be cleared to expand farming
operations.

New York's plateau area has some of the most prosperous farms.
Dairying is encouraged by a nearby market of dense population occupying
the Mohawk-Hudson lowland from Buffalo to New York City. Most of
New York State's 15,000,000 people live in this lowland. Hill lands need
no cultivation for grass and hay; ample precipitation stimulates growth of
these bulky crops and also provides liberal quantities of good drinking
water for the cattle. Prosperous-looking dairy barns and silos feature New
York's farming landscape.

Concord grapes grow on slopes facing Lake Ontario and Lake Erie as
well as upon hill land bordering the Finger Lakes. Slopes assure air drainage, and protection against frost, and proximity to large water surfaces also
provides some insurance against low temperatures. Many of the grapes
reach market in the form of wine.

The large local market, which gives a good outlet for dairy products,
assures production of truck crops such as asparagus, beans, beets, cabbage,
and sweet corn. Buckwheat is a money crop on many farms because of
favorable adjustment to a short growing season and mediocre soils. New
York State accounts for one-half of the nation's buckwheat crop.

Ohio's plateau section, to the west of New York, forms the eastern
boundary of the Corn Belt. Land too rugged for row crops can be utilized

for sheep as well as for cattle; and a map showing sheep distribution will include several dots in eastern Ohio as well as in plateau sections of Pennsylvania and West Virginia. Dual-purpose animals—production for meat and wool—are most numerous. Some farmers plan the breeding season for early spring lambs. Protection against spring rain and cold is necessary for this type of sheep raising; the farmer must have warm barns or sheds.

The raising of livestock to graze land too rugged for cultivation is widespread throughout the plateau country. But so is the growing of corn. Cultivating corn has brought serious soil erosion, and in no section of the United States are conservation practices more necessary. Most of the land should be left in forest or grass; if cultivated crops are planted, contour plowing, terracing, strip farming, and a dominance of hay and tree crops are essential.

Tourism. The regional economy is strengthened by tourist attractions. Pleistocene glaciation in the New York section has contributed the Finger Lakes and other water bodies of scenic quality; too, in this area, glaciation has softened and rounded the land forms to make them attractive to many people. Besides attractive scenery, the northern part of the plateau possesses a market advantage. It is much more accessible to dense centers of population than the southern part of the highland. The latter may have forests, mountains, streams and other physical features of scenic quality just as attractive as those of the north, but the southern area lacks easy accessibility to a large market.

The Tennessee Valley Authority

(Figure 13)

The TVA is one of the greatest social and economic experiments of modern time, known not only throughout the United States, but all over the world as well. Its local control center is Knoxville, Tennessee, in the Ridge and Valley subregion; but TVA extends through other subregions of the Southwest Appalachians, and involves the entire Tennessee Valley and its tributaries. The major river system drains an area of 40,000 square miles, a territory as large as Belgium, Denmark, and the Netherlands. Parts of seven states are affected by the project, Alabama, Georgia, Kentucky, Mississippi, North Carolina, Tennessee, and Virginia, with a total population of more than 2,000,000 people.

The TVA started in 1933, during an economic depression that affected the United States as well as the rest of the world. Its primary aims were to lift the social and economic status of Tennessee Valley people by the development of flood control, hydroelectric power, and navigation.

Flood Control. The best farm land of the Tennessee drainage basin is

Fig. 13. Norris Dam: TVA Bulwark. This dam and 25 others are operated as a unit. Reservoir levels are balanced against power needs and flood dangers. Nearly all Tennessee Valley farms get electricity from this vast federal project; Oak Ridge experiments also receive power from Norris Dam. (Courtesy Paul A. Moore, Tennessee Conservation Department.)

along the valley lowlands. Before TVA, floods on these low plains often destroyed farm crops and left farmers without any dependable source of income. Floods may be due primarily to heavy rainfall, but rainfall reaches stream valleys faster and less water soaks into the ground when the rain falls upon land stripped of protective forest and grass cover. Man, during his long occupance of the area, removed the timber recklessly, thereby accelerating runoff and increasing flood danger. Although building dams to regulate stream flow was a primary TVA aim, part of the planning program is to replace forests in order to slow up runoff. Today, more than two dozen dams hold back river waters so that they move oceanward more evenly throughout the year, and even flow is also assisted by a planned reforestation program.

Hydroelectric Power. The building of dams not only provides flood control, but also gives an assist to power development. Below each of the dams there is a power plant, and within that structure there are raceways through which water moves against blades of large turbines. This generates electricity that can be carried on transmission lines for use on farm and factory. Before TVA, electric power was available for use on less than 5 per cent of the farms in the Tennessee Valley; now many farmers possess this necessity of modern living, and factories have moved in to profit from reasonable power rates.

Navigation. Prior to the establishment of TVA, falls and rapids, as well as seasonal periods of shallow water, made navigation hazardous if not impossible. With the building of the dams, locks were also constructed so that ships could move along the Tennessee River with a minimum of delay. At present, a nine-foot depth is maintained for a distance of over 600 miles between Knoxville, Tennessee, and Paducah, Kentucky. As a result of these improvements, river cargo has increased significantly.

When Congress passed TVA legislation, it not only planned to improve navigation, flood control, and hydroelectric power, but many other conditions as well. At the time of the depression of the 1930's, when TVA was started, thousands of people who were out of work moved back into the valley thereby making worse economic conditions that were already bad. Construction of the TVA gave many of these people something to do.

Tennessee Valley agriculture in the 1930's involved too much exploitation of farm land rather than conservation. TVA planning deplores exploitation and encourages conservation practices such as terracing, crop rotation, close cover crops, contour plowing, and acceptance of farm bureau extension service advice. All these farming improvements may not be necessary for lowland farms, but they are vital on the slope lands.

Improvement in farm practices contributes to national defense; but TVA strengthened the war effort in other ways. It furnished hydroelectric power for factories that produced quantities of aluminum, super phosphates, powder, shells, weapons, and many other articles of military importance.

Possibly one of TVA's greatest national contributions is the experience it gave in regional planning when applied to a river basin in economic and social difficulty. Partly as a result of TVA planning experience, an MVA has started to improve similar difficulties in the valley of the Missouri River.

TVA has not developed without encountering considerable opposition. Private power companies oppose the Authority because of what they call unfair competition. Private industry argues that TVA's rate structure can charge off expenses to navigation and flood control that rightfully belong to charges on power development. Steam power facilities have been added to supplement TVA's original hydroelectric equipment. Although opposition to TVA has occurred, most people, even some private power companies, will agree that it has been a successful experiment for the millions of people living in the Tennessee Valley.

The Ozarks

(Figure 14)

The Ozark physiographic province has a midcontinental location, and is separated from the remainder of the Southwest Appalachians by a broad expanse of the Central Lowland.   However, the subregion is included with the major region because of several similarities.   (*a*) Much of the Ozark area is a plateau; the Appalachian Plateau makes up a large fraction of the Southwest Appalachians.   (*b*) The Ouachita Range, south of the Ozark Plateau, is developed upon an Appalachian type of structure with ridges and valleys providing most striking features.   (*c*) The Ouachitas are not far from the Arbuckle Mountains, which were uplifted and base-leveled in common with the great Appalachian province east of the Mississippi.   Geologically therefore, there is similarity between Ozark and Appalachian areas, and there is also considerable similarity in land use.

Surface Features.   The Ozarks may be divided into several minor divisions; the Ozark Plateau to the north is separated from the Boston Moun-

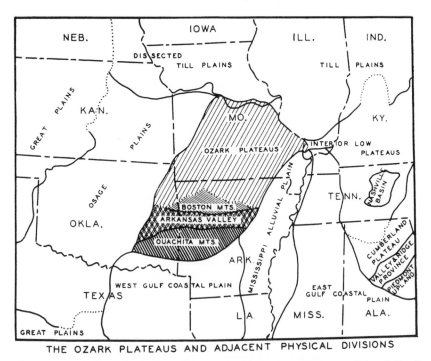

THE OZARK PLATEAUS AND ADJACENT PHYSICAL DIVISIONS

Fig. 14.   The Ozark Plateaus and Adjacent Physical Divisions.   The White River Valley lies between the Ozark Plateaus and the Boston Mountains, and the Arbuckle and Wichita Mountains lie to the west.   They are not shown on the map.   (After Nevin F. Fenneman and Arthur B. Cozzens.)

tains on the south by the White River; south of the Boston uplands is the broad Arkansas Valley; and south of the broad lowlands of the Arkansas are the Ouachita Mountains. Western outliers of the Ouachitas are the Arbuckle and Wichita Mountains. The Ozark province includes parts of four states, large portions of Missouri and Arkansas and smaller sections of Oklahoma and Kansas.

Rocks in the Ozark Plateau are mainly sedimentaries, with wide expanses of limestone, dolomitic limestone, and sandstone. Granites and other igneous rocks occupy small sections such as the St. Francis Knobs, whose sedimentary rocks topping a structural dome have been removed by erosion. Domed sedimentaries have also been eroded from the outlying Wichita Mountains, which are composed of igneous rocks, chiefly granites. The highest elevations in the Ozark province, approximately 2,800 feet, occur in the Ouachitas.

Climate, Vegetation, and Soils. The Ozark province lies in two climatic regions; the southern portion belongs to the humid subtropical type and the northern part possesses the humid continental variety. Continentality is probably the most important climatic control; a long distance from the sea brings colder winters and warmer summers than those of coastal locations in the same latitude. Altitude is insufficient to cause significant differences in either temperature (Fig. 3) or precipitation. The latter increases to the east and south and so does the temperature.

Cutover forests of deciduous trees such as oak and hickory are dominant over the Ozarks, but conifers, mainly pine, occur on the poor soils and at higher elevations. There are several reasons why these forests should remain dominant in the land use pattern. (*a*) Soils contain much cherty material resulting from the geologic processes of erosion and solution in large areas of limestone rock. (*b*) A large section of rugged relief makes crop agriculture difficult, and the planting of row crops accelerates dissection by streams. (*c*) Finer soil has been carried too far beneath the surface to be available for many farm crops.

The most productive soils occur on wide flood plains such as those of the White and Arkansas rivers. About 75 per cent of the Springfield Plateau surface shows less than a 5 per cent slope, a condition that lessens the danger of soil erosion.

Agriculture. As previously indicated, outside the Springfield Plateau and the river valley lowlands, which can be utilized for cultivated crops, Ozark land forms are too rugged and soils too light for the widespread planting of row crops. However, soils will support alsike and red clover, Kentucky blue grass, lespedeza, and timothy, but fertilization may be necessary to get a good first seeding. Some dairying is carried on, but environmental conditions generally are not ideal. Summer rainfall is variable in amount and distribution; low rainfall and light soils causes grasses to dry out quickly and may result in pasture deficiency; the lack of many large cities lessens opportunity for sales of liquid dairy products.

Beef cattle, especially Hereford and Shorthorn, are better adapted than dairy animals for grazing the grass and tree-covered hills. In fact, the growing of cattle for fattening in the nearby Corn Belt—not enough corn is produced locally for fattening cattle—is proving a good way to utilize the less rugged hill land.

The growing of fruit offers another Ozark farming opportunity. Southern Missouri and northern Arkansas are well known for their apples, grapes, and strawberries.

Subsistence agriculture is more characteristic of the Ozarks than commercial farming, and in many cases the settler may be called a Jack-of-all-trades. He may mine a little barite, cut a few trees for forest products, fish from nearby streams, and in the winter hunt and trap wild animals for food and skins.

Forestry. Forests include climaxes of oak-hickory and oak-pine. In no other part of the United States are there the large pure stands of oak that so clearly and characteristically distinguish the Ozark upland from the neighboring regions to the north, west, and east. Since the best soils are in the river bottoms, most of the forests there have been removed. On the other hand, over widespread areas of the rugged uplands, forests have never been completely cleared, only culled of their marketable timber.

Forest products include fuel, barrel staves, furniture, lumber, railroad ties, and mine props. Some tree country is used for mast feeding and all forest vegetation serves as an attraction for tourists. Nearly one-fifth of the region has been set aside for national forests.

Mining. The Ozarks hold a high position in producing lead and zinc. In Missouri, about 80 miles southeast of St. Louis, mines contribute nearly one-third of United States galena. The ore occurs at considerable depths and shaft mining is necessary. Unique features of the mines are huge man-made underground caverns with ceilings supported by enormous limestone columns. Great piles of tailings surround the surface openings of the mine shafts.

Southwestern Missouri, southeastern Kansas, and northeastern Oklahoma are included in the Tri-state mining region, widely known for its production of zinc and lead. The principle ore is sphalerite, the sulphide of zinc, although galena, calcites, pyrite, and quartz are present in small quantities. Shaft mines are used because the ores lie at considerable depths beneath the surface. Large mounds of white chert or flint, dug from the zinc mines, dot the landscape. This material is not entirely waste, for it is utilized in the construction of motor highways and in resurfacing railroad rights of way. In 1953, the district accounted for more than 10 per cent of United States zinc production. Normally Oklahoma ranks first among the Tri-state group, Kansas second, and Missouri third.

The region ranks high in the production of barite, a heavy white mineral often stained with brown limonite. Barite may be ground to a fine powder called baroid, and used on oil drilling machinery; it is so heavy that it aids in forming mud valuable in controlling high gas pressure. The mineral is used also in chemicals, lithopone, glass, paint, and rubber. In 1953, three-fourths of United States barite came from Missouri and Arkansas.

Additional minerals of the Ozarks include iron ores—iron deposits were exploited for many years at Iron Mountain in the St. Francis Mountains, and new shafts will soon tap rich deep iron deposits at Pea Ridge—building limestone, marble, clay, coal, and others of lesser importance.

Tourism. Tourism is increasing in the Ozarks, but the industry has several drawbacks: mountains are not high; forests are not so luxuriant as those in the Northwest, the East, and the South; summers in the continental interior are hot; winter snows are not heavy enough and do not remain on the ground long enough to permit winter sports; and few large population centers are close by.

In spite of these handicaps, there is a certain charm about this isolated region that attracts more people every year and tempts them to return again and again.

Regional Summary

In the opening paragraphs of the chapter, attention was called to regional differences between the physical environment of the Northeast Appalachians and that of the Southwest Appalachians. Only a small portion of the Southwest was affected by glaciation in contrast to the widespread glacial action in the Northeast. The mountains of the Southwest are higher than those of the Northeast. No broad plateau like the Southwest's great coal-bearing upland is present in the Northeast. Neither of the great mountain regions is rich in developed metallic minerals, but the Southwest has significant iron deposits at Birmingham, Alabama, and valuable zinc and lead resources in the Ozarks. Forest vegetation is dominant in both regions, but that of the Southwest is almost entirely deciduous, whereas that of the Northeast is a mixture of coniferous and deciduous.

Man's adjustments to differing regional physical environments also show contrasts. The Northeast has no large iron and steel centers like Pittsburgh, Pennsylvania, and Birmingham, Alabama; no great coal mining industry adds to Northeastern economy as it does to that of the Southwest. Forest practices differ in the two regions largely as a result of contrasts in forests and contrasts in climate. The Northeast produces better and more paper and paper pulp and better and more lumber. Northeast winter snows and spring thaws bring forest exploitation practices differing from those of the Southwest. The Southwest produces more tobacco and more beef cattle.

Both regions emphasize manufacturing, but many of the Northeast textile mills have moved to the Southwest; both regions compete for tourists, but the Northeast has more glacial lakes, cooler summers, greater proximity to the sea, and greater nearness to dense centers of population. Finally, the Southwest contains one of the greatest social and economic experiments of all time in the TVA. More contrasts may be cited, but enough have been listed to show that in spite of great diversity within the Southwest, many items give regional unity when comparison is made to the bordering Northeast.

QUESTIONS, EXERCISES, AND PROBLEMS

1. Give the location, boundaries, subregions, and general environmental features of the Southwest Appalachians. What differences exist between the Northeast and the Southwest Appalachians? Describe the physical environment of the Piedmont in some detail. Comment on the agriculture of Lancaster County, Pennsylvania. Trace the seasonal activities in growing tobacco in the central Piedmont. How do major crops in the southern Piedmont influence the practices of soil conservation? Give the geographic background for Piedmont manufacturing.

2. Compare the physical features of the Ozark region with those of the Blue Ridge Mountains. Give the advantages of each for tourism, agriculture, forestry, mining, manufacturing, etc.

3. Describe the surface features and the regional economy of the Ridge and Valley region. Show the influences of limestone upon past and present economy.

4. Tell of the mining, forestry, agriculture, manufacturing, tourism, etc., of the Appalachian Plateau. Contrast the geology of the plateau with that of the Ridge and Valley region. Describe the geography of the TVA.

5. West Virginia's Great Kanawha Valley is sometimes known as Chemical Valley. Show how the urban development is related to basic factors in industrial location—market, raw materials, power, labor, transportation, water supply, capital, land values, taxation, living costs, and the human factor. Do the same for Pittsburgh and other industrial areas.

6. Each of the following cities has approximately 100,000 people or more in its urban district: Akron, Altoona, Binghamton, Canton, Charleston, Chattanooga, Harrisburg, Knoxville, Pittsburgh, Scranton, Wheeling, Wilkes-Barre, and Youngstown. Name the major activities for these centers of population.

7. Locate, and indicate important economic and other activities for each of the following towns and cities: Asheville, Florence, Fort Smith, Hot Springs, Huntington, Johnson City, Joplin, Muscle Shoals, Oak Ridge, Roanoke, Spartanburg, Springfield, Missouri.

8. Identify the following: Stone Mountain, Amish, Lehigh Valley, St. Francis Mountains, feeder cattle, air drainage, lespedeza, kudzu, mast, Mount Mitchell, White River, Ouachita, Boston Mountains, solution processes, wind gap, anthracite, dissected plateau, drift mining, Zebu, Eastern Quadrilateral, Pittsburgh-Plus, barite, galena, Tri-state mining region, Pea Ridge.

9. Describe the best practices that should be employed in the conservation of natural resources throughout the Southwest Appalachians. Describe the distribution of population in the region.

SELECTED REFERENCES

Bowman, Isaiah, *Forest Physiography,* John Wiley and Sons, 1911, pp. 585–635 and 665–706.

Broadhurst, Sam D., "The Mining Industry in North Carolina from 1946 to 1953," *Economic Paper No. 66,* North Carolina Department of Conservation and Development, 1955.

Brown, J. D., "Twenty-Five Years of TVA," *The Americas,* May 1958.

Cozzens, Arthur B., "Analyzing and Mapping Natural Landscape Factors of the Ozark Province," *Transactions of the Academy of Science of St. Louis,* Vol. 30, May 31, 1939.

Crissler, Robert M., "Recreation Regions of Missouri," *Journal of Geography,* Vol. 51, 1952, pp. 30–39.

Deasy, George F., and Phyllis R. Griess, "Some New Maps of the Underground Bituminous Coal Mining Industry of Pennsylvania," *Annals of the Association of American Geographers,* December 1957, pp. 336–349.

Durand, Loyal, Jr., "Mountain Moonshining in East Tennessee," *Geographical Review,* April 1956, pp. 168–181.

Durand, Loyal, Jr., and Elsie T. Bird, "The Burley Tobacco Region of the Mountain South," *Economic Geography,* July 1950, pp. 247–300.

Federal Reserve Bank of Cleveland, *Changing Fortunes of Bituminous Coal,* 1956.

Fortune, "Rise of the Rubber Railroad," April 1951.

Foscue, Edwin J., "Gatlinburg: A Mountain Community," *Economic Geography,* Vol. 21, 1945, pp. 192–205.

Glenn, L. C., "Denudation and Erosion in the Southern Appalachian Region," *Professional Paper No. 72,* U. S. Geological Survey, 1911.

Gottman, Jean, *Virginia at Mid-Century,* Henry Holt and Co., 1955.

Mattoon, M. A., "Appalachian Comeback," *Trees,* U. S. Agricultural Year Book, 1949, pp. 304–309.

Miller, E. Willard, "Strip Mining and Land Utilization in Western Pennsylvania," *Scientific Monthly,* Vol. 69, 1949, pp. 94–103.

Miller, E. Willard, "The Southern Anthracite Region, Problem Area," *Economic Geography,* October 1955, pp. 331–350.

Moke, Irene A., "Canning in Northwestern Arkansas: Springdale, Arkansas," *Economic Geography,* April 1952, pp. 151–159.

Ohle, E. L., and J. S. Brown, "Geologic Problems in Southeast Missouri Lead District," *Bulletin of the Geological Society of America,* March 1954.

Popular Mechanics, "130-Mile Belt to Carry Coal and Ore," April 1949.

Rich, John L., "A Bird's-Eye Cross Section of the Central Appalachian Mountains and Plateau, Washington to Cincinnati," *Geographical Review,* October 1939, pp. 561–586.

Shaw, Earl B., "The Geography of Mast Feeding," *Economic Geography,* July 1940, pp. 233–249.

Shearer, M. H., and Ralph S. Harris, "The Ozark Region of Missouri," *Journal of Geography,* May 1943, pp. 181–187.

Shirley, Hardy L., "Company Forests," *Trees,* U. S. Agricultural Year Book, 1949, pp. 255–274.

Smith, J. Russell, "The Great Valley, Function of Limestone," *Journal of Geography,* September 1921, pp. 234–238.

State of Tennessee, Department of Conservation, Division of Geology, *List of Publications,* July 1954.

U. S. Bureau of Mines, "Mineral Facts and Problems," *Bulletin 556,* 1956.

Woodruff, James F., and Eldon J. Parizek, "Influence of Underlying Rock Structures on Stream Courses and Valley Profiles in the Georgia Piedmont," *Annals of the Association of American Geographers,* March 1956, pp. 129–139.

8 · The Interior Seaboard

(Figure 1)

The dream of an interior seaboard is not of recent origin. In the seventeenth century, Champlain visualized the possibility of a canal linking the Great Lakes to the Atlantic; this vision is described in the diary of the French explorer. After the War of 1812, Canadians drew blue prints of a canal that would sidetrack falls and rapids between the western Great Lakes and the Gulf of St. Lawrence. A canal 7½ feet deep was completed on the Canadian side of the St. Lawrence between 1824 and 1833. By 1850, the canal had been deepened to 9 feet; and the depth was increased to 14 feet in 1902. The trouble with depths of 7½ feet, 9 feet, and 14 feet is that they will not accommodate many ocean-going ships. However, the new 27-foot channel of the Great Lakes-St. Lawrence Seaway will provide passage for most of the big ocean freighters as far as the western tip of Lake Superior, about 1,700 miles away from the Pacific Coast.

Land use is not the same for all lands bordering the interior sea. But one important factor of the geographic environment is similar everywhere along its shores—the availability of water transport. This advantage has been important in both past and present economy of all areas contiguous to the waterway. In the section south of the Great Lakes, a major United States manufacturing area, sometimes called the North American Ruhr, several influences are responsible for great industrial progress. These include proximity to Appalachian coal, nearness to iron of the Lake Superior region, location near the heart of the big Eastern market, and availability of Great Lakes transport; the last factor may be the most important of all.

North and west of the interior sea, a highly mineralized portion of the Laurentian Shield is rich in iron ore and other metals. Availability of Great Lakes shipping has been extremely important in the exploitation of this area.

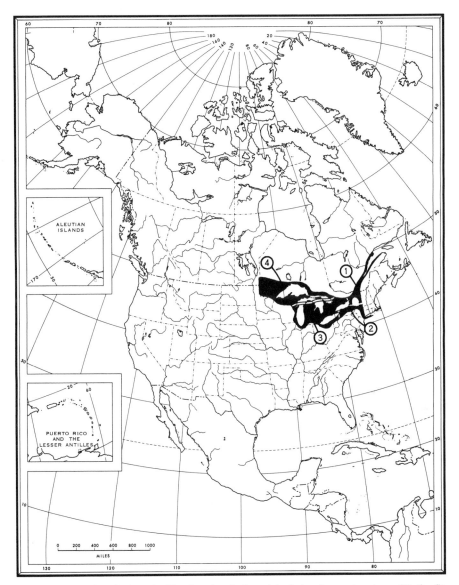

Fig. 1. The Interior Seaboard. The Interior Seaboard includes four subregions: (1) the St. Lawrence-Lake Champlain Lowland; (2) the Mohawk-Hudson Gateway: (3) the Lower Lakes region; and (4) the Upper Lakes region.

Easy access to water transport has been significant in the farming development throughout the St. Lawrence Valley and the Lake Champlain Lowland since early days of European settlement. Farmers chose land facing the water in order to obtain shipping facilities for local and distant markets. And transport more than anything else is responsible for the great economic growth in the Hudson-Mohawk Valley region lying tributary to the St. Lawrence-Great Lakes Seaway.

All along the shores of the interior sea, in the Northern Lake subregion, the Southern Lake subregion, the St. Lawrence-Lake Champlain Lowland, and the Mohawk-Hudson valleys, water transport is a dominant factor in the geographic environment. It is the one factor that provides a reason for considering the large area as a geographic region. A better understanding of the Interior Seaboard may be gained by discussing separately each of the subregions mentioned above.

The St. Lawrence-Lake Champlain Lowland

Geology. Geologically, the St. Lawrence-Lake Champlain Lowland is made up largely of sedimentary rocks, mainly shales, lying between resistant igneous and metamorphic rocks on both sides. To the north of the St. Lawrence is the Laurentian Shield, to the south are the Adirondacks and the New England uplands.

During Pliocene time, uplift of several hundred feet occurred in the present St. Lawrence Valley, beginning just west of Montreal and extending east to the Atlantic. At that time, water eroded the gorgelike St. Lawrence Valley, leaving more resistant rocks on either side standing out as steep cliffs. With the coming of the continental ice sheet in Pleistocene time, subsidence of several hundred feet took place; and with the departure of the glacier, the Atlantic invaded the St. Lawrence, the Lake Champlain Trough, and the valley of the Hudson. Following the sea invasion, uplift occurred again; however, tidal influences are still felt as far inland as the city of Quebec.

Not all of the St. Lawrence possesses the gorgelike valley that the river has worn in the weak rocks between Montreal and Quebec. Southwest of Quebec, the river occupies a shallow valley where stream erosion has made but little headway. Two reasons for less erosion west of Montreal than there is east of the city are, (*a*) the St. Lawrence has occupied the valley west of Montreal only since Pleistocene time, and (*b*) more resistent rocks are present west of Montreal.

History. The St. Lawrence has been a significant transport artery throughout human history because, with the Great Lakes, it forms the best natural gateway to the heart of the continent. When Jacques Cartier discovered the river in 1535, he thought that he had found a short route to China; and the early French explorers called the rapids west of Montreal, the Lachine (China) rapids, for they believed them to be a part of the Northwest Passage to the Orient across a relatively narrow continent. These were mistaken beliefs, but the French did discover an inland passage that led them to the Mississippi Valley and the Great Plains—that led them to an expanse of territory on which they spread out so thin that they failed to hold much of their conquest over succeeding centuries.

Permanent French settlement took place at Quebec in the early 1600's; the name Quebec is probably derived from an Indian word meaning the narrows. Here, the constricted river is only about 3,500 feet wide, a distance across which guns of the seventeenth century could control passage up- or downstream. Here, also was high ground, another protective factor for the settlement which later became the capital of New France.

Quebec harbor is commodious enough for hundreds of ships of early seventeenth century draft, and the junction of the St. Lawrence with the St. Charles gave the harbor a sheltered position. West of the harbor, navigation is more difficult than to the east; the current is more rapid; tides have little effect upon the river; and shallows are a hazard for ships of more than 10-foot draft. Geography had much to do with the location of an important settlement at Quebec.

Settlement at Montreal, named after Mount Royal, the volcanic hill rising nearly 1,000 feet back of the city, took place a few decades after that of Quebec. However, like Quebec, the upriver location had certain geographic advantages. Location with reference to the fur trade was important in the seventeenth century. Montreal is at the node of a Y, with the Ottawa and Upper St. Lawrence forming the two limbs. Both limbs were useful for the transfer of furs and trade goods used in exchange for furs. The Ottawa limb was the most important for it offered a fairly direct route to Mackinac Island, which became a significant post within the French fur country. Besides the gateway position on the Ottawa and Upper St. Lawrence, Montreal is well located for contact with the south along the Lake Champlain Trough and Hudson Valley.

Geography was a stronger influence than history upon the settlement pattern of the river valley between Quebec and Montreal. Foremost in the settler's mind was a desire for frontage on the St. Lawrence and its navigable tributaries. The rivers furnished travel by water in summer and by ice in winter at a period and in an environment where other means of travel were either costly or wholly unobtainable. The natural result was a distribution of habitations like beads on a string, each one within easy reach of the river. Village life, a characteristic of the feudal system in France, was thus eliminated. This situation distressed the authorities, who felt that such a dispersal of people subjected them more easily to surprise Indian attack. It seemed impossible, however, with attractions of the river as they were, to legislate villages into existence.

The long narrow farms (Fig. 2) gave another advantage besides river frontage. Extending well inland, the holdings included higher and rougher pasture land and woodland, with varied soils that contributed to the self-

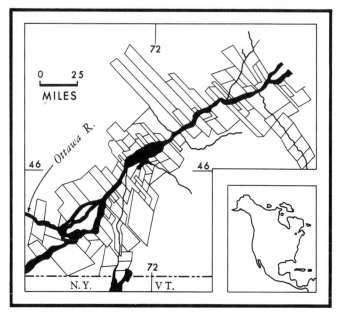

Fig. 2.   Farms Along the St. Lawrence and Its Tributaries, About 1800.   An almost unanimous desire for access to the best means of transportation influenced the shape of early farms along the St. Lawrence. (After Ralph H. Brown, *Historical Geography of the United States,* Harcourt, Brace and Co., 1948.)

sufficient economy of the people.   Many who have condemned the method of land subdivision that developed here have failed to appreciate the fact that each unit included a variety of soils and other resources that another system might not have provided.

In the early nineteenth century, French-Canadian agriculture was self-sufficing, with arable land used for crops such as potatoes, onions, corn, and some small grains.   Sheep, horses, and cattle were grazed on meadows and upland pastures in the wooded tracts.   The family produced its own dairy products and meat, and made clothing from wool woven in the household.   Woodland areas furnished raw materials for building and cordwood for fuel, as well as maple sap for syrup and sugar, a substitute for cane sugar. Apples were abundantly produced, and from them cider was pressed.   In addition, each farmer maintained a garden and kept poultry, and there was always the river from which fish could be secured.   Commercial towns found little place in this type of economy.

Agriculture Today.   Today, farmers retain a few elements of subsistence agriculture, but major emphasis is placed upon dairying.   The environment favors dairy cattle and the feed they eat.   Climate permits root crops such as potatoes, beets, and turnips.   Hay and small grains, especially oats, grow well. Cold winters do not kill fall wheat because of the heavy snow cover; but the grain can be grown cheaper on the Canadian prairies and thus local production is unprofitable in the face of western competition.

Well-distributed, adequate rainfall provides good drinking water. Cool summers encourage heavy milk flow. About the only unfavorable factor of the physical environment is the winter cold and deep snow. These climatic conditions necessitate good barns and shedding, and the storage of feed crops grown in the summer season.

Tariffs on dairy products bar St. Lawrence commodities from the United States market, a sales area much closer than Great Britain, where most dairy concentrates are sold. Much of the milk surplus goes into cheese, a dairy item that will keep better than milk during the long sea journey to Europe.

Dairying is a major farm enterprise in the Lake Champlain Lowland adjoining the St. Lawrence on the south. But this subregion within the United States has a tariff-free advantage over its Canadian neighbor. Distances to densely populated urban centers are short, and much milk is sold in fluid form.

Water Power, Wood Pulp, and Newsprint. The St. Lawrence Lowland combines with adjoining regions to produce a large percentage of Canada's water power. That commodity is based upon suitable land forms and adequate surface water. It has been mentioned previously that the St. Lawrence Valley was worn down by stream erosion on relatively weak sedimentary rocks, mostly shales. On each side of the valley are resistant igneous and metamorphic rocks, part of them in the Canadian Shield to the north, which were more resistant to erosion agencies and remain in the steep cliffs bordering the St. Lawrence. Thus, valley and adjoining land forms are ideal for creating waterfalls, and abundant water is available from local precipitation.

Canada's pulp and paper industry, much of it in the St. Lawrence Valley—Quebec produced 49 per cent of the national total in 1952—is first in the use of Canadian hydroelectric power. Canadian pulp and paper stand first in other ways: first in production, with a 1953 gross ouput valued at $1,100,000,000; first in salaries and wages paid to employees with an annual payroll of about $380,000,000; first in value of exports with a 1953 figure of $876,000,000; and first in the purchase of goods and services and in the employment of transport facilities.

Canada's paper and pulp industry has been aided by availability of clean water, required in enormous volume by paper and pulp factories, and by the proximity to the United States market.

Besides providing power for the paper pulp and paper industry, the St. Lawrence and its tributaries furnish hydroelectric power for the manufacture of aluminum. Prior to the construction of the hydroelectric plant at Kitimat-Kemano, British Columbia, the Aluminum Company of Canada power development at Arvida, on the Saguenay in Quebec, was the largest in the world. Here, between Lake St. John and tidewater, a distance of 30 miles, the Saguenay drops 330 feet. Another large aluminum plant uses power of the St. Maurice tributary of the St. Lawrence at Shawinigan Falls. Still another large hydroelectric development is the 1954 installation on the Bersimis tributary northeast of the Saguenay. It is well to remember that the St. Lawrence flows through two Canadian provinces, Quebec and Ontario, but Ontario's actual hydroelectric development is a much higher proportion of potential than is that of Quebec. The eastern province is less developed industrially.

The Tourist Industry. The St. Lawrence Valley attracts tourists both in summer and winter. In summer, the trips up and down the St. Lawrence bring in many visitors from the United States and from the rest of Canada. In winter, the snow favors ski resorts, ice skating, and the use of bobsleds. In both summer and winter, the St. Lawrence Valley competes with similar sports activities in New England; the latter location is nearer centers of dense population, giving a market advantage. Whenever the Canadian dollar is quoted at a discount below the United States dollar, people from the United States receive an added influence to cross the border, but that situation has not occurred for years. In 1958, the United States dollar was selling at a discount below the value of the Canadian dollar.

The St. Lawrence Seaway (Fig. 3). In May 1954, after Canada announced intention to construct the St. Lawrence Seaway without United States help, Congress voted approval for a project that has been in United States politics for more than a half century.[1] One of the most decisive factors in changing congressional attitude was the rapid depletion of high-grade iron ore in the Mesabi region, and the discovery of enormous iron deposits in Labrador only a few hundred miles north of the St. Lawrence (Fig. 4). Owners of steel mills along the Great Lakes recognized high-grade Labrador iron as a replacement for the vanishing high-grade ore of the Mesabi region, and gave strong encouragement to congressional passage. Here, was a strong economic and strategic argument for the seaway.

Congress also was impressed (*a*) by the fact that the contemplated 27-foot channel will open the Great Lakes to ship building on a far greater scale than was possible in World War II; (*b*) by the certainty that completion of the seaway will diversify and increase the efficiency of our transport facilities for use in wartime; and (*c*) by the assurance that power development in connection with canal building through the international rapids

---

[1] For a good short geographic analysis of forces causing the delay see Blair Bolles, *Foreign Policy Association Bulletin,* March 15, 1946.

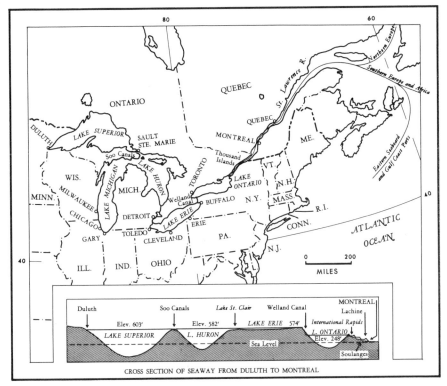

CROSS SECTION OF SEAWAY FROM DULUTH TO MONTREAL

Fig. 3. The Great Lakes-St. Lawrence Seaway. The greatest problems in seaway improvement occurred in the 182-mile stretch between Lake Ontario and Montreal, where rapids have always made river navigation hazardous. Here, old canals have been deepened and new canals and locks have been constructed to at least 27-foot depth. Power facilities have been added capable of an electrical output three times that of the Colorado River's Hoover Dam.

will create three times as much power as that of the Hoover Dam and almost as much as that of the Grand Coulee.

Most seaway projects will be completed by 1960 at a cost of over a billion dollars. Major projects involved are the deepening of the following areas: the St. Mary's River channel near Sault Ste. Marie, the Straits of Mackinac, the St. Clair River, Lake St. Clair, the Detroit River, and the Welland Canal; dredging the Thousand Islands channel; building two ship canals, two locks, two dams, and a powerhouse at International Rapids; enlarging the Lake St. Francis channel; building a lock on the Beauharnois power canal; and building a ship canal and locks that will bypass the Lachine Rapids.

Depth will be sufficient to accommodate three-fourths of the world's sea-going ships. More than 8,000 miles of coast line will be added to the

Fig. 4. Seven Islands Iron Ore Terminal. Iron ore travels over 300 miles by rail from Schefferville, Labrador, to Seven Islands on the St. Lawrence. Notice the ore boats, the piles of iron
ore, and the long string of railroad cars. (Courtesy Youngstown Sheet and Tube Company.)

United States and Canada; and such lake cities as Chicago, Cleveland,
Duluth, Buffalo, Toronto, Toledo, Milwaukee, and Hamilton will become
genuine deep water ports; they are already improving harbors to take care
of expected expansion in water transport. Power development associated
with the seaway will be helpful, especially to power-deficient Ontario Province. The seaway is not a project like the TVA, for there is no planned
development for the whole region.

Future Trends. The St. Lawrence portion of the subregion will continue
utilization and expansion of hydroelectric facilities for power-hungry
industries, such as aluminum, paper pulp, and paper. Tree farming and
other improved timber practices will strengthen the region's forestry activities. Physical and man-made environment may attract more tourists during each succeeding year. Dairying will expand, and other specialized
farming types may develop.

The Lake Champlain Lowland will probably expand its farming and
tourist activities more than those connected with power and manufacturing.
It is largely because of similarity in background of the St. Lawrence and
Lake Champlain lowlands for tourism and agriculture, and because of the
corridor character of Lake Champlain's location between the St. Lawrence
and the Hudson opening to the Atlantic that the Lake Champlain and St.
Lawrence lowlands were joined in a subregion.

Finally, the St. Lawrence River, the heart of the subregion, will carry more tourists than it does now; local exports of aluminum, paper pulp, paper, farm products, etc., will increase; and through cargo, both import and export commodities will expand. All this shipping emphasizes the important part transport plays not only in the economy of the subregion, but also in the entire region of the Interior Seaboard.

The Mohawk-Hudson Gateway

(Figure 5)

There are several reasons for making a subregion out of the Mohawk-Hudson portion of the Interior Seaboard: (*a*) The Mohawk-Hudson corridor to the Great Lakes and the continental interior differs from the St. Lawrence-Lake Champlain opening by being entirely within the United States; (*b*) the United States subregion is much more densely populated than the St. Lawrence-Lake Champlain Lowland—a population density based upon greater manufacturing development; (*c*) railroad and road traffic is heavier than similar transport through the St. Lawrence Valley; and (*d*) the Mohawk-Hudson corridor is a major reason for the growth of North America's largest city, New York.

The Mohawk-Hudson Gateway extends from the Great Lakes to the Atlantic Ocean; and has had a great influence upon national growth, upon state growth (New York State), and upon city growth (New York City).

Geology. Geologic history has contributed more to the transport efficiency of the gateway than any other factor in the physical environment. Subsidence in recent geologic time drowned the mouth of the Hudson and the adjoining coastal area. Drowning deepened the river mouth harbor so that until the early 1930's New York harbor could accommodate the world's deepest draft ships without resorting to much dredging. Subsidence also affected former hills of the slightly irregular coastal surface and surrounded them with water, thus making islands. In fact, New York Harbor has so many islands that New York has been called the city of islands. These islands provide protection from stormy seas and have greatly extended water frontage. Such frontage made possible the building of many piers, without which New York's shipping could not function effectively. Sinking of the land changed the formerly shallow Hudson into a deep river with practically no current. Between Albany and New York, about 150 miles, the stream falls approximately 5 feet, less than a half inch a mile. From New York to Albany, the Hudson really is an arm of the sea.

West of the north-south flowing Hudson, at 43° 10′ north, is the Mohawk Valley; it forms a broad east-west opening through the Appalachian Mountains where the system is relatively low and narrow. This gateway developed near the close of Pleistocene glaciation. At that time,

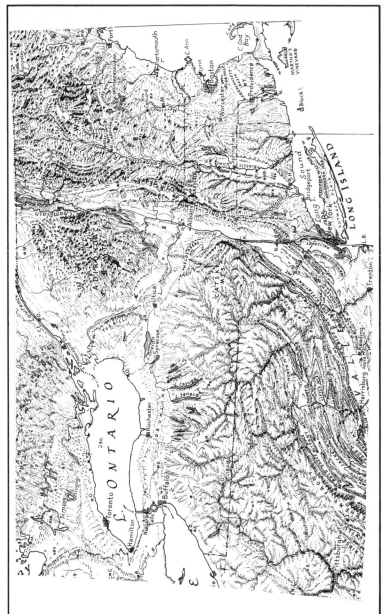

Fig. 5. The Hudson-Mohawk Gateway to the West. The trade of New York City was greatly encouraged by its splendid natural harbor and by its easy accessibility to the productive central plains of the United States. Easy access could be attained by the Hudson-Mohawk Valley and Great Lakes route. Note the absence of shading, showing plains topography, in the Hudson Valley and on west from Albany by way of the Mohawk Valley to Buffalo and the Great Lakes. (Source: W. W. Atwood, *Physiographic Provinces of North America*, Ginn and Co.)

when ice still blocked the St. Lawrence to the north, the Great Lakes drainage reached the sea through the Mohawk-Hudson opening. Erosion by glacial waters moving over relatively weak sedimentary rocks fashioned this continuous east-west gap, the only low passage through the Appalachians between Canada and Alabama.

From the Mohawk gateway westward lies an ice-formed plain made by the erosion and deposition of the Pleistocene glacier. So nearly level is this plain that the Erie Canal builders needed no locks for a stretch of about 50 miles. The only difficulty came with the rise of the Ontario plain to the higher level of that bordering Lake Erie, which necessitated a series of locks at Lockport.

Human History.[2] The geology of the Mohawk gateway made easy the building of canals and railroads between Albany and Lake Erie. The original Erie Canal, 40 feet wide and 4 feet deep, was completed in 1825. With occasional improvements, the waterway did its work for 75 years. Today, the New York State Barge Canal, completed in 1918, carries on at a different tempo from that of the Old Erie with its towpath, mules, drivers, and wooden boxlike barges. In the mid-1940's more than 100 tugs operated on the New York State Barge Canal, plus 22 motor ships, 418 general cargo barges, and 68 tankers or tank barges.[3]

In the first decade of the Erie Canal's history, the population of Buffalo, Rochester, Syracuse, and Utica increased about 300 per cent. New York City rose from 125,000 to about a half million between 1820 and 1850.

After 1850, railroads, taking advantage of the nearly level topography on the Hudson-Mohawk Gateway, paralleled the canal and moved goods and people faster than movement on the canal. A century later, New York's paved toll road carries thousands of motor vehicles over the water level route.

Within, or in close proximity to the Eastern Gateway, live more than

[2] A required reading for background on this section should include R. H. Whitbeck, "Geographical Influences in the Development of New York State," *Journal of Geography*, January 1911, pp. 119-124.

[3] Pertinent statistics on the New York State Barge Canal include the following: at point of contact with the Hudson near Albany, the elevation is approximately sea level; going west, it rises to 420 feet; at Syracuse, it drops to 370 feet; at Lockport, the altitude is 564 feet; the canal enters the Niagara River at Tonawanda. The length of the canal, including branches, is about 525 miles, but there are also approximately 400 miles of canalized rivers and lakes. Channel depth is 12 feet, surface width minimum 123 feet, bottom width minimum 75 feet. The number of locks is 35 and the highest lock, 40½ feet, is No. 17 at Little Falls. High water sometimes blocks locks, and ice closes the canal about November 30 until April 15. The state waterway system links the Atlantic Ocean and Lakes Erie, Ontario, Champlain, Cayuga, and Seneca. The canal is not a common carrier and no carriage rates are established. Traffic is largely oil, grain, etc., bulky goods for which speed of delivery is of little significance. Cargo is carried mainly by big corporations who can afford to operate a fleet of their own barges.

three-fourths of New York's 15,000,000 people, most of them in large urban centers. It may be informative to examine the background and economic character of several of these cities.

New York City (Fig. 6). It has already been indicated that New York

Fig. 6. New York's Skyscrapers. Land is so valuable on Manhattan Island that buildings expand perpendicularly rather than horizontally. (Courtesy Skidmore, Owings & Merrill.)

is a city of islands. Island status has created many problems, among which are bridges, tunnels, and tall buildings. In 1950, Manhattan had a total of 20 bridges and 20 tunnels. The latter are gaining on the former; unlike a tunnel, a bridge needs vast aboveground areas for approaches, and property left standing in the vicinity is often blighted by ramps. Manhattan's highly valued real estate places an enormous cost on these ramps. The same property is not devalued or destroyed when traffic disappears underground.

With the limited opportunity for horizontal expansion on an island, vertical extension has been necessary. New York's elevator shafts, laid end to end, would almost equal its more than 1,000 miles of rapid transit tracks. Some people, to get to work, travel further vertically than horizontally.

Fortunately, New York is located in a relatively stable earth zone; danger from earthquakes is much less than in an unstable region such as Chile, Japan, or the Philippines. Foundations for high buildings are also favorable. Anyone traveling by Central Park can see the solid basement rocks all over the surface, and such outcrops give evidence of firm support for New York's many storied structures.

New York is a city of superlatives. These include the nation's largest port, tallest buildings, biggest department stores, most crowded subways, and unquestioned business leadership.

A long list of locational and economic advantages contribute to continued leadership. New York has easy accessibility through the Mohawk-Hudson Gateway to an extremely productive hinterland, an accessibility already described in some detail. Its harbor is deep and well protected from winds and waves by a whole series of islands. Tidal scour makes dredging a minor problem; and tidal range is so slight that difficulties in loading and unloading cargo lack the seriousness characteristic of London, with its great tidal range. Ice never interrupts shipping, and fogs, although an occasional handicap, cannot compare in frequency to the number at St. John's, Newfoundland. New York pioneered in establishing a free port in the Staten Island Foreign Trade Zone, and thereby gained an advantage over its competitors. Other cities now possess free port foreign trade zones, but New York has the advantage of an early start.

New York is well situated near the center of a solid urbanized belt extending from Washington, D. C., to Hartford, Connecticut, and faces Western Europe across the world's most traveled shipping lane. It is also well placed with respect to both the east coast and the west coast of South America, and lies near the great-circle route from the Caribbean to northwestern Europe.

In 1950, the city handled a total of 145 million short tons of merchandise, as compared with 68 million tons for Philadelphia and 35 million tons for New Orleans. Despite this impressive figure, New York, unlike Baltimore or Norfolk, is not primarily a bulk-handling port. It caters above all to general cargo of high unit value which calls for skilled operations. This is the reason the value share of the nation's foreign trade cleared through New York is about twice as large as its share measured by volume. The activities connected with storing and handling some 300 different types of commodities call for a large specialized labor force; the port provides work, directly or indirectly, for one out of every 10 persons employed in the metropolitan area. New York clears about one-fourth of United States foreign trade if measured by volume, and more than 40 per cent if counted by value.

Matching the sea-borne traffic are more than 300 common-carrier motor truck lines, plus innumerable private and contract trucks, which in 1950, accounted for 40 per cent of all pierside loadings. The balance of overland freight, or about 80 million tons, was carried by the 12 railroads, which have terminals and storage yards accommodating more than 35,000 freight cars in the port area.

New Yorkers, who think of their city as a great port, a mecca for tourists, and a hub of wholesale activities, are seldom aware that it is also the nation's leading manufacturing center, first since 1824 in the number of industrial establishments and in the value added by manufacture. A most unusual characteristic of New York's industry—and incidentally the reason why few recognize its preeminence—is the workshop nature of its establishments. In 1951, the average manufacturing plant employed about 20 wage earners.

The industries that find conditions in New York City especially attractive are the makers of non-standardized products, who depend upon ingenuity of design, adaptability to changing styles and uses, initiative, promotional efforts, and rapid distribution rather than upon low unit cost or mass production methods. These industries also value their proximity to the nation's leading wholesale markets, which attract buyers from everywhere.

Despite the rise of Hollywood as a major style center, and the congested streets and workshops of New York's garment district, the manufacturing of apparel and its accessories continues to dominate all other industrial activity in the city. Over 350,000 production workers, heavily concentrated in Manhattan, contribute more than 20 per cent of the total value added by the city's manufactures.

The combined circulation of New York's daily newspapers totals 6 million; this circulation, plus the national influence of these dailies, is matched only by the country's leading periodicals, whose editorial offices are also found here.

New York's other major industries—food processing and the manufacture of fabricated metal products, machinery, and chemicals—have spread out beyond the narrow confines of Manhattan Island. The larger ones in particular and those dependent upon water-borne deliveries have lined most of the Brooklyn and Queens waterfront along the East River; Newton Creek, one of the nation's shortest waterways, is also one of the busiest.

Few heavy industrial plants are found within the New York City limits. They are concentrated near the lower New Jersey waterfront, where large and relatively low-cost sites provide the added advantage of direct rail communication with the hinterland. In Manhattan, competition for the country's most valuable real estate has prevented all but one railroad from establishing freight classification yards on the island, and has practically eliminated open spaces near the piers that can be used to improve trailer-truck maneuverability.

New York does have certain weaknesses as a port city. The fragmentation of the waterfront of more than 500 miles, the insularity of Manhattan at the heart of the port district, and the abrupt barrier of the Palisades have imposed great obstacles to land transport and are largely responsible for making the port more expensive to operate. Possibly New York's greatest weakness is a man-made one. Today, New York loses trade not because of any depreciation in the harbor's splendid physical background, but because groups of organized gangs steal and extort from shippers who use this fine port of entry into the United States.[4]

Other Mohawk-Hudson Gateway Cities. At the western end of the Mohawk gateway, where a break in transportation occurs between valley lowland and the Great Lakes waterway, stands Buffalo. Here, on the threshold of the East and the portal of the West, a great city was bound to develop. Not only is there a break in transport between land and lake waters, but there is also a serious break in the water route from Lake Erie to Lake Ontario. Near Buffalo, at Niagara Falls, the north-flowing Niagara River drops over 100 feet to interrupt navigation (Fig. 7); about 90 per cent of the water drops approximately 160 feet over the Canadian Falls. The total drop on the 34-mile long Niagara River is about 325 feet; this drop gives Buffalo transshipping advantages and Niagara Falls facilities for hydroelectric power.

Location has encouraged manufacturing as well as commerce. The city lies close to Pennsylvania coal and at the edge of the water route to Lake Superior iron and Michigan limestone, three basic materials required for the manufacture of iron and steel. Another advantage, often overlooked, is that every minute of the day Buffalo receives 1,230,000 gallons

---

[4] Much of the material on New York City is based upon "New York City," *Focus,* June 15, 1952, American Geographical Society.

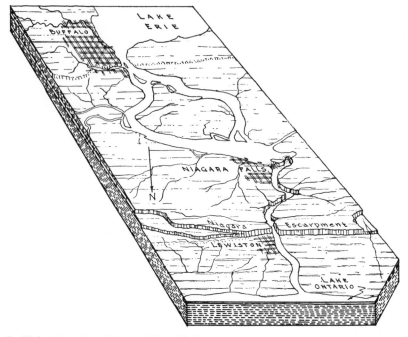

Fig. 7. Vicinal Location, Niagara Falls. Bird's-eye view of Niagara River and Falls. Greatest length of the block is 35 miles and the vertical exaggeration is two times. A new hydroelectric project, to be completed about 1960, will tap the Niagara river above the rapids and carry water downstream to Lewiston. This will almost double Niagara's head and make Niagara the second largest hydroelectric development in the United States. (Source: C. R. Longwell, A. Knopf, and R. F. Flint, *Physical Geology,* 2nd ed., John Wiley and Sons, 1939.)

of fresh water. Not the least of the reasons for Bethlehem Steel's investment of millions in the Lackawanna steel plant is that it uses 200,000,000 gallons of lake water in each 24-hour period.

One of the most conspicuous features in Buffalo's skyline is the large number of grain elevators and flour mills (Fig. 8). The city ranks high in milling flour, and enormous amounts of grain from the Spring Wheat Region just west of Lake Superior move through Buffalo.

Further diversification is shown in the manufacture of rubber goods, chemicals, rayon, etc. In fact, the city's industry includes all but one of the major lines of manufacture recognized by the United States Department of Commerce. In the early 1950's, Buffalo ranked eighth among the nation's leading manufacturing centers.

Three cities, Albany, Troy, and Schenectady, are located near the confluence of the Mohawk Valley with the Hudson Valley. Troy lies on the east side of the Hudson, and the other two manufacturing centers on the west side. To the north, there is an easy opening to Canada by way of the

Lake Champlain lowland; to the south, ocean tides reach Albany by way of the Hudson; and to the west, is a water-level valley lowland. Only on the east do mountains block easy passage across New England. No doubt Albany's location was an important influence in encouraging urban growth. Albany became the capital of the Empire State; Troy, an important manufacturing center, is famous for its output of men's shirts; and Schenectady is known for its industrial contributions to General Electric.

Syracuse has a good location approximately half way in an east-west direction between Albany and Buffalo; there is easy access over lowland plain to Lake Ontario on the north and by the Finger Lakes gateway to the south. Local resources of salt supplemented Mohawk gateway location in encouraging the early growth of Syracuse. Today, broad diversity in manufacturing gives support to more than 200,000 persons.

About halfway between Syracuse and Buffalo, lies Rochester, a city well known throughout the country as the home of Eastman Kodak. Cameras, films, and optical goods feature its manufacturing; but early industrial growth centered on flour milling, powered by the 205-foot water falls on the Genesee River. The rocks over which this water plunges belong to the same sedimentary group as those causing the falls at Niagara. Rochester has easy east-west transport by way of the Mohawk gateway; Lake Ontario lies only a few miles to the north by way of a nearly level lake plain; and

Fig. 8. Grain Elevators and Flour Mills, Buffalo. Buffalo ranks high among United States cities in milling flour; and large amounts of grain from the Spring Wheat Region, just west of Lake Superior, move through Buffalo. (Courtesy Buffalo Chamber of Commerce.)

to the south the Genesee Valley reaches close to that of the Chemung River, a tributary of the equatorward-flowing Susequehanna.

Many other cities, besides the above-mentioned urban centers, line the Mohawk gateway. These include Utica, known for its textile factories; Rome, a leader in copper manufacture; Amsterdam, ranking high in carpet and rug making; Gloversville, an important producer of gloves and mittens; and many more. Other factors in addition to transportation advantages have encouraged city growth. But no student of geography would fail to stress the Mohawk gateway in analyzing causes for site location and industrial progress.

The Upper Lakes Region

Differences between the Upper and Lower Great Lakes subregions include, (*a*) the Upper Lakes country is dominated by igneous and metamorphic rocks of the Laurentian Shield in contrast to the wider occurrence of sedimentary rocks in the Lower Lakes subregion; (*b*) the northern subregion is more of a raw materials-producing land with an emphasis upon exploitation of minerals; and (*c*) the borders of the Lower Lakes are much more densely populated with a large percentage of the people engaged in manufacturing.

All of Lake Superior, the northern part of Lake Michigan, and the northern and western parts of Lake Huron are included in the Upper Lakes subregion. It also includes the lands bordering this water area, namely, northeastern and north central Minnesota, northern Wisconsin, the northern section of Michigan, together with the Upper Peninsula—all within the United States. The Canadian section includes southwestern Ontario and a narrow Ontario rimland, which borders lakes Superior and Huron over to the northeast edge of Georgian Bay.

Physical Background. Much of the area belongs to the Laurentian Shield, described by Fenneman as a "submaturely dissected recently glaciated peneplain on crystalline rocks of complex structure." The words *glaciation* and *crystalline* are two terms of geographic importance in the land use of this region. The glacier provided the land directly west and south of Lake Superior with thousands of lakes. This provision was accomplished by gouging and damming action of the ice and by glacial interruption of former stream courses. Thousands of Upper Lakes water surfaces provide a fisherman's paradise.

The word *crystalline* suggests the igneous and metamorphic rocks that underlie lands north of lakes Superior and Huron and the Minnesota and Wisconsin parts of the Upper Lakes region. These crystalline rocks, and sedimentaries derived from them, contain iron and other metallic minerals, which provide a feature industry of the region.

Interior location furnishes a continental influence upon the climate, although widespread water surfaces give a conservative trend to summer heat and winter cold. Water surfaces also induce cloudiness, and the Great Lakes region is one of the cloudiest sections of the continent. A relatively high latitude, 45° to 50° north, cuts short the growing season, and frost is an almost constant threat to agriculture. Precipitation of more than 20 inches is not a limiting factor upon farming.

The word *glaciation* in Fenneman's description of land forms should be mentioned again in connection with soils and vegetation. Pleistocene ice stripped off much of the soil and left many surfaces suitable only for tree growth, some of them not adaptable for any vegetation at all. Thin podzol soils are characteristic, and they support a mixed forest with a large percentage of conifers.

Forest Industries. In the middle of the nineteenth century, after the New England forests had been cut over ruthlessly, lumbermen went west and started the same practice on the forests around the Great Lakes. Fires frequently got out of control on cutover lands, killing seedlings and damaging soils; no attempt was made to replant trees; and when the lumbermen were through, there was little left but wasteland. Fortunately, America is no longer following such practices in Great Lakes forests or in those of any other section of the continent. It may take a long time for the midcontinent forests to return to a healthy state like that of the 1850's, but ruthless exploitation no longer applies to our national forest policy.

Agriculture. Forest vegetation, thin soils, a short growing season, and a large percentage of the surface covered by water are a combination of factors that suggest little encouragement for crop agriculture. Those who attempt farming grow root crops, pasture, and hay, all of which do well on the better soils of the cool cloudy region. Hay and pasture may be fed to dairy animals. Unless the farm land is close to a town or to one of the few large urban centers, milk is likely to be sold in concentrated form, such as butter or cheese. Besides pasture land, hay ground, and fields for cultivated root crops, the farmer may have a large acreage in tree crops, some of which may be sold annually to the lumber or paper mill. Tree farming is becoming widespread among farmers in all of the country's forested regions.

Mining (Fig. 9). Probably the most important industry is mining; and the Upper Lakes region has provided United States manufacturers with at least three-fourths of the iron ore processed in this country for the past 50 years. A large part of this has come from rich hematite ores in the Mesabi region, one of several of the Upper Great Lakes iron deposits.

Geologic history has made it easy for man to exploit the ore. A highly generalized and simplified history includes the following main events. Millions of years ago, mountains, as high as the Alps, whose roots were loded

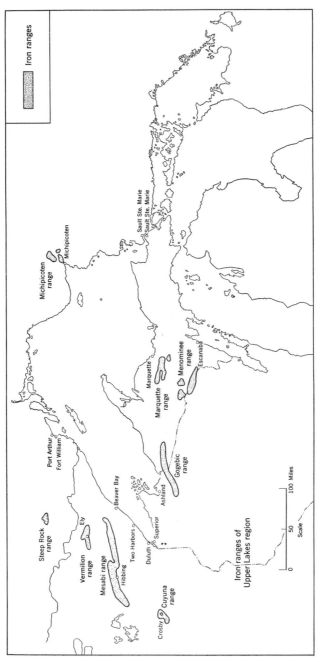

Fig. 9. Iron Ranges of the Upper Great Lakes. In 1948, iron production from the eight ranges amounted to nearly 84,000,000 gross tons averaging more than 50 per cent metallic content. The Mesabi Range contributed nearly 77 per cent of the total. Shipments of ore move from Superior and Ashland, Wisconsin; Two Harbors and Duluth, Minnesota; Escanaba and Marquette, Michigan; and Port Arthur and Michipicoten, Ontario. These ports possess 21 iron ore docks with over 5,000 pockets and a storage capacity of more than 1,500,000 tons. (Source: John H. Garland, *The North American Midwest*, John Wiley and Sons, 1955.)

with iron dominated the area. Erosion leveled these mountains and brought the ore closer to the surface. The peneplaned lands were then invaded by the sea and covered with layers of limestone and sandstone. After uplift took place, the Pleistocene glaciers removed the limestone and sandstone covering the Mesabi area, and deposited unconsolidated glacial drift over the previously uncovered deposits. Today, giant steam shovels (Fig. 10) easily remove the morainic overburden and then load the rich hematite ore into railroad cars, which move downgrade to the glacially formed Great Lakes, on which the iron may be transported to steel centers along the shores of the Lower Lakes region.

Here in the Mesabi, the type of occurrence (iron ore that lies near the surface under glacial sands and gravels) influences the manner of exploitation—removal of the ore by the open pit method. The man-made landscape is also influenced by the manner of mineral occurrence. Giant steam shovels, scores of them, may be seen, and temporary rail lines, extending into a huge open pit, on which locomotives pull cars to be loaded with ore. No deep mine shafts covered with tall buildings are seen here; no elevators move deep into the rocks to lift minerals hundreds and thousands of feet to the surface. Just a huge open pit, steam shovels, temporary railroads, and open pit-mining machinery—these are the features that dominate the man-made landscape of Mesabi.

Fig. 10. Hibbing, Minnesota, on the Edge of the Mesabi Open-Pit Mine. The present city of Hibbing borders the edge of a huge open-pit iron mine. In the 1920's, part of old Hibbing was moved. The underlying iron was so valuable that mineral exploitation became more important than the permanence of the town site. Note the glacial boulders in the foreground.

The approaching exhaustion of high-grade hematite ores in the Mesabi has forced American steel men to spend millions of dollars in research for practical processes, permitting the use of billions of tons of low-grade Upper Great Lakes ore still remaining. Not far from the Mesabi ore, containing approximately 51 per cent metal, lie enormous supplies of 25 to 30 per cent metallic ore called taconite.

This ore bed, about one hundred miles long, several thousand feet wide, and up to 200 feet thick, has been known to steel men for years; but because of low metallic content and the difficulty of beneficiating the ore—changing it to a higher percentage of metal—the use of the mineral has been delayed. With depletion of high-grade ore only a few years away, possibly twenty-five, and with unit production slower and unit costs mounting as better deposits near exhaustion, steel producers are turning to taconite and to foreign sources. The weakness in any national economy depending upon foreign supplies of strategic material such as iron lies in the fact that war may cut off expanded needs at any time. Foreign ore is satisfactory for stockpiling in peacetime, but it loses its attraction with the declaration of war. Then, local resources are far more dependable. With these facts in mind, magnetic taconite scattered through the Lake Superior ore-bearing hard rock is being crushed and ground to fine pieces; iron particles are separated magnetically from the gangue; and powdered metal is concentrated into small pellets (Fig. 11) or balls that are usable in blast furnaces. It is probable that equipment for beneficiating up to 20,000,000 tons annually will be ready by 1960, and twice that amount by 1970.

Besides the billions of tons of taconite and the rapidly declining rich hematite of the Mesabi, other iron deposits occur in the Cuyuna and Vermilion ranges of Minnesota, the Gogebic and Menominee ranges of northern Wisconsin and the Upper Peninsula of Michigan, and the Marquette Range in the Upper Peninsula. Extraction if iron ore from the majority of these ranges is by shaft mining, for most of the ore lies deeply buried beneath the surface. One advantage of shaft mining over open-pit exploitation in this latitude is the possibility of all year mining. Freezing stops open-pit work during the winter period.

The Upper Lakes Canadian iron ore comes mainly from Steep Rock (Fig. 12) and Michipicoten. Annual production does not approach the tens of millions of tons taken yearly from Mesabi, but proven reserves are large. These amount to 500,000,000 tons for Michipicoten and geological estimates exceed a billion tons. Ore is predominantly siderite, which has about one-third metallic content, and requires beneficiating at the mine before it is shipped to blast furnaces. Production in 1953 amounted to 1,300,000 tons of beneficiated ore, with plans for an increase to 3,000,000 tons in the near future. Steep Rock proven reserves approximate a half

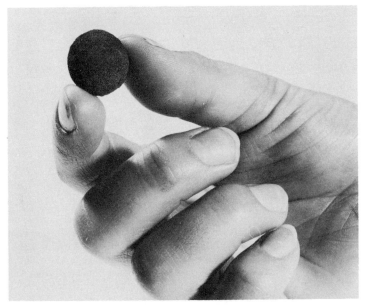

Fig. 11. An Iron Pellet Produced from Taconite. Taconite was actually the mother lode from which deposits of high-grade iron ore were formed by nature. Man is now duplicating on a much faster scale nature's process of concentrating the iron content of the rock. First steps are drilling and blasting for the taconite. At the concentrating plant the native rock is crushed; magnets pick up the magnetic material and leave the non-magnetic. Powdered coal is mixed with the finely ground concentrate. The mixture of iron ore, coal, and water then goes to a rotating drum, where it is formed into pellets about the size of a walnut. These pellets are fired in furnaces so that they will be hard before they are fed into blast furnaces. Pellets contain about 60 per cent of the element iron, compared with approximately 50 per cent contained in the hematite ore of the Mesabi region and about 25 per cent in the taconite rock. (Courtesy Reserve Mining Company.)

billion tons of high-grade ore with the 1953 output 1,500,000 tons. Beneficiating is unnecessary, and output is growing rapidly.

Upper Lake iron ore (Figs. 13, 14) moves out over the Great Lakes from several ports; Steep Rock ore moves to the blast furnaces from Port Arthur; Michipicoten iron is loaded at the Lake Superior harbor of Michipicoten; Vermilion ore seeks an outlet at Two Harbors, Minnesota; Cuyuna ore moves to Superior, a port just south of Duluth; Mesabi ore moves out of Superior, Duluth, and Two Harbors, Minnesota. Ore from the Gogebic Range reaches Lake Superior at Ashland, Wisconsin; Menominee ore goes out of Escanaba on Michigan's Upper Peninsula; and Marquette iron is taken to Marquette on the Upper Peninsula for shipment. Practically all the ore moves from the Upper Lakes to blast furnaces located in cities upon

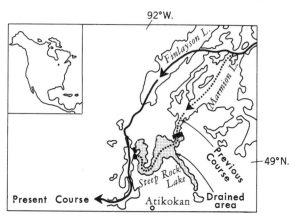

Fig. 12. Mining Operations at Steep Rock, Ontario. To get at Steep Rock iron ore the following operations were necessary: (1) Finlayson Lake, whose surface was 33 feet higher than Marmion Lake, was lowered 53 feet; (2) the flow of the Seine River through Marmion Lake into Steep Rock Lake was reversed so that water moved from Steep Rock Lake to Marmion Lake and on to Finlayson Lake; (3) 75 billion gallons of water were pumped from Steep Rock Lake to reach iron ore near the bottom of the lake; (4) open-pit mining is used to extract the ore. (After map by Tris Coffin, "Pay Dirt at Steep Rock," *The Beaver,* Spring, 1957.)

Lower Lakes shores. Most of it moves through the Sault Ste. Marie (Soo) Canal, probably the busiest commercial waterway in the world (Fig. 15).

For over a century, Michigan's Keweenaw Peninsula has been known for its copper. At one time, the shaft mines, which are now very deep, gave up enough copper to place the state first in United States production. Yields have declined until only about 20,000 tons were recovered in the early 1950's, leaving Michigan a poor sixth among United States producers, far behind the Western states of Arizona, Montana, New Mexico, Nevada, and Utah.

A new mining development occurred in the Upper Lakes region during the early 1950's, when one of the largest uranium deposits in the world was discovered near Wind River, Ontario, on the shores of Lake Huron.

Upper Lakes Cities. Mention has been made of ports on Lake Superior which are forwarding cities for the region's iron ore. For most of them a transfer function for Great Lakes commerce is their main industry. Metals move out through their harbors to processing cities in the Lower Lakes region. Returning ore boats may bring coal from the Appalachian coal fields to be used as fuel in Upper Lakes ports or to be transferred to interior locations lacking high-grade bituminous coal. Freight rates on coal moving west are likely to be lower than those on east-moving iron ore. More competition exists for Great Lakes shipping space going east than for that traveling west. Westward moving general cargo may supplement coal movement to the Upper Lakes entrepôt ports.

Duluth is the only one of the Upper Lakes shipping centers that has an important steel mill to fabricate the iron produced in such large quantities within the region.   Duluth and Superior, because of their position at the western end of Lake Superior, also act as entrepôt ports for United States spring wheat moving east by rail to the Great Lakes for shipment. Grain from the Canadian Spring Wheat region may funnel through Fort William and Port Arthur, similarly situated at Canada's western portion of Lake Superior.

Future Trends.   The future land use of the Upper Lakes subregion looks quite similar to that practiced today.   Although most high-grade hematite has been exhausted, billions of tons of low-grade iron ore remain to feed steel mills of the Lower Lakes region when properly beneficiated.   It is

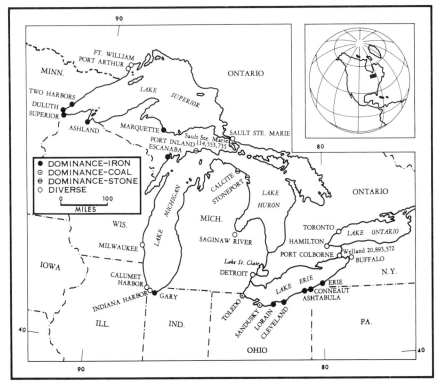

Fig. 13. Shipping on the Great Lakes. The map shows the 4,000,000-ton ports on the Great Lakes together with tonnages for the Soo and Welland Canals. The downbound tonnages of the Soo and Welland waterways are 101,686,587 and 16,633,580 tons respectively—much greater than upbound cargo. No legend is given for grain, but it is a dominant commodity at Fort William-Port Arthur and at Port Colborne. Besides the 4,000,000-ton ports, there are 22 U. S. ports and 7 Canadian ports with tonnages of over a million tons. (After map by Albert G. Ballert, 1957.)

Fig. 14. Winter Ice on the Great Lakes. One of the main arguments used by opponents of the Great Lakes Seaway is the fact that ice makes shipping difficult for four or five months of the year. (Courtesy U. S. Department of Commerce, Weather Bureau.)

possible that the rich iron deposits of Labrador, together with the St. Lawrence waterway improvement, may slow down iron shipments from the Upper Lakes. Regional uranium development may increase. Other minerals may be discovered to expand outgoing metal shipments from Upper Lakes ports. Forestry will become more important as modern conservation policies increase the products from natural forests of beech, fir, hemlock, maple, spruce, and white pine. The cool forest environment also offers opportunity for trapping and hunting and for fur farms.

Not the least of land use opportunities may be tourism. The thousands of glacial lakes with many fish, other glacial features, attractive forest vegetation, cool summer climate—all within easy reach of dense populations of Lower Lakes cities—provide a good background for tourist development.

Outlook for great expansion in farming is not bright. Soils are not consistently good, tree vegetation is expensive to remove, summer seasons are short, winters are long and cold; these and other disadvantages will discourage farmers. Those who do use the land for agriculture will continue to emphasize grass, hay, root crops, and dairying, and will sell much of their produce to growing mining centers, tourist resorts, and busy commercial lake ports.

The Lower Lakes Region

The Lower Lake subregion is well located for its major land use, manufacturing. On the north is the highly mineralized Upper Lakes subregion, from which metals can move easily by water transport to factories along the Lower Lake shores. To the west and southwest are large supplies of livestock and farm crops, the raw materials from farm, ranch, and range, many of which are processed in the Lower Lake industrial plants. To the east and southeast are the coal fields of the Appalachian Plateau, with high-grade bituminous coal to power many of the heavy industries scattered along the Lower Lake borders. And within short distances to the south and east is the biggest market on the North American continent, with millions of people accustomed to high living standards and demanding a large variety of manufactured products.

A few examples will indicate the size of this market. South of Lake Michigan are Illinois and Indiana with 15,000,000 people; east of Lake Michigan and south of Lake Huron is Michigan with 7,000,000 people; south and east of Lake Erie are Ohio, Pennsylvania, and New York with

Fig. 15. The Soo Locks. The Soo Locks of the Sault Ste. Marie Canal, which link Lake Superior with the other Great Lakes, handle an enormous tonnage of bulky materials, principally iron ore, coal, and grain. More than 70 per cent of the iron ore shipped annually from mines in the United States passes through the Soo Locks. More than 2,500,000,000 tons of ore have gone through since the first lock opened in 1855. (Courtesy Corps of Engineers, U. S. Army.)

35,000,000 people. Moreover, the peninsular lowland of Canada included in the Lower Lakes subregion is one of the most densely populated parts of that country. It is not surprising that the area bordering the Lower Great Lakes has been called the North American Ruhr.

The Lower Lakes subregion includes the central and southern parts of lakes Michigan and Huron, all of lakes Erie and Ontario, and the land that borders these water bodies. Included in this land are all of Michigan south of the 45th parallel north, the Door Peninsula, and Wisconsin's other shores to the south, the Lake Michigan urban area of Illinois and Indiana, the Lake Erie coast of Ohio, as well as the entire northeastern part, northwestern Pennsylvania, New York State's lake borders, and the fertile Canadian peninsula extending south towards the United States among southern Lake Huron, Lake St. Clair, Lake Erie, and Lake Ontario.

Manufacturing (Fig. 16). An examination of manufacturing development in a few of the major industrial cities may illustrate the most important use of the land.

Detroit. Detroit is one of the leading automobile manufacturing cities of the world. The city is located on the river of the same name between Lake St. Clair and Lake Erie. Location on the Interior Seaboard gives access by cheap water transport to many North American raw materials and markets as well as to those on other continents. A great railroad net, located south of the Great Lakes to avoid the water barrier for land transport, provides easily accessible overland carriage for raw materials and finished products.

Detroit lies near the center of the automobile market. The market may be seen as a circle, slightly more than 600 miles in diameter with its center at Detroit, that includes Boston, New York, Philadelphia, Baltimore, Washington, Atlanta, Memphis, Kansas City, Omaha, and Montreal, as well as other cities. This area now owns a large portion of United States cars and about half of those in the entire world. Nowhere else does a similar circle include as many autos. Cheap transport by water on the Great Lakes, and to a much lesser extent on the St. Lawrence, makes central location still more important. Cars can be carried by water to within 300 miles of practically the entire area. Thus, from the standpoint of transport to the main market for motor vehicles, Detroit's location is good. From the standpoint of raw materials and fuel, the location is almost equally as good. Detroit can bring iron ore at a small expense by water from the Upper Lakes region; coal can come cheaply from mines in Pennsylvania and Ohio. It is not an accident that Michigan and other states bordering the Great Lakes produce such a large per cent of the world's motor cars.

Chicago. The making of heavy types of agricultural machinery is another kind of manufacturing in which transport is especially important. The location of the market is even more significant than that of the raw

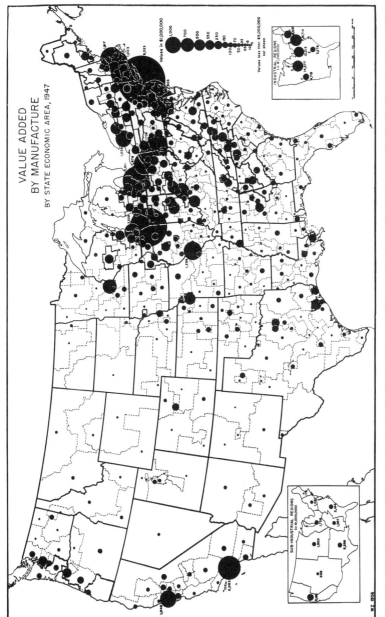

VALUE ADDED
BY MANUFACTURE
BY STATE ECONOMIC AREA, 1947

Fig. 16. Distribution of Manufacturing in the United States. The greatest manufacturing area in Anglo-America lies within the Interior Seaboard. Although manufacturing is increasing elsewhere on the continent, growth also continues in the North American Ruhr. (Source: Wilbur Zelinsky, and *Economic Geography*, April 1958.)

materials, but both locations play a part. Many agricultural machines are bulkier than automobiles and more expensive to ship. Much of the market lies farther west than that for automobiles. This is not only because large sections of the Middle Atlantic and New England states are too rugged for profitable farming, but also because those states, generally, have small farms which require less bulky machinery. As yet, the South, with many small tobacco farms, and much cotton and corn still harvested by hand, does not purchase as much bulky farm machinery as the Middle West. The large market lies mainly in the plains of the North Central States from Ohio to Kansas, Nebraska, and the Dakotas, with a southward extension to Oklahoma and Texas.

Chicago's position at the southern end of Lake Michigan causes railroads from all directions except north and northeast to converge there. Thus, it lies in an admirable position for shipping agricultural machinery to the entire prairie region, from Ohio west. It is also well located for bringing coal, iron, and wood by water from Pennsylvania, the western end of Lake Superior, and the forests of northern Michigan. Southern Wisconsin shares these advantages, and is especially well located in respect to the northern wheat region of Minnesota and the Dakotas, where much large machinery is needed.

With the deepening of the St. Lawrence-Great Lakes waterway and the improvement of port facilities in the Lower Great Lakes, increased shipments of agricultural machinery to foreign countries may result. No place in the world has better farm lands to use as a laboratory for testing agricultural machinery than the United States, and any decrease in transport costs will give further advantage. Whether ocean shipping to the North American interior will improve export of automobiles is a question. Western Europe is producing large numbers of small, cheap cars, and a lowering of transport cost may give advantage to the foreign car salesman.

Raw materials for the manufacture of iron and steel, used in automobiles and agricultural machinery, lie within easy transport distance of the Lower Lakes region. Appalachian coal, Lake Superior iron, Michigan limestone, Great Lakes water, all are nearby in large amounts; capital, labor, and market are near there too. Most of the iron and steel furnaces in the United States find advantages in a Lower Lakes location. The Chicago district steel plants, on broad acreages of the Lake Michigan plain, are well located topographically for any future expansion (Fig. 17).

Besides being well located with reference to raw materials for iron and steel fabrication, the region, and especially the Chicago district, is nicely situated for the slaughter and processing of livestock. Chicago, although not generally considered a part of the Corn Belt, lies at the north-central edge of this greatest of all livestock producing regions, and millions of corn-fattened hogs and cattle are easily accessible to the packing center.

Fig. 17. Steel Plant, Indiana Harbor. Enormous amounts of flatland are available for plant expansion on the broad plain adjoining Lake Michigan. The location is also easily accessible to cheap water transport for raw materials as well as for the finished product. (Courtesy The Youngstown Sheet and Tube Company.)

The invention of the refrigerator car helped Chicago's meat packing industry, as well as that of the whole country. Livestock could be shipped to Chicago for slaughter in the ordinary stock car; but fresh meat needs refrigeration en route to the large Eastern market. Chicago received a great boost when William Davis of Detroit patented the first refrigerator car in 1868. Students of geography should never forget that man himself is an important contributor to effective use of the physical environment. Chicago's proximity to the Corn Belt livestock is important in meat packing, but meat must be sold after the animals are slaughtered; the refrigerator car facilitates the sale, not only by carrying meat to near and far away markets, but also by keeping it in excellent condition until it reaches its destination.

Chicago is now one of the greatest rail centers in the United States. Lake Michigan, which contributes so much to the city's water transport, also has been partly responsible for the focus of many rail lines on the city. All the railroads moving east-west to the north of, or in the same latitude as, Chicago must pass the southern tip of the lake to continue the journey east or west. In this way the barrier nature of Lake Michigan compels many railroads to converge on Chicago. The availability of an enormous amount of cargo is a positive factor that encourages rail lines to enter the city. Much petroleum and natural gas comes by pipeline. Whiting and East Chicago in the Calumet district are great oil refining centers.

Milwaukee. Milwaukee, less than 100 miles north of Chicago, is sometimes described as belonging to the Chicago-Milwaukee manufacturing district. The city is the nation's third largest consumer of steel, behind Detroit and Chicago, and produces enormous amounts of durable goods such as machine tools, metalwork, farm implements, tractors, and earth moving machines. It is also well known for its beer, meat packing, glass, and textiles.

Commercially, Milwaukee's location in relation to the Corn Belt and Spring Wheat country makes it an easily accessible port for shipping large quantities of farm products by cheap water transport. Milwaukee has achieved fame as the leading car ferry port of the world. Many rail cars, instead of going around the southern tip of Lake Michigan, may be moved on to boats and save railroad mileage by a water trip to the Michigan side of the lake.

Most of Milwaukee's commerce is concerned with moving the 9,200,000 tons of commodities (1955) among the United States and Canadian ports; but in 1955, over 200 foreign vessels belonging to 16 different shipping lines called at the port. Overseas shipments were made to 98 foreign ports in 29 countries of Europe, Africa, South America, and the Caribbean. Between 1917 and 1956 Milwaukee spent $10,000,000 on port development; plans are well underway to spend over $5,000,000 more on projects tied directly with the St. Lawrence Seaway and $4,000,000 more on other waterfront improvements.

Cleveland. Cleveland has been the leading iron ore port on the Great Lakes for many years. When iron from the Lake Superior region was first exploited in the 1850's, Cleveland was already an important Lake Erie city. Cleveland financiers made heavy investments in iron from the Marquette Range and in shipping facilities for moving it to lake ports. With these investments in Marquette iron and in a large number of lake boats to haul it, the city maintained a dominance in iron shipping for several decades. However, in the early 1890's, Mesabi ore gained leadership over Marquette iron, and ore carrying ships became larger—too large to move easily along Cleveland's Cuyahoga River front. These two changes—new ore discoveries and delayed improvement of Cleveland harbor facilities to handle large boats—lessened the city's leadership in iron shipping and in handling other bulky commodities, always so important in Great Lakes trade.

In 1939, Cleveland began spending approximately $11,000,000 to straighten the Cuyahoga—Cuyahoga is an Indian word meaning crooked—and in making other harbor improvements. Now Cleveland again dominates iron ore movement among lake ports. Leadership is a result of several factors besides harbor improvements: chief among these are (*a*) an early start in handling Lake Superior ores; (*b*) the city's financial interest in iron-coal fleets; (*c*) heavy financial investments in Labrador ore; (*d*) the large consumption of iron ore in local furnaces; and (*e*) a favorable location for supplying ore by rail to interior iron and steel centers, such as the Pittsburgh, Shenango Valley, and Steubenville districts.

With the building of the St. Lawrence Seaway, Cleveland is looking forward to an increase in overseas trade. Already ships from more than a dozen foreign lines make more than 250 calls annually. To take advantage of expanded overseas trade and greater lake trade, Cleveland is planning to spend at least $5,000,000 on harbor improvements.

Cleveland is not only an important lake port, but is also a great manufacturing city. In 1955, Cleveland had 292,103 industrial workers with a payroll of $1,380,627,000 and a value added by manufacture of $2,404,-708,000. Leading manufactures include transport equipment, primary and fabricated metal goods, machinery, chemicals, food products, printing and publishing materials, and many other items.

One of the most important problems facing Cleveland's lake shipping and that of many other lake ports as well, is the lack of balance between imports and exports. In 1955, Cleveland had over 20,000,000 tons inbound cargo, 15,000,000 tons of which was iron ore, and only 200,000 tons of outbound lake tonnage.

Toledo. Toledo is located at the mouth of the Maumee River, the largest river emptying into the Great Lakes, and at the extreme western tip of Lake Erie. Unlike Cleveland, which is a leader in iron ore shipments, Toledo is the world's leading coal port and accounts for over half of all Great Lakes coal tonnage. In 1954, total shipping tonnage at Toledo was 27,549,366 tons; 20,779,879 tons of this cargo was coal.

Toledo's coal comes by rail from the Appalachian coal fields of Kentucky and West Virginia. This coal, moving out of Toledo by lake freighters with capacities of about 12,000 tons per vessel, goes to practically all the ports of the Upper Lakes, both in the United States and in Canada. Toledo has two coal docks, one with a capacity of 4,500 cars daily and the other with a capacity of 5,500 cars.

Toledo plans to increase its overseas coal trade as a result of the St. Lawrence Seaway improvement; it also hopes to increase overseas grain cargo. An increase in grain cargo may be possible because completion of a 27-foot channel between Lake Erie and Lake Huron may be delayed until

1960 or 1962. If this delay occurs, large ships will have an advantage in loading grain at Toledo rather than at Chicago. Both cities are easily accessible to the great Middle West grain belt.

Over 100 foreign ships from 14 different lines called at Toledo in 1955. The city, in 1956, arranged to issue $20,000,000 in bonds for harbor improvements to take advantage of the Great Lakes-St. Lawrence Seaway.

Toledo's manufacturing does not equal that of Cleveland. In 1954, the city had a total of 62,002 workers in industry, with a payroll of $298,617,000 and value added by manufacturing of $536,474,000. Leading manufactured items include transport equipment, machinery, machine tools, food products, glass, and other commodities. The city long has been famous for its glass manufacture.

Besides Toledo and Cleveland, Ohio has eleven other lake ports: Ashtabula, Conneaut, Fairport, Huron, Lorrain, Marblehead, Port Clinton, Put-in-Bay, Rocky Harbor, Sandusky, and Vermillion. Ashtabula, Conneaut, and Lorrain lake tonnages each exceed 10,000,000 tons annually. Most of this, as in all lake ports, consists of bulky commodities; and most of the commodities enter domestic commerce. In 1955, 88 per cent of the commerce carried on the Great Lakes consisted of five items—iron ore, 45 per cent; coal, 23 per cent; stone, 11 per cent; petroleum, 5 per cent; and grain, 4 per cent.

Location with reference to cheap water transport and to market, a variety of raw materials, water supply, labor, capital, etc., has given Great Lakes ports great advantages in manufacturing and commerce, and has been responsible for great industrial expansion. There are, however, certain disadvantages in too much expansion of manufacturing in the Lower Lakes region. In the unsettled political world of today, any huge concentration of industry is an excellent target for enemy planes or missiles. Accessibility to a wider market may also result from less industrial concentration in one location. Several corporations, such as those producing automobiles, are finding that a wider distribution of factories and assembling plants is profitable, especially in the modern period of standardized parts for most all machinery. Again, in some Lower Great Lakes cities, such as Detroit, there has been too much emphasis upon one industry. Too much emphasis on a single commodity makes a community more susceptible to economic losses in the downward phase of the business cycle. On the other hand, diversification of industrial production cushions the shock of an economic downturn, for it is seldom that financial depressions are equally serious for all types of manufacturing. A city with diversified industries, just as a person with well-diversified investments, usually weathers a financial storm.

Canadian Manufacturing. The Canadian manufacturing section is centered largely in two areas: (*a*) around Windsor, across the Detroit River from Detroit, and (*b*) at Toronto, a short distance from Buffalo, New York.

It is not surprising that a major emphasis rests on automobile manufacturing at Windsor. American automobile companies find it easy to establish branch factories, standardized parts are readily available, and the Lower Lakes Canadian peninsula pointing towards the United States is densely populated enough to afford a good local market. This peninsula is one of four sections of Canada, all densely populated, which are separated from one another by sparsely populated portions of the country. The other three are the St. Lawrence Valley, the prairie provinces, and the British Columbia southeast coast. The manufacturing of agricultural machinery also is stressed in the Windsor area. Factories started there a long time ago, and the advantage of an early start has encouraged their continuance in spite of a large market in the Spring Wheat Region to the west.

Hamilton, on the western shores of Lake Ontario, is the largest Canadian iron and steel center. Canadian coking coal is far away, near Sydney, Nova Scotia, and much coal is imported from the United States. Canadian iron ore is available by water transport from Steep Rock and Michipicoten, Ontario, Bell Isle, Newfoundland, and from Seven Islands, port for the Labrador ore. Local limestone and water supplies are easily accessible. Production costs are higher than those of many plants in the United States, but tariff protection has encouraged Canadian production.

Niagara Falls power, used on both sides of the international boundary, has stimulated chemical and metallurgical factories in Canada and in the United States. St. Lawrence waterway development will add additional power facilities to Ontario manufacturing. Flour mills and other cereal factories provide another of the many types of manufacturing in the Toronto district.

Agriculture. Manufacturing and commerce are leaders in Lower Lakes economy, but farming is by no means neglected. Agriculturally the Wisconsin, Michigan, and Ontario portions form a part of the American Dairy Region. The relatively moist, cool climate is not ideal for commercial corn production, but is better for hay, grass, oats, corn for silage—all good feeds for dairy cattle. Furthermore, the large concentration of manufacturing gives an excellent market for dairy products.

Fruit growing, including grapes, cherries, peaches, apples, pears, etc., supplements the care of dairy animals in regional farming. Concentration of fruit trees is greater on eastern and southern lakeside locations (Fig. 18). In the spring, cold lake water and ice chill the prevailing west and north winds as they move east and south; thus, they arrive on the opposite sides of the lake somewhat cooler. By this action, temperatures are kept lower and budding is delayed until danger from frost is unlikely. In autumn, lake waters are warmer than the surrounding land, and winds are warmed as they move over the lake. The consequent higher temperatures encourage a longer maturing season for the fruit.

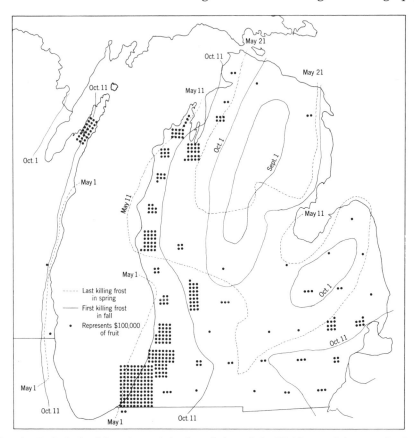

Fig. 18. Fruit Orchard Location and the Great Lakes. Lake Michigan and the westerly winds are significant factors in modifying the climate of western Michigan, and in influencing the location of crops. In the narrow belt, along the leeward shore of Lake Michigan, nearly seven-tenths of the total value of all fruit grown in Michigan is raised; the seven-tenths of Michigan's total fruit value is nearly four times the value of all fruit grown in Wisconsin, a state located on the western or windward side of Lake Michigan. (Source: G. J. Miller, A. E. Parkins, and B. Hudgins, *Geography of North America,* John Wiley and Sons, 1954.)

Fishing. During the past few decades, commercial fishing on the Great Lakes has been seriously affected by a parasitic fish known as the sea lamprey. This parasite reached interior waters by way of the St. Lawrence, and has all but destroyed the lake trout fishing. Catches declined on Lake Huron from 1,743,000 pounds in 1935 to 1,000 pounds in 1949 and on Lake Michigan, from 4,873,000 pounds in 1935 to 343,000 pounds in 1949. Authorities are studying the habits of the lamprey to gain information which will enable them to eliminate the parasite from the Great Lakes. No doubt the right poison, trap, electric current, or other method of extermination will be found, but it may take years before the lake trout fisheries return to their former productivity.

Regional Trends

Cheap water transport has always been and will continue to be a great advantage for both Lower and Upper Lakes regions. Soon two important transport changes will provide economic stimulation for the entire area: (*a*) completion of the Great Lakes-St. Lawrence waterway, and (*b*) harbor improvements for many lake ports. Two other developments already have brought assurance to the Lower Lakes steel centers that their extremely valuable iron and steel manufacturing equipment will not be idle when the high-grade Mesabi iron ore is depleted in the near future. These developments are (*a*) the discovery of the great Labrador iron deposits, and (*b*) the increased and improved facilities for processing taconite of the Lake Superior region.

At present, the water route from lake cities for overseas cargo saves at least 15 per cent of transport costs, compared to shipping by rail and transferring the cargo to a ship in New York or some other Atlantic port. Moreover, with the improved seaway, exporters are likely to prefer shipping direct. It must be remembered, however, that all water shipments will be limited to seven or eight months a year because of winter ice; and, too, carriage by rail to the Atlantic Coast may be preferable for commodities unable to stand the relatively slow carriage on the seaway. Again, railroads and Atlantic ports may lower shipping charges for overseas cargo when confronted with lower rates offered by all-water carriers using the Great Lakes-St. Lawrence route.

Increased overseas trade on the seaway may depend somewhat on United States tariff policy. Great Lakes port cities may have to bring pressure upon Washington for lower tariffs, for lower tariffs may mean more trade and more trade means more shipping and busier ports.

QUESTIONS, EXERCISES, AND PROBLEMS

1. What gives regional unity to the Interior Seaboard? Give the geologic history and the human history of the St. Lawrence-Lake Champlain Lowland. Comment upon the present-day economy of the subregion.

2. Outline the history and the geography of the St. Lawrence Seaway. Describe Canadian-United States relations with reference to the construction and operation of the seaway. Why has the problem of tolls on the St. Lawrence-Great Lakes waterway involved so much study and research? Will the opening of the seaway lessen commercial activities for Atlantic and Gulf Coast ports? What factors in the economic geography of Canada and the United States cause commercial and political friction?

3. Give the geologic and human history of the Mohawk-Hudson Gateway. Point out geographic relationships in the growth of New York City; describe present industries in New York's urban district.

4. Of what geographic significance are the terms *crystalline* and *glaciation* when applied to the Upper Lakes region? Show how the regional economy is related to the geographic environment. Point out the relationships between the occurrence of minerals and methods of exploitation. Name and locate major ports on the Great Lakes.

5. Give the general background for manufacturing in both the Canadian and United States portions of the Lower Lake subregion. Be sure to consider the various bases for locations of industrial sites. Describe agricultural activities in the Lower Lake subregion. Indicate major problems of the Great Lakes fishing industry.

6. Each of the following cities has approximately 100,000 people or more in its urban district: Albany; Buffalo; Chicago; Cleveland; Detroit; Duluth; Erie; Gary; Grand Rapids; Lansing; London; Milwaukee; Montreal; Niagara Falls, New York; Pontiac; Quebec; Rochester, New York; Saginaw; Syracuse; Toledo; Toronto; Windsor. Name major activities accounting for these heavy concentrations of population.

7. Locate the following cities and indicate the most important economic activities for each: Amsterdam, Arvida, Calcite, Chicoutimi, Gloversville, Hamilton, Kenosha, Ludington, Massena, Michipicoten, Racine, Rome, St. Thomas, Schenectady, Steep Rock, Thorold, Troy, Utica, Wind River.

8. Identify the following: Lachine Rapids, Mesabi, taconite, hematite, Keeweenaw, Soo, sea lamprey, North American Ruhr, Saguenay, beneficiate, Cuyuna, Vermillion, Mackinac, Shawinigan Falls, Thousand Islands, milling-in bond.

9. Describe the distribution of population in the Interior Seaboard region.

SELECTED REFERENCES

Alexander, John W., "Industrial Expansion in the United States, 1939–1947," *Economic Geography,* April 1952, pp. 128–142.

Ballert, Albert G., "The Great Lakes Coal Trade, Present and Future," *Economic Geography,* January 1953, pp. 48–59.

Ballert, Albert G., "The Million-Ton Ports of the Great Lakes, 1955" (Map), Great Lakes Commission, 1957.

Bank of Montreal, "The Manufacture of Wood Pulp," *Business Review,* Feb. 23, 1954.

Carmer, Carl, "Erie Canal," *The Lamp,* December 1946.

Cleveland Chamber of Commerce, "Port of Cleveland," *The Clevelander,* November 1956.

Federal Reserve Bank of Cleveland, *Northwestern Ohio,* December 1956.

Great Lakes Commission, *Great Lakes Overseas Commerce,* 1957.

Heimonen, Henry S., "Low Grade Iron Ores in the Lake Superior Region," *Journal of Geography,* March 1958, pp. 130–135.

Hoan, Daniel W., "The St. Lawrence Seaway—Navigational Aspects," *Canadian Geographical Journal,* Vol. 36, 1948, pp. 52–69.

Ioanes, Raymond A., "The St. Lawrence Seaway—Effect on Grain Marketing," *Foreign Agriculture,* January 1958.

Johnson, Gilbert R., "United States-Canadian Treaties Affecting Great Lakes Commerce and Navigation," *Inland Seas,* Vol. 3, 1947; Vol. 4, 1948.

Langdon, George, "The Mesabi Range—A Fabulous Iron Ore Producer Shows Evidence of Decline," *Journal of Geography,* March 1958, pp. 119–129.

Mayer, Harold M., "Great Lakes-Overseas, an Expanding Trade Route," *Economic Geography,* April 1954, pp. 117–143.

Mayer, Harold M., "Prospects and Problems of the Port of Chicago," *Economic Geography,* April 1955, pp. 95–125.

Pfeiffer, John, "The Iron Sea," *Steelways,* December 1953.

Rodgers, Allan, "The Iron and Steel Industry of the Mahoning and Shenango Valleys," *Economic Geography,* October 1952, pp. 331–342.

Smith, Villa B., "Overseas Trade on the Great Lakes-St. Lawrence Waterway," *Journal of Geography,* October 1955, pp. 327–339.

Vicker, Ray, "Seaway's Start," *Wall Street Journal,* Feb. 9, 1959.

White, Langdon C., "Water—A Neglected Factor in the Geographical Literature of Iron and Steel," *Geographical Review,* October 1957, pp. 463–489.

9 · The Central Farming Region

(Figure 1)

The richest farming region in North America, the Central Farming Region, and one of the most productive in the entire world lies entirely within the United States. The heart of this agricultural area is the well-known American Corn Belt. The other two subregions include (*a*) the western part of the North American Dairy Region, which joins the Corn Belt on the north; and (*b*) the General Farming and Tobacco Region, which joins it on the southeast.

The Central Farming Region is bounded on the north and west by the Great Lakes, on the east by the northern portion of the Appalachian Plateau, on the south by the Cotton Belt, and on the west by the Great Plains.

The Corn Belt

The Corn Belt received its name because of the large acreage, yield, and production of corn in parts of twelve central states: Illinois, Indiana, Iowa, Kansas, Michigan, Minnesota, Missouri, Nebraska, Ohio, Oklahoma, South Dakota, and Wisconsin. On all farms, corn dominates the field pattern, but it is not the only crop grown. On the contrary, there are also hay, oats, pasture, soybeans, and wheat, as well as livestock, including cattle, hogs, sheep, and poultry. In short, the word *corn* in the name *Corn Belt* does not signify a one-crop region, for no region in the world is more diversified in its farm economy than the heart of the Central Farming Region.

Boundaries. The physical boundaries are approximately as follows: on the north, the 70°F. isotherm for the three summer months; on the east, the foothills of the Appalachian Plateau in eastern Ohio make mechanized agriculture difficult; on the southeast, the rolling terrain of the Interior Low Plateaus discourages large-scale cultivation; on the south, rugged land forms

220

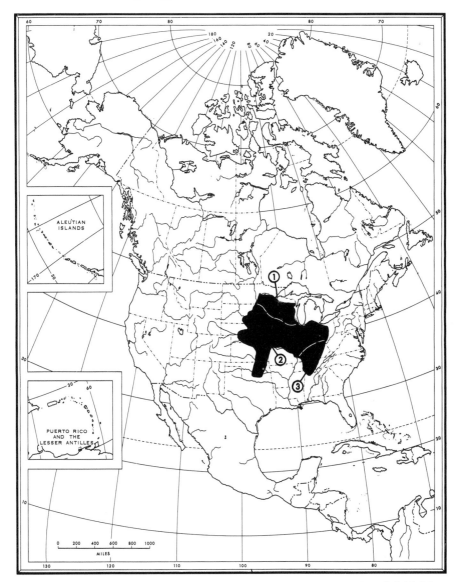

Fig. 1. The Central Farming Region. This rich agricultural region may be subdivided into three subregions: (1) the western part of the North American Dairy Region, (2) the Corn Belt, and (3) the General Farming and Tobacco Region.

of the Ozark Plateau limit large-scale corn planting; and south of the Ozarks, cotton competes successfully with corn because the former is a more valuable commercial crop; on the southwest, the hot winds of July and August ruin the growing corn; and on the west, little corn is grown west of the 20-inch annual rainfall line or that of 8 inches for the three summer months.

As already indicated, the above boundaries are approximate; in the last three decades, 1925–55, hybrid corn has been developed which is resistant to drouth, cold, insects, disease, etc. This seed has permitted a shift of northern, southern, and western boundaries; further man-made inventions may cause other boundary changes in the future.

Climate. All authorities agree that high temperatures and ample precipitation provide optimum conditions for commercial corn production (Fig. 2). In the summer, the sun reaches its highest point in the sky. High sun makes easy the solar transmission of much heat to corn fields. Moreover, at the season of high sun, the length of daylight is greatest. In the poleward part of the Corn Belt, summer days may be fifteen hours in length. Fifteen hours of sunshine contribute heat necessary for growing corn, just as the high sun does. Another factor stimulating rapid plant growth is the large number of hot nights, so characteristic of the Corn Belt.

Corn needs rain in the right amounts at the proper times. An annual rainfall of 20 inches or more, with at least 8 inches during the three summer months, is the characteristic precipitation of the Corn Belt. What are the causes for the 8 inches or more of summer rainfall? In the Corn Belt's continental location, the long days and the high sun produce rapid heating, a condition favorable for low pressures on land, higher pressures on the adjoining seas, and winds blowing from sea to land. This favors frequent thundershowers. Although cyclonic storm control is weaker during summer, convectional precipitation brought about by the high sun is supplemented now and then by rainfall, induced by the passage of infrequent, slow moving, poorly developed low pressure areas.

Short periods of rainfall not only furnish needed moisture, but they permit the farmer to return to his fields when cultivation is necessary, a situa-

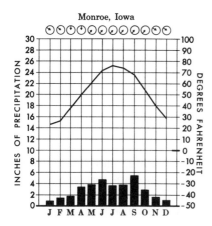

Fig. 2. Monroe, Iowa (41° 30′ N., 93° 1′ W.; altitude 861 feet; mean annual temp. 49.6° F.; mean annual precip. 31.90 inches). Monroe lies in the heart of the Corn Belt and has a humid continental climate, Da, sometimes called the Corn Belt type. Notice the arrows at the top showing prevailing wind direction. Winter winds show a tendency to reverse the direction of those in summer.

tion not always true with the more persistent cyclonic precipitation. Another advantage is the tendency for many thunderstorms to precipitate in the early evening or at night. Moisture falling at this time is more efficient than that falling during daytime hours, for evaporation is less.

Glaciation. Pleistocene glaciation prepared most preglacial land forms and soils for corn production. When the great ice sheet came, it smoothed the preglacial hilly topography, filling in the valleys with material taken from the hill tops. The comparatively level land resulting from glacial action shows greatest significance when it is realized that the Corn Belt is one of the most highly mechanized farming regions in the world.

Not only did the ice level the hills and fill in the valleys, but it ground up parent rocks into finer materials, mixed these materials, and even carried soil from Canada—where it left many rock surfaces almost bare—south into what is now the Corn Belt; thus, United States agriculture gained and Canada's farming lost through glacially forced Canadian soil contributions.

It took the glacier thousands of years to make these changes, but seasonally frozen ground makes a geographic contribution every winter. Frost of several months duration in the north not only lessens soil leaching, but also lessens disease and insect attack on Corn Belt plants and animals.

Vegetation. A natural growth of grasses covered much of the Corn Belt for thousands of years before man appeared on the scene. This vegetation gave fertility to soils already enriched by glacial processes. It is a well-known fact that natural grasses of middle latitudes give more fertility to the soil than do forests.

Why did grasses rather than trees cover much of the Corn Belt before the coming of the commercial farmer? Several geographic factors were probably involved. These include (*a*) the eating of seedling trees by vast herds of herbivorous animals which once grazed here; (*b*) the pushing of the forest eastward by grass fires set by the Indians; and (*c*) a climate with cold and relatively dry winters characterized by more and longer summer drouths than those occurring in forested areas to the east.

Since corn growing is but one part of Corn Belt crop activity, we should consider the adaptability of the physical environment for oats, wheat, soybeans, clover, alfalfa, pasture, and other plants that make up the whole crop picture. Oats, soybeans, and wheat demand less cultivation than corn, but all are favored by relatively level Corn Belt topography; and all grow better because of the fertility in the Corn Belt's prairie-earth and chernozem soils. Hay crops such as clover and alfalfa, together with pasture, demand even less disturbance of the soil for planting and early growth than any of the previously mentioned crops, and they add fertility to the soil rather than taking nutrients away.

Oats. It should be added that the physical environment permits or favors production of all these crops, but probably not with the encourage-

ment given corn. For example, oats grow best in cool moist climates such
as are found in most of the northern European countries, in northeastern
United States, and in southern Canada. But the center of production in
the United States in the early 1950's appeared in Illinois, near the heart of
the Corn Belt. Influencing this condition is the fact that oats serves so well
as a nurse crop for clover; because of this advantage, it is chosen by many
farmers as one of the principal crops in the rotation plan (Fig. 3).

Wheat. Wheat or some other small grain may also be used as a nurse
crop for legumes. Like oats, wheat does not find the most ideal physical
environment in the Corn Belt. Grain of the best quality thrives in a drier
climate with more continental influences or Mediterranean conditions. It
needs a cool, moist growing period and a dry, sunny ripening season. Corn
Belt winters may be too cold and lack snow enough to protect plants from
winter killing; and if they survive the winter, the summers may be too humid
for anything except soft wheats. The best wheats of the Corn Belt grow in
the southwest part.

Soybeans (Fig. 4). Until World War I, soybean production was a
monopoly of the Old World, where China and Manchuria led in acreage
and yield. After the war, and especially after the beginning of World War
II, the soybean became a highly essential and vital crop in the international
war-emergency program. Climate favors soybeans in the Corn Belt with
a longer growing season than that of Old World lands. Furthermore, the
crop matures in a much shorter period than corn, and in years when corn
seeding fails, soybean planting can be made on the same ground as late as
July, with near certainty that there will be a good harvest. Like hay crops,
soybeans may add fertility to the soil and fit nicely into Corn Belt crop
rotations.

Clover. Clover is an important crop, for it not only provides hay for

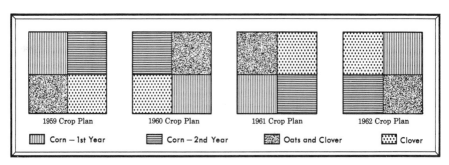

Fig. 3. Crop Rotation. Corn, oats, and clover may be used to illustrate a four-year rotation
cycle. Other crops may be added to or substituted for oats and clover; for example, sweet clover
planted in place of oats and clover can shorten the crop cycle to three years. Choice of crops
depends on soil conditions, disease hazards, relative prices of crops, major farming aims, and
many other factors.

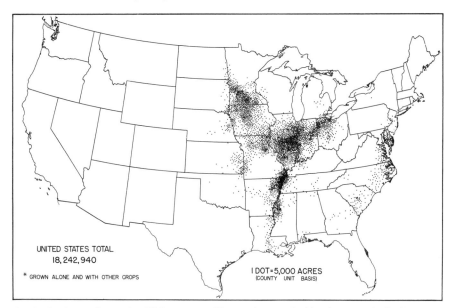

Fig. 4. Soybeans Grown for All Purposes. (Grown alone and with other crops.) Soybean production is widely distributed over eastern United States, but greatest acreage lies in the Corn Belt. (Courtesy U. S. Department of Commerce, Bureau of the Census.)

feed but it also adds fertility to the soil. Because it fits well into crop rotation with corn and oats, farmers are willing to risk an occasional winterkill and the trouble and expense involved in replacement with another crop when misfortune strikes. Winterkill may be due to low temperatures, to alternating low and high temperatures, or to heaving of the soil.

High summer temperatures are not fatal to clover, provided soil moisture is abundant and plant root systems are large enough to absorb moisture to replace that lost by transpiration. Often, however, even among favorable conditions, the removal of a mature companion grain crop like oats from a vigorous growth of red clover, exposing the young plants to the direct rays of the sun, results in the death of many plants.

Alfalfa. For best results, alfalfa needs a comparatively dry summer climate and soils that are not acid. Neither Corn Belt climate nor soil are entirely favorable, yet alfalfa has become an important crop in parts of the region. It is not so well adapted to the eastern section as it is to the west; this is because acid soils are more prevalent in the east; and with humidity greater than in the west, diseases are more destructive. Winter cold may kill alfalfa the same way that it causes the death of clover. But the high yields, several cuttings a year, coupled with the fertility added to the soil make it attractive to the farmer.

Permanent Pasture. Ground left continuously in pasture for grazing animals occupies acreages of various sizes. Although most of the Corn Belt has nearly level topography, some of the moraines left by glacial action provide surfaces that are more than gently rolling. Furthermore, stream erosion since Pleistocene time has etched hills and valleys in a good many sections. To make proper agricultural adjustments to the more rolling lands, farmers leave them in grass, which prevents serious erosion and provides needed pasture.

Seasonal Crop Activities. In central Iowa (Figs. 5, 6, 7, 8, 9), in the heart of the Corn Belt, the crop season starts about the last of March or the first of April, when signs of spring encourage preparation of ground for planting oats and clover, or for some other nurse crop and legume. These two crops form an important part of a rotation cycle followed by many farmers— a four-year cycle, including corn, two years; oats and clover, one year; and clover, one year (Fig. 3). The choice of the cycle is based on the fact that since corn is a soil robber, two years of land for corn necessitates replenishment of soil nutrients. The legume, clover, is selected to add the desired fertility, and oats serves as a nurse crop.

After oats and clover have been planted, ground preparation for corn occupies the farmer's attention. Land must be plowed, disked, and harrowed, in short, placed in condition to receive hybrid corn seed about the last of May or the first few days of June. In preparation of his fields for planting hybrid corn, the farmer may decide to use commercial fertilizer to increase yields and to put the soil in better condition.

Fig. 5. Iowa Farms. Nearly 500 square miles of Iowa farms are shown on this photograph. Light patches show harvested small grain such as oats and wheat; dark-colored areas include corn, pasture, and forage. Note the rectangular fields so characteristic of the nearly level Corn Belt topography. (Courtesy of the *Des Moines Register.*)

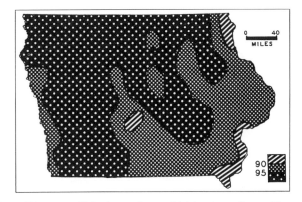

Fig. 6. Percentage of Area in Farms. Iowa's nearly level topography probably contributes more to its high proportion of farm land than any other feature of the physical environment. In the area enclosed by the 95 per cent isarithm, a mantle of glacial drift changed sharply rolling preglacial topography into gently rolling plains. More rolling areas lie (1) in the northeast on a part of the Driftless area; (2) in the southeast which has been dissected by the Cedar, Des Moines, Iowa, Mississippi, and Skunk rivers; and (3) where urban development is encouraged by the state's largest city, Des Moines. County percentages of farm land range from 84 to 99 per cent. (Source: Helen L. Smith, "Agricultural Land Use in Iowa," *Economic Geography,* July 1949.)

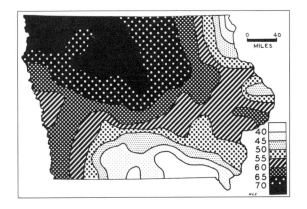

Fig. 7. Percentage of Farm Land in Crops. Iowa, in the heart of the Corn Belt, has 59 per cent of its total farmland in crops. (Source: Helen L. Smith, "Agricultural Land Use in Iowa," *Economic Geography,* July 1949.)

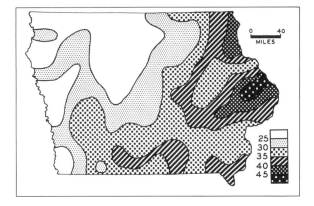

Fig. 8. Livestock Units per 100 Acres of Cropland. The production of livestock by counties in Iowa, a typical Corn Belt state, ranges from 20 to 46 per 100 acres of cropland. (Source: Helen L. Smith, "Agricultural Land Use in Iowa," *Economic Geography,* July 1949.)

Fig. 9. Winter Windbreak. Trees planted to protect farm buildings and livestock from cold winter winds may be seen on most Corn Belt farms. These trees result in a saving of at least 25 per cent in fuel bills, and may lessen snow accumulation in yard and driveway. (Courtesy American Forest Products Industries.)

Hybrid corn brings to agriculture the industrialized techniques of standardized parts and mass production. It is based on the fact that certain characters can be fixed in a corn plant by inbreeding, that once fixed they do not change, and that the continued crossing of these inbreds in a certain way will always produce the same result. Here is an example of the importance of man-made factors in geography. Physical conditions are more or less ideal for corn production; but man is constantly making progressive improvements in seed types, in rotation cycles, in fertilization, in mechanization, and in many other ways in order to utilize the physical environment to the best advantage.

After the farmer has prepared his fields for planting hybrid corn and has planted the seed, he will be busy for several weeks. Oats will be ready to harvest during the latter part of June or early July; his first crop of seeded clover from the previous year will be demanding attention; and he must keep the corn field free from weeds by cultivation. Most corn needs to be cultivated three times before the corn plants are high enough to shade the ground and discourage competition from weeds.

Throughout June, July, and the early part of August, the farmer finds little time for other activities besides caring for his crops and livestock. But in late summer and early autumn with corn cultivation long completed, small grain harvest over, and hay crops cared for, he has an opportunity to look after his building and fencing needs. In the eastern part of the Corn Belt he may take this opportunity to spread lime over the fields which he has selected for planting legume crops the coming season. As previously indicated, alfalfa and certain other legumes do not thrive well in acid soils.

Corn harvest may begin the last of October, and with the mechanical corn harvester this job takes less time and is less difficult than it was when maize was picked by hand. In fact, the highly mechanized character of all crop activity makes the task much less irksome than it was in bygone days, and a much smaller amount of labor is necessary on the average size farm. The days of the hired man are almost over on most Corn Belt farms.

With corn harvest completed, the grain may be sold on the market if the farmer lives close to a great grain center, such as Chicago. If not, he may follow a practice that can almost be considered a principle in the geography of the Corn Belt. Farmers living far distant from a large grain buying center are likely to market their corn on the hoof—feed it to live-stock and market them—to save transport costs. It is during the autumn and early winter season that feeding and caring for livestock may take up much of the farmer's time.

Livestock Raising and the Seasons. Livestock raising adds further diver-sity to farming activities beyond that already evident in the growing of pasture, alfalfa, clover, soybeans, wheat, oats, corn, and other crops. Many factors encourage growing domestic animals: (*a*) several crops are available for feed; (*b*) animal manures enrich the soil; (*e*) grazing animals utilize per-manent pasture and hay; (*d*) greater economic stability may be achieved by this additional diversification; (*e*) animal culture gives better distribution of labor throughout the year.

Swine (Fig. 10). Swine are found on more farms and in larger numbers than either cattle or sheep. Most farmers plan their sows' farrowing time so that the period of growth and fattening of young pigs will correspond to the warm season. Consequently the majority of pigs come in the spring during April or May, when the cold of winter has passed and when there is little danger of a delayed spring with its raw, wet days, so damaging to the young animal's progress. Although the larger pig crop is born in the spring, an important fraction is farrowed in the fall. Pigs will arrive no later than September or early October, so that they can attain considerable size before the winter season advances.

As the sun is always below the zenith and in the southern sky during the entire year, both portable and large stationary hog houses generally face south, thereby gaining an advantage of longer and more intense sunlight with the consequent increase in light, warmth, and dryness. Doors and windows are seldom found on the poleward side. Moreover, hog buildings, where possible, are built on the north side of the farm house so that this dwelling will be to the windward of the pigpens in summer, an advantageous position when the prevailing winds of the season pick up unpleasant odors while sweeping across the hog lot. In winter, the wind almost reverses its direction, suggesting a monsoonal tendency (Fig. 2), but doors and win-dows of the farmhouse are closed most of the time, and frozen ground over which the air blows yields a minimum of the rank smell.

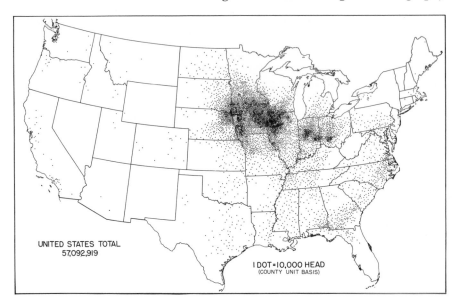

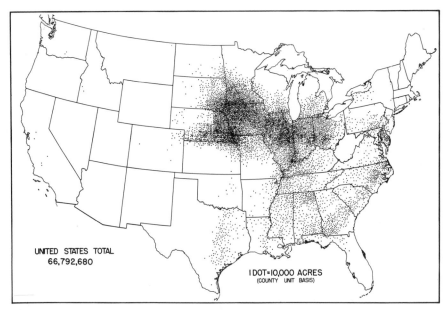

Fig. 10. Hogs, Number in 1954, Top; Corn, Acreage in 1954, Bottom. Marked similarity exists between heavy concentration of corn and swine in the Corn Belt. (Courtesy U. S. Department of Commerce, Bureau of the Census.)

Many methods are followed in feeding swine, but corn has always been the major feed. Shelled or on the cob it may be fed to animals at regular periods, or placed in a self-feeder which eliminates evening and morning chores. Swine also eat corn wasted by feeding cattle. In following corn-fed cattle, swine utilize much feed that would otherwise be of no value.

Hogging down corn is another well-known method of swine feeding. In the autumn, when corn is ripe, farmers may enclose a portion of their corn field with a temporary fence and turn the hogs into the enclosure. This method of feeding permits the animals grain and forage when they want it, saves labor in feeding, and assures soil fertilization through well-distributed animal manures.

Feeding hogs gives an opportunity for a more continuous use of labor than farming without them. Moreover, duties conincident with swine culture do not seriously conflict with the raising of grain. In the spring, summer, or fall, the farmer may do his chores before and after working in the field, and in the winter, when no planting, cultivating, or harvesting is possible, he has time for the extra chores brought about by the colder season. Adding diversity and stability to the labor problem is just one more way in which hog raising strengthens the system of diversified farming in the Corn Belt.

The bulk of the Corn Belt swine go into commercial channels to supply large urban markets. At present, with large trucks so common, and sur-faced roads crisscrossing the belt in every direction, buyers pick up droves at the farm and transport them direct to the packing plants. For the small percentage of hogs marketed during hot weather, so characteristic of the Corn Belt summers, truck men arrive at the farm before dawn. Fat hogs suffer greatly from heat, and loading in the coolest period of the day mini-mizes danger from death loss and shrinkage in weight, which may occur when the sun is high above the horizon.

Beef Cattle (Fig. 11). Beef cattle rearing and fattening add further variety to the farm activities. Cattle change large quantities of hay, straw, silage, and grain into meat, a more concentrated and more easily marketed product; they graze the pasture found on areas of more rolling topography; and they make possible a better utilization of labor during the winter season.

Many cattle, unlike hogs, are shipped into the Corn Belt from other regions, especially from the Great Plains pastures to the west. It is cheaper to graze cattle on the Western Range country to the age when they may be fattened on corn than it is to graze them to a fattening age in the Corn Belt. The higher value of Corn Belt land, and the possibility of its more profitable utilization for grain farming largely account for this situation.

A large percentage of the yearly cattle movement into the Corn Belt comes during August, September, October, and November, and the animals are very soon placed on a grain ration. The large movement from the range

Fig. 11. Fattening Cattle. These Angus cattle are feeding upon shelled corn. About nine-tenths of the Midwest corn crop is fed to livestock, mainly hogs, beef cattle, and poultry. Cattle may be taken off grass and fed several weeks on a ration including grain, hay, and some concentrate such as cottonseed meal, or molasses. Hogs usually follow feeders in order to utilize grain wasted by the cattle. (Courtesy U. S. Department of Agriculture.)

at this time is occasioned by the feeder's desire to take advantage of the new corn crop, the fall pastures, the corn stalk pasture, and the available supply of farm labor during the winter. October is often the month of heaviest feeder movement into the Corn Belt, whereas in June, the month when the farmers are busiest with their crop work, and the month just before the summer period of short pasturage, the movement is generally the lightest.

Corn provides the dominant item in the fattening ration. However, this grain may be supplemented by hay, and lesser quantities of many other items such as cotton seed meal, oil meal (from flax seed), and even corn-cobs and molasses. Concentrates have been added to the ration in large amounts in recent decades, not only because of their own feeding values, but also because the high price of corn has encouraged the use of supplementary feeds.

Barns and sheds are needed to protect livestock from winter storms, and especially from blizzards, which may occur any winter. The farmer has learned that aside from the hazard of loss of livestock by death, there is no economy in attempting to keep up the animal's bodily heat entirely with high-priced corn and other feeds.

The feeding of cattle involves a larger capital outlay, and is more speculative, than the feeding of hogs; thus, it is not surprising that most of the cattle fed are handled by large feeders. A few own tracts of land in the Western Range country from which they ship cattle to be fattened in the Corn Belt.

The cultural features on farms where cattle are fed in considerable number are likely to be different from those where only hogs are fattened. The man-made landscape may include corn cribs of large capacity, long stretches of cattle barns, and numerous bunks from which the cattle feed on corn, hay, and concentrates. The feeder usually owns a set of scales for periodic weighings of cattle so that he may tabulate the rate of gain and the amount of feed used in fattening.

Dairy Cattle. Dairy herds are generally not so numerous as the beef cattle, except near large cities. However, a few milk cows may be found on nearly every farm, and the daily or weekly checks from dairy and poultry products supplement the larger, but less frequent, returns resulting from major activities of grain farming and fattening livestock.

Dr. Loyal Durand, probably the best authority on American dairying, has the following to say about Corn Belt dairying:

The eastern Indiana-western Ohio portion of the Corn Belt has a large dairy-cow population, and is important in milk production. In part this is a response to the numerous cities of these two states, located in the region, and in part a response to the small-sized farms of this portion of the Corn Belt, a factor promoting more intensive use of the land. The western Corn Belt is a large producer of butter. In fact, Nebraska is the fourth state in American production. This is the so-called Centralizer Belt, which stretches along the Great Plains border from eastern Kansas to eastern North Dakota. Cream from a very large area is shipped to large creameries, known as centralizers. No one farm contributes much, maybe only a can or two per week, but collectively the butterfat output is important, and individual centralizers may draw their supplies from 200 miles or more. Long distance shipment is made possible because of the fact that the butter is manufactured from sour cream. It would be impossible to manufacture cheese under these conditions. This phase of dairy manufacture extends into the Corn Belt portions of Iowa and, in conjunction with the butter production of Iowa's northeast, helps place the state high in American butter output.[1]

Sheep. The raising and feeding of sheep and lambs is not so important as swine and cattle feeding. Some farmers keep a small flock of sheep to raise lambs, which they sell in the autumn, and also for the yearly spring crop of wool. Other farmers buy lambs from the Western Range country to fatten on corn, oats, and hay.

[1] Loyal Durand, Jr., "The American Dairy Region," *The Journal of Geography,* January 1949.

Horses and Mules. The Corn Belt uses fewer and fewer horses and mules with every passing year. They are declining there just as they are throughout the entire United States. A few figures will illustrate the situation. In 1920, the country's horses and mules numbered 25,742,000; in 1951, 6,753,000. In 1920, tractors numbered 246,000; in 1950, 3,800,000. In 1941, corn pickers numbered 120,000; in 1950, 410,000. Other figures could be given, but enough are shown to indicate the trend toward more and more mechanization in agriculture. In fact, farming has become so highly mechanized that the accident rate among farmers is relatively high, and accident insurance has risen accordingly.

Manufacturing. For a long while about the only diversity in Corn Belt economy was in agriculture. But the situation today is far different from that of the early 1900's. Manufacturing has become important even in a state like Iowa, in the very heart of the Corn Belt.

During World War II, Iowa factories received encouragement from the national trend toward decentralization of industry, and Iowa factories processed many finished products for the war machine. Encouragement has also come from local sources. Mechanization of agriculture has released many workers for industry. Again, the coming of the motorcar has encouraged good roads; good roads have made it possible for farmers to bypass small towns for larger ones in order to purchase food, clothing, housing, farm equipment, and other supplies. Lack of employment in declining small towns makes more workers available in the factory and commercial centers. Good roads also aid transportation, a necessary factor in manufacturing development. Capital, like labor, is extremely flexible in its movements; wherever profit opportunities are present, capital moves in.

The preliminary report of the 1954 Census of Manufactures for Iowa showed the total number of manufacturing establishments as 3,327, the number of employees 161,700, and the value added by manufacturing $1,219,100,000. Comparing this with similar manufacturing items for the state of Ohio—a state in the heart of the American Manufacturing Belt and a state partly in the Corn Belt, the Interior Seaboard, and the Appalachian Plateau—Iowa does not show up well. In 1954, Ohio had 14,632 manufacturing establishments, 1,270,200 manufacturing employees, and added a sum of $10,153,700,000 by manufacture. In comparison with one of the Great Plains-Rocky Mountain states, Colorado, the position of Iowa looks better. In 1954, Colorado had 2,089 manufacturing establishments, 63,200 workers, and added $471,500,000 by manufacture. Moreover, Iowa's changes between 1947 and 1954 for payroll and value added by manufacture were up 72 per cent and 82 per cent respectively, whereas national changes for the same items were up 67 per cent and 56 per cent. A comparison of Iowa's value added by manufactures with the value of agricultural production for the state shows $1,219,100,000 for the former or almost 60 per cent of the $2,079,014,000 for the latter.

The most important manufacturing industries in Iowa are those closely linked with the farm, food processing plants and the farm equipment industry. But the gain in these two types of manufacturing between 1947 and 1954 has not been as great as in other types of manufactures such as rubber products, with the 1954 value added by manufacture three times that of 1947; primary metal products, over four times for the same period; transportation equipment over three times for the same period, etc.

Examples of specific factories may be informative. At Ottumwa, Iowa, John Morrell and Company has a packing plant slaughtering tens of thousands of hogs and cattle annually; at Davenport, International Harvester Corporation manufactures farm machinery that is sold not only in the Corn Belt, but also throughout the world; Cedar Rapids is the home office for the Quaker Oats Company (Fig. 12), with branches in many states and in numerous foreign countries. The company processes cereals into several types of human food and into feed for animals as well. At Newton, the Maytag Corporation, and other companies as well, manufactures washing machines, and at one time Newton was called the washing machine capital of the world.

Bases for manufacturing in the Corn Belt are not insignificant. The region is underlain with large supplies of medium- and high-volatile bitu-

Fig. 12. The Quaker Oats Plant, Cedar Rapids, Iowa. The Quaker Oats factory is typical of grain processing plants in the Corn Belt. (Courtesy of The Quaker Oats Company.)

minous coal (Fig. 13) of the Interior fields.   These deposits are important in five Corn Belt states, Illinois, Indiana, Iowa, Kansas, and Missouri. Large quantities of coal lie only a few feet deep, and many farms yield coal worth hundreds of crops of grain and hay grown on the surface.   Strip mining may produce profits, but it also brings huge piles of unsightly earth dumps called *spoils.*   Most states have laws that force mining companies to restore these dumps into an attractive cultural landscape.   United Electric Coal Company, a large, strip-mining corporation in Illinois, has converted hundreds of acres in dumps to bearing orchards of peaches and apples and to broad stretches of pasture land.   Some large tracts have been landscaped into picnic parks.

At least two states, Illinois and Kansas, have significant reserves of oil. In Illinois, farmers cultivate corn, soybeans, and other crops right up to the pumps of numerous oil wells.   Mt. Carmel petroleum fields have yielded nearly 10,000,000 barrels since 1940, and were producing almost a thousand barrels a day in the early 1950's.

Fig. 13. Growing Corn and Mining Coal. Notice the steam shovel in the center as seen a short distance from the corn field. This photograph was taken among the corn stalks to emphasize growing crops above ground and power resources below. Strip mining of coal is widespread in the Corn Belt.

In 1955, the monument marking the center of population in the United States stood near Olney, Illinois, and that state with more than 9,000,000 people ranks fourth in total population. Thus, the local Corn Belt market for manufactured goods is significant. Moreover, most of the region is within reach of the big Eastern market, and market is constantly becoming of greater importance as an influence in the location of factories.

The American Dairy Region: Western Part

The western part of the American Dairy Region is located west of Lake Michigan and includes northwestern Illinois, northeastern Iowa, southeastern and east-central Minnesota, and nearly all of Wisconsin. The western part of the Corn Belt lies to the south, the Spring Wheat Region to the west, the Upper Lakes region to the north, and the Lower Lakes region to the east.

Climate (Fig. 14). Most of the Dairy Belt lies north of the 70°F. isotherm for the three summer months in the humid continental, short summer climate. The cool summers, the drizzly frontal rainfall of fairly long duration, the cool and damp spring season, and the low rate of evaporation resulting from cool temperatures, cloudy skies, and winds of moderate velocity, all combine to produce good pasture and hay land; timothy, clover, and oats are at their best; but meteorological conditions are not favorable for corn because the short growing season prevents complete ripening. However, maturity is not necessary for good silage, and silos are a characteristic feature of the cultural landscape.

Another man-made feature is the large and substantial basement barn. Cattle must be housed during the long cold winters, and great quantities of hay must be stored for winter feeding.

Surface Features. The most recent glaciation, the Wisconsin, left land forms such as drumlins and moraines that are gentle to sharply rolling; but outwash and till plains contain fairly large acreages of relatively flat land. Numerous lakes, marshes, and swamps are a result of drainage disruption. In the Driftless Area (Fig. 15) of northeast Iowa, northwest Illinois, southeast Minnesota, and southwest Wisconsin—the section unaffected by glaciation—the surface is one of rolling plain, low hill country, undulating ridge tops, steep hill sides, and flat floored valleys. Nearly every dairy farm contains combinations of land which permit grass on rolling ground and crops on land with little relief.

Vegetation and Soils. Mixed forest of conifer and broadleaf furnishes a contrast to the natural grass cover originally growing on much of the Corn Belt. Soil types include gray-brown podzolics in the south and podzols in the north.

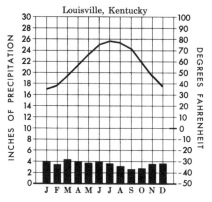
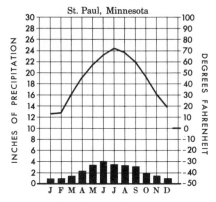

Fig. 14. Louisville, Kentucky (38° 15′ N., 85° 45′ W.; altitude 525 feet; mean annual temp. 57° F.; mean annual precip. 43.49 inches); St. Paul, Minnesota (44° 57′ N., 93° 5′ W.; altitude 848 feet; mean annual temp. 44.1° F.; mean annual precip. 27.4 inches). Louisville climate is characteristic of the General Farming and Tobacco subregion; St. Paul lies in the Dairy subregion. Louisville is situated near the equatorward boundary of the humid continental warm summer climate (Da) and the poleward limit of the humid subtropical climate (Ca). St. Paul belongs to the humid continental short summer climate (Db). Both charts show climatic conditions encouraging for agriculture.

The Human Element. Ancestors of the present population were largely from northern Europe where they followed the dairy industry before coming to America. They include Germans, Scandinavians, Swiss, Dutch, and Poles. In northern Europe and in the American dairyland, the farmer tends his cattle 365 days a year, milks them twice a day, and has an evenly spread work year—crop production and milking during the summer, barn feeding and milking during the winter. There are no vacations. Those individuals who are willing to engage in this form of a livelihood do so. Most of the present farmers have been brought up to it as a part of their life pattern, and accept an industry started by their forebears in response to environmental factors.

Dairying has been stimulated by many public-spirited citizens. In Wisconsin, Professor S. M. Babcock, of the state university, gave the industry everywhere an enormous boost by the invention of a dependable test for the butterfat content of milk and cream. Wisconsin governor W. D. Hoard, who served one term beginning in 1888, also gave the dairy industry much encouragement. Even before election, his farm paper, *Hoard's Dairyman,* was a leader among the nation's dairy periodicals. Once in office, he employed many means to stimulate the dairy farmer. One of the best influences resulted from his sponsorship of dairying at the University of Wisconsin, where research has brought advances that continue today.

Another man-made factor favoring progressive dairying is the broad development of cooperative associations. In the last analysis, man has contributed as much to farm success in the American Dairy Region as the physical environment.

The Dairy Farms. Dairy farms average about 120 acres in size. They are smaller than farms in the western part of the Corn Belt, but slightly larger than landholdings in the eastern corn county. Monthly work hours are practically the same both in summer and in winter, a labor regime which differs from that of the Corn Belt and other farming regions where the growing season is the busy one.

Farm ownership is high. This situation may be influenced by several factors. (*a*) Many farms will not support an absentee owner in addition to the tenant. (*b*) Ownership of a herd of dairy cattle involves a large investment, and handling them carefully to get highest milk production requires conscientious responsibility. Many men are not willing to take such responsibility, or are incapable of doing so; and dairymen are often hesitant to trust tenants, even if the latter are willing. (*c*)Where tenancy exists it may be a family affair, such as rental to a son-in-law or son. In contrast to the Corn Belt, most dairy farms keep a hired man who may be needed as much in the winter feeding season as during the summer crop season.

Cows on the farm, like the people who own the land, are nearly all of northwest European origin. The Holstein, which gives a large quantity of milk with medium to low butterfat content, leads in number; the animal is Danish in origin. There are Ayrshires from Scotland, Brown Swiss from

The Driftless Area

Fig. 15. The Driftless Area. Parts of four states lie in the driftless area: northeastern Iowa, southeastern Minnesota, southwestern Wisconsin, and northwestern Illinois. Here, the terrain lacks the nearly level character of the surrounding land once covered by the ice sheet. (Map drawn after Nevin M. Fenneman, *Physical Divisions of the United States.*)

Switzerland, and Guernseys and Jerseys which originated on small islands off the coast of Britain. Toward the southern margin of the Dairy Region, where corn may mature with careful handling, some farmers keep dual-purpose cattle, suitable for milk and beef, such as the Shorthorn, which was developed in England.

Holsteins, because of their large milk production, are numerous near urban centers or cheese factories. Jerseys and Guernseys give less milk, but milk that has a higher content of butterfat. For this reason they predominate where creameries specialize in butter, and near urban districts where brand names for milk have a special value.

The large barn, silo, and night pasture distinguish dairy farms from those of other agricultural regions. Generally good buildings, well painted and in excellent repair, also reflect high standards of most farmers and the stable weekly or monthly income provided by the milk check. These frequent payments to dairy farmers are in sharp contrast to the seasonal payments received by grain farmers, cotton growers, meat producers, and many other farmers.

Marketing. The dairy farmer's income is derived principally from the sale of milk products. Milk may be sold to city market, to creameries, cheese factories, condenseries, powdering establishments, malted milk factories, casein plants, and to other outlets. Because the western part of the American Dairy Region is far removed from most urban markets for milk, the liquid is manufactured into a concentrated product that is higher in value per unit of weight, and one that will bear transport costs to distant markets.

The main butter producing area is in the western part of the region, centered in western Wisconsin, northeastern Iowa, and eastern and southeastern Minnesota. The cream, received two or three times weekly is manufactured into butter by private and cooperative creameries. The skimmilk, remaining after cream is separated from whole milk on the farm, is fed to calves or swine, or is mixed with grain to form a swill for hogs. Butter regions, as a result of the skimmilk by-product, usually engage in the raising of swine.

Cheese, in contrast to butter, is made from whole fresh milk; several conditions account for localization of cheese factories. (*a*) They are likely to operate in cool-summer sections where milk is kept fresh easily. (*b*) National origin of the population is an influence of importance. Some of the Wisconsin districts were originally localized by settlers from cheese areas of Oneida and Herkimer counties, New York, and others were founded by Swiss settlers from Canton Glarus. (*c*) The economic advantage of an early start accounts for persistence of cheese factories in certain localities as well as factors of (*d*) name, and (*e*) advertising value. Once established the industry usually continues in the area.

Wisconsin manufactures half of the nation's output of American cheese, and from 80 to 90 per cent of differing foreign varieties. Milk for American cheese factories is delivered daily. Milk for some of the foreign varieties of cheese, such as limburger, is delivered twice a day during hot weather, following both the evening and morning milking; and, pending cessation of this type of weather, the cheesemaker engages in twice a day cheese-making, from 7 A.M. until noon, and from 7 P.M. until midnight. After delivering his milk to the factory, the farmer returns home with the whey, drawn off from the cheese vat after the curd has formed. Whey is fed to swine.

Condensed and evaporated milk is canned at large plants called condenseries. The factory is commonly corporation owned, in contrast to the private cooperative creameries and cheese factories. A key factor in condensery location is an intensive dairy district with large milk production per unit of area. Large size, abundant capital, corporate connections, and efficient management have usually permitted condenseries to compete successfully with the smaller dairy plants, and they have often forced the latter from the competitive market.

Cream, either in whole form or in specially concentrated jellylike form, known as *plastic cream,* is shipped daily from Wisconsin, Iowa, and Minnesota to such distant markets as Boston, New York, and Philadelphia. Milk may be shipped daily in tank cars to these same areas if needed. During the winter tourist season fresh milk from Wisconsin is dispatched to Miami, Florida, and other resort towns whose local milksheds are unable to meet the seasonal demand. During World War II, shipments from Wisconsin went to many Southern cities. War-boom communities, such as Knoxville, Tennessee, and its satellite city, Oak Ridge (which grew from zero to a population of 80,000 in two years), had to obtain over 40 per cent of their day-to-day milk supply from Wisconsin, and during the winter obtained as much as 55 per cent from this source. Modern refrigeration and rapid transport have made possible these long distance shipments, and have modified the oft-repeated economic statement that "a heavy, bulky, perishable product such as market milk is produced immediately adjacent to the market." [2]

General Farming and Tobacco Subregion

This subregion lies southeast of the Corn Belt in the Lower Ohio Valley; it occupies part of the physiographic province that Fenneman calls the Interior Low Plateaus. Two states, Kentucky and Tennessee, contain most of the subregion, but small portions are also included in southwestern Ohio, southern Indiana, southestern Illinois, and northern Alabama.

[2] Much of the material on dairying is based on Loyal Durand, Jr., "The American Dairy Region," *The Journal of Geography,* January 1949.

Surface Features. Although classified as a part of the large physiographic division of the Central Lowland or Interior Plain, land forms are hilly. One cause for the hills is the uplift that has taken place. Two well-known uplifts are the Cincinnati Anticline and the Nashville Dome. The former lies to the north and is made of rock layers unequally resistant to erosion, resulting in the formation of the Bluegrass lowland and the Kentucky Knobs. These land forms developed when the top of the anticline was truncated, leaving the stronger upper layers as a rim—the Kentucky Knobs—surrounding the Bluegrass plain; the plain was fashioned on the weaker and older rocks in the center of the anticline. The Nashville Basin to the south, developed in the same way as that of the Bluegrass area, but the rim around the plain occupying the center of the Nashville Basin is called the Highland Rim.

Solution work has aided uplift and doming in making uneven surfaces; numerous sinkholes, caves, and underground passages have developed as water, percolating through crevices, has dissolved and removed lime from the rocks. One of the world's most famous underground passages occurs in midwestern Kentucky, Mammoth Cave.

Climate (Fig. 14). The subregion's humid subtropical climate has an annual rainfall of about 40 to 50 inches, well distributed throughout the year with a slight summer maximum. The growing season averages 160 days in the north and about 200 days in the south, placing the area just north of the Cotton Belt. Climate does not separate the subregion from the Corn Belt to the north, but corn loses commercial importance, partly because the non-glaciated topography is more rolling than the glacial plains of the Corn Belt.

Vegetation and Soils. Climax vegetation of oak-ash-maple adds more fertility to the gray-brown podzols than the conifer climax of much of the Cotton Belt. Pages have been written about the richness of the blue grass that covered parts of the land when early settlers moved west through the Cumberland Gap to Kentucky. These pioneers came in such numbers that Kentucky preceded Ohio in becoming the first state west of the Appalachian mountain barrier. It is entirely possible that prairie grasses of the Corn Belt were just as nutritious as those of the Bluegrass country; but the pioneers were so impressed by the bluegrass after years and years in deep forests and rugged mountains that they may have placed a higher value on the blue green pasture than it deserves.

Much of the soil of the lowlands comes from limestone, but not all of it even in the Bluegrass country. Here there are three concentric belts; the innermost is underlain by highly phosphatic limestone having a gently rolling relief except along the larger streams, where dissection has carved out hills and valleys. This belt is also characterized by sinkholes and big springs from underground streams. The shale belt, which encircles the central limestone area, is much more rugged, with high hills often terminating in sharp ridges and numerous deep narrow valleys; beyond the shale belt and constituting the outermost section of the Bluegrass area, lies a more nearly level country like that of the innermost belt. Most of the rimland around the Bluegrass region, as well as that of the Nashville Basin, is made up of less fertile soils.

Agriculture. Farming is the major occupation. The rimlands, with more rugged topography and less fertile soils, have larger acreages in hay, pasture, and woodland. Some gently rolling Bluegrass country is also left in pasture, and here some of the world's best race horses are grown. The choice of utilizing land for pasture is influenced more by man than by the physical environment. On much of the three lowlands—the Bluegrass country, the Nashville Basin, and the Ohio flood plains—man chooses to grow tobacco, wheat, and corn.

Tobacco is an important money crop in the Bluegrass country and less significant in the Nashville Basin and along the Ohio-Indiana, Kentucky boundary. Humid subtropical climate favors tobacco, and so do the phosphatic limestone soils. Potash and nitrate are needed more than phosphorus; fertilization and crop rotation are used on the better managed farms. The rotation cycle may include tobacco, a legume hay crop like lespedeza, wheat, and corn.

Much of the tobacco is a burley type, useful in cigarette and pipe mixtures, and it is grown in small acreages. Size of the plot is determined largely by available labor to take care of planting in seed beds, replanting, weeding, removing worms, treating plants for disease and insect pests, plucking buds, harvesting, curing, and other tasks. The large landowner may rent small sections to sharecroppers, or with the aid of his family and hired help he may plant his own tobacco. The small farm owner may put much of his land in this money crop.

Wheat also provides a money crop. Climate permits winter or fall wheat to be grown successfully. The seed, planted in the autumn, makes a good growth before the cool season advances. Plants remain more or less dormant during the winter period, and mature rapidly in late spring or early summer. With the green grass cover—wheat is a grass—during the winter season, rains cause little erosion; moreover, fall planting and early summer harvest distribute the labor load more evenly throughout the year.

Although corn is not so important as it is in the Corn Belt, the frost-free season is long and the well-distributed rainfall is sufficient for good growth. Limestone soils are naturally fertile, and cultivation brings little erosion on gently rolling to flat land if conservation practices such as contour farming and strip cropping are employed. Most of the crop is fed to livestock, especially to hogs.

Farming contrasts are noted between lowlands and highlands. The choice of crops is largely the same; but with much less cultivable land on the uplands, tobacco, wheat, and corn acreages are lower. Most of the Kentucky Knobs and similar land forms in Tennessee should be utilized for pasture land and tree crops. These could include various fruits such as apples, nut crops such as pecans, or deciduous and conifer trees for lumber and paper pulp. For many years, mast feeding was important in the rolling lands of Kentucky and Tennessee. There still may be advantages for use of rugged lands with dual-purpose trees—to feed animals and to provide materials for lumber and paper.

Most of the hill country does not possess the prosperous look of the lowland, and most landowners on the rugged terrain are not so prosperous. Yet, these hill farmers survived the depression of the 1930's better than their lowland neighbors. The hill people had not extended their credit beyond means of payment like some of the people on the plains; in fact, much of their production could be called subsistence farming.

Commerce and Manufacturing. Transport has always been important in the subregion. In the early days, just as today, the Ohio River was an important traffic artery. Louisville, on the falls of the Ohio, became a large city partly because waterfalls made it a bulk-breaking point. Goods had to be unloaded and carried around the falls. At present, ships use locks to get around the barrier.

Most people associate this second largest city of the subregion with the Kentucky Derby, but city growth is based upon many other factors. Now it is a great railroad center, a tobacco market, home of famous distilleries, manufacturer of wood products, one of the most famous of which is the Louisville Slugger of baseball fame, and producer of many other commodities.

The growth of Cincinnati, the subregion's largest city, is also associated with transportation. It is a big-bend-river city located near the confluence of several tributary streams with the Ohio. It is still a great river port, but other conditions have stimulated growth. Though not as important as Chicago in meat packing, it continues to slaughter thousands of animals daily. More significant than meat packing, however, is the city's high rank in the manufacture of machine tools and many other products. A convergence of railroads gives advantages for a rail center.

In the decade 1945–55 there were 300 new manufacturing plants located in the Greater Cincinnati area; and of those already there, 930 completed expansion or improvement programs. Capital expenditures reached over a half billion dollars; local payrolls increased nearly 200 million dollars to take care of workers on 51,000 new jobs.

Cities in both the Lower Ohio and Upper Ohio valleys have many advantages for commerce and manufacturing. (*a*) Coal reserves in and near the valleys are enough to last 1,000 years at present rates of consumption. (*b*) Although local markets are limited, the valleys lie close to the great eastern market. (*c*) Labor supply is plentiful. (*d*) Land near the river is available at relatively low prices for industrial sites. (*e*) Local salt deposits are plentiful and have already attracted factories using chlorine and chlorine products. (*f*) Commodity shipments from port to port move cheaper by barge than by rail and easy availability of water transport keeps rail rates down.

Recently, aluminum manufacturing, attracted by nearby coal and market, has come into the Ohio Valley (Fig. 16). It is true that steam power, based on coal, costs about 4 mills per kilowatt hour against approximately 2 mills per kilowatt hour for hydroelectric power in plants along the Pacific Coast of British Columbia. But Ohio River aluminum plants are close to market and do not have the long haul necessary to bring Pacific Coast aluminum to the large areas of consumption.

Although there are many commercial and industrial advantages along the Ohio River there are also disadvantages.

Fig. 16. Manufacturing Is Increasing in the Ohio Valley. Aluminum plants are moving into the Ohio Valley to take advantage of cheap Appalachian coal, river transport, and relative proximity to the large Eastern market. (Courtesy Olin Mathieson Chemical Corporation.)

1. Locks and dams have been built to maintain a 9-foot depth; but these locks and dams were constructed many years ago with an expected capacity of 13,000,000 tons annually. In 1955, the river carried more than 65,000,000 tons by barge, which is more than the tonnage carried by any other United States river. Half of the tonnage consists of coal, one-fourth is petroleum, and the remainder includes iron and steel, sulfur, chemicals, and other commodities.

2. Many delays occur, especially in waiting to go through the locks.

3. Furthermore, many of the installations are becoming old and are in need of repair.

4. Most valley roads paralleling the river are either poor or mediocre in quality.

5. Tax systems leave much to be desired for industrial progress.

6. Labor leadership has lacked the vision for proper industrial expansion.

7. Many industrial plants have been built too close to the river to escape flood damage. Further comment on this latter disadvantage seems pertinent.

Sizable floods have swept down the Ohio and its branches for thousands of years, but flood damage has increased with the settling and development of the country during the last two centuries. Rivers out of their banks caused little or no loss to the Indian civilization because most villages were located above the lowlands.

In contrast, modern cities like Cincinnati and Louisville build industrial districts, railroad yards, highways, warehouses, and mills near the stream. When floods come, the river climbs into buildings, houses, and mills, many of which are ruined.

Man has done other things to increase flood damage. He has cut forests, and in many instances failed to replant them; his paved city streets and roads afford quick runoff for rain; he has plowed hillsides carelessly; smoke and fumes from home and factory have denuded hillsides; and large areas have been covered with buildings whose roofs are no check to runoff of rainfall.

Ohio River cities are not the only urban centers that suffer from floods, for the problem is a national one. In 1955, drenching rains from Hurricane Diane caused over a billion dollars damage to urban districts in New England, most of which lay too close to river banks. Local and national action for flood control is needed.

Landscapes: Changes and Similarities

The physical environment of the Central Farming Region, so well suited to modern farming, has supported several different cultural landscapes. For example the first white settlers to appear in Jasper County, Iowa, in 1843, found the Indian cultural landscape made up of villages built along the streams. Here, the environment was good for hunting, trapping, and fishing. Forests bordering the streams gave protection from cold winter winds and provided wood for fuel and wikiups. During the summer, fields of Indian corn grew well on the alluvial flood plains.

Some of the early pioneers also established homes along the streams, but many built log cabins on the interstream prairie land. On the wooded flood plains and the prairie uplands, the settlers fashioned a cultural landscape based upon subsistence agriculture, but their farming was more diversified than that of the Indians. Furthermore, the fields of corn, wheat, and oats, enclosed with rail fences, were larger than Indian grain fields. The early settlers' domestic animals, grazing on the native grasses, also furnished contrast to the Indian landscape. A few grist mills and small trading centers added further cultural diversity.

In 1865, when the first railroads were built and provided transport to distant markets, the landscape changed from that of subsistence farming to one of commercial agriculture. Several surplus crops and domestic animals were raised for shipment; and as time went on, the farms began to assume an aspect somewhat similar to Corn Belt farms of today.

However, there are many differences between the commercial farm of the late nineteenth and early twentieth centuries and that of the Jasper County farm in the 1950's. Crops now show more diversity, provide higher yields, and are produced with more agricultural machinery. Livestock has increased, is of better quality, and is better housed and fed. And there are other man-made features in the county besides farms; manufacturing, commerce, mining, power, and other industries make their separate contributions to the cultural pattern. Throughout the entire Central Farming Region, sequence occupancy has been somewhat similar to that of Jasper County.

Even though land use is generally similar throughout each of the Central Farming subregions, it should be stressed that differences do exist. It is true that most Corn Belt farms raise hogs, beef, and dairy cattle, and poultry. But there are farms that show most diversity in crop pattern whereas animal culture is dominated by a single type; on other farms there is diversity in animals and an emphasis on one field crop. Still other farms may be devoted entirely to raising grain or livestock.

In spite of the contrasts just described, there seems to be as much of a trend towards regional uniformity as towards regional differences. For example, hybrid corn is extending the boundaries of the Corn Belt farther north, west, and south. Although domestic animals suffer greater disease hazards on southern edges of the Central Farming Region than to the north, animal culture is increasing towards the south. Dairying is not confined to the dairy subregion, but is increasing both in the Corn Belt and in the

Tobacco and General Farming area.   Other examples of the trend toward regional uniformity may be cited.

Finally, it may be emphasized again and again that the Central Farming Region possesses one of the world's largest and richest food producing environments.   Some years ago, a book entitled *Farmers for Forty Centuries* was written about people on the plain of China's Hwang Ho.   If man uses proper conservation measures on the Central Farming Region, this area may be described truly in 6,000 A.D. by a book of the same name.

QUESTIONS, EXERCISES, AND PROBLEMS

1. Indicate factors making for unity in the Central Farming Region. What are the physical boundaries of the Corn Belt?   Point out relationships between the physical environment of the Corn Belt and the major crops grown.   Trace the farmer's activities through the seasons.   Why are farmers living far away from large grain markets likely to sell their corn on the hoof?   Tell of relationships between cattle grazing on the Great Plains and cattle feeding in the Corn Belt.   List the advantages of diversified farming.   Describe the cultural landscape of a Corn Belt farm.   Comment on Corn Belt manufacturing, minerals, and power resources.   Why is tourism a minor industry in the Corn Belt?

2. How have climate, land forms, and history encouraged dairying in the American Dairy Region?   Describe major features of a typical dairy farm.   Indicate the final products of dairying and tell how they are marketed.   Give similarities and differences between the American Dairy Region and the Corn Belt.

3. What are the major money crops of the Lower Ohio Valley?   Point out contrasts between land use in the lowlands and in the rimlands.   Read Edward Higbee, *American Agriculture,* pp. 286–294 and 306–310, for a description of farming in the Kentucky Bluegrass area and in the Nashville Basin.   What manufacturing developments are occurring in the Lower Ohio Valley?   What can be done to prevent disastrous flood losses?

4. Each of the following cities has about 100,000 people or more in its urban district: Cincinnati; Columbus; Davenport-Rock Island-Moline, sometimes known as the tri-city area; Dayton; Des Moines; Evansville; Fort Wayne; Indianapolis; Kansas City; Lincoln; Louisville; Madison; Minneapolis; Nashville; Omaha; Peoria; Rockford; St. Louis; St. Paul; Sioux City; South Bend; Springfield, Illinois; Topeka; Tulsa; Waterloo.   Name major activities encouraging the growth of each population center.

5. Locate the following cities and indicate the most important economic activities for each: Cedar Rapids, Dubuque, Frankfort, Lexington, La Crosse, Newton, Ottumwa, Sioux Falls, St. Joseph.

6. Identify the following: hybrid corn, McLean system, corn-hog ratio, nurse crop, crop rotation, ensilage, Driftless Area, Babcock test, Nashville Dome, Cincinnati Anticline, sinkholes, L-shaped groves, geographic variable.

7. What trends in the Central Farming Region and other farm areas of the United States are likely to weaken the political strength of the farm bloc?   Why is it that American farmers usually prosper greatly during war periods?   Suggest a solution for the problem of farm surpluses in the United States.   Why is it that population in Corn Belt small towns has been declining for years and promises to continue that trend?   Describe the distribution of population in the Central Farming Region.

SELECTED REFERENCES

Alexander, John W., "Manufacturing in the Rock River Valley, Location Factors," *Annals of the Association of American Geographers,* September 1950, pp. 237–253.

Alexander, John W., "Rockford, Illinois: A Medium-Sized Manufacturing City," *Annals of the Association of American Geographers,* March 1952, pp. 1–23.

Des Moines Register and Tribune, *Facts About Iowa,* July 1955.

Durand, Loyal, Jr., "The Migration of Cheese Manufacture in the United States," *Annals of the Association of American Geographers,* December 1952, pp. 263–282.

Garland, John H., editor, *The North American Midwest: A Regional Geography,* John Wiley and Sons, 1955.

Geographical Record, "A Swiss Colony in Wisconsin," *Geographical Review,* October 1956, pp. 568–569.

Harris, Chauncy D., "Agricultural Production in the United States: the Past Fifty Years and the Next," *Geographical Review,* April 1957, pp. 175–193.

Hewes, Leslie, "Some Features of Early Woodland and Prairie Settlement in a Central Iowa County," *Annals of the Association of American Geographers,* March 1950, pp. 40–57.

Hewes, Leslie, "The Northern Wet Prairie of the United States: Nature Sources of Information, and Extent," *Annals of the Association of American Geographers,* December 1951, pp. 307–323.

Hewes, Leslie, and Phillip E. Frandson, "Occupying the Wet Prairie: The Role of Artificial Drainage in Story County, Iowa," *Annals of the Association of American Geographers,* March 1952, pp. 24–50.

Johnson, Hildegard Binder, "The Location of German Immigrants in the Middle West," *Annals of the Association of American Geographers,* March 1951, pp. 1–41.

Roepke, Howard G., "Changing Patterns of Coal Production in the Eastern Interior Field," *Economic Geography,* July 1955, pp. 234–247.

Shaw, Earl B., "Fertilization: Route to a New Continent," *Journal of Geography,* October 1948, pp. 284–290.

Smith, Helen L., "Agricultural Land Use in Iowa," *Economic Geography,* July 1949, pp. 190–200.

Smith, Richard Austin, "The Boiling Ohio," *Fortune,* June 1956.

U. S. Department of Agriculture, "Family Farms in a Changing Economy," *Agriculture Information Bulletin 171,* March 1957.

U. S. Geological Survey, *Circular 293, Coal,* Jan. 1, 1953.

U. S. Geological Survey, *Fuel Reserves of the United States,* prepared for the Senate Committee on Interior and Insular Affairs, 1951.

U. S. Weather Bureau, "Weather and Alfalfa Seed," *Daily Weather Map,* Oct. 10, 1956, Washington, D. C.

U. S. Weather Bureau, "Weather and Corn," *Daily Weather Map,* Sept. 14, 1951, Washington, D. C.

Wallace, Henry A., and William L. Brown, *Corn and its Early Fathers,* Michigan State University Press, 1956.

Weaver, John C., "Changing Patterns of Cropland Use in the Middle West," *Economic Geography,* January 1954, pp. 1–47.

Weaver, John C., "Crop-Combination Regions in the Middle West," *Geographical Review,* April 1954, pp. 175–200.

Weaver, John C., Leverett P. Hoag, and Barbara L. Fenton, "Livestock Units and Combination Regions in the Middle West," *Economic Geography,* July 1956, pp. 237–259.

10 · The South

(Figure 1)

Evidence that the South is a region comes from many sources. Politicians and statesmen frequently speak of the Southern vote; a Southern dialect may draw attention to a person's regional origin when no other characteristic would identify him; the song beginning "Way down South in the Land of Cotton" suggests the South as a geographic area, together with one of its major commodities; slavery persisted in the South largely because regional climates favored the growth of cotton, sugar, rice, and other crops —crops for which slaves could be employed more profitably than in factories of the North; people go to the South in the winter to take advantage of the region's warmer climate. These and other conditions suggest the South's regional character.

However, the term *South* has many connotations; the areas included in the region now to be considered correspond generally to all of Fenneman's Atlantic Coastal Plain except the part of the embayed section lying north of the 35th parallel and the extreme northern part of the Mississippi alluvial plain. For a better understanding of the large region, it seems best to divide it into two subregions, (1) the Cotton Belt, and (2) the Humid Subtropical Coast.

The Cotton Belt

Boundaries. The Cotton Belt is not a continuous section of cotton growing land; on the contrary, it is a broad stretch of farming country, in parts of which cotton dominates the field pattern, and in parts of which cotton is either not grown at all or is of minor importance. It is important to remember this.

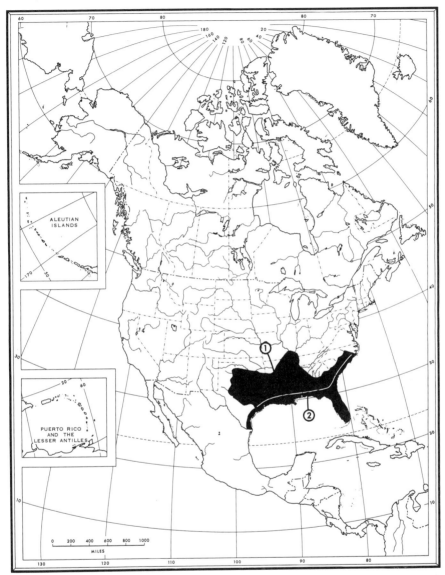

Fig. 1. The South. The South may be divided into two major subregions, (1) the Cotton Belt on the north and (2) the Humid Subtropical Coast on the south.

The ten states, large parts of which belong to the belt, are Alabama, Arkansas, the Carolinas, Georgia, Louisiana, Mississippi, Oklahoma, Tennessee, and Texas; small acreages of cotton appear in the Panhandle of Florida, southwest Kentucky, southeast Missouri, southeast Virginia, and even in southeast Illinois.

In general, the physical boundaries of the subregion are as follows: on the north, little cotton is grown poleward from the 200-day growing season or the 77° isotherm for the three summer months; the western border is a result of rainfall insufficient to grow cotton without irrigation; rainfall is also critical in the southern boundary, but here it is the occurrence of too much rainfall in the autumn when the white fluffy fiber bursts out of the boll.   Little cotton is grown south of the ten-inch rainfall line for the three autumn months; the ocean is the final limit of production on the east.

Climate (Fig. 2).   The entire Cotton Belt lies in the humid subtropical climate. Precipitation declines from east to west and from south to north. The maximum comes in summer from Tropical Atlantic and Tropical Gulf air, which holds large amounts of moisture and gives up much of it during heavy thundershowers.   The belt also receives rainfall during the cool season from the same air masses, but in lesser amounts than in summer.

No freezing temperatures occur for a period of 200 days or more. During the summer, sensible temperatures may be uncomfortable, with hot humid air present during both day and night; however, maximum temperatures seldom rise as high as those in the Corn Belt. Winter snow falls infrequently and accumulations are light; moreover, they are not likely to last beyond a 48-hour period. Besides the harmless cyclonic storms which move across the region in a general west-east direction, mainly during the winter period, tropical cyclones may bring winds of hurricane force during the autumn.   The lack of mountains across the Central Lowland in an east-west direction permits an occasional polar air mass to drift across the Cot-

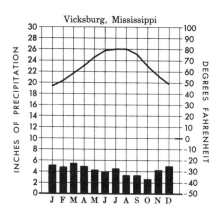
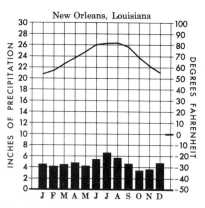

Fig. 2. Vicksburg, Mississippi (32° 20′ N., 90° 54′ W.; altitude 247 feet; mean annual temp. 65° F.; mean annual precip. 52 inches); New Orleans, Louisiana (30° 0′ N., 90° 5′ W.; altitude 51 feet; mean annual temp. 68.4° F.; mean annual precip. 56.5 inches). The climate of both stations is classified as humid subtropical, Ca; but notice that the autumn rainfall for New Orleans, on the Humid Subtropical Coast, is heavier than that of Vicksburg, in the Cotton Belt. Heavy autumn rainfall is damaging to the maturing cotton boll.

ton Belt from the north; such a winter storm may bring a day or two of low temperatures.

Surface Features. As previously indicated, the Atlantic Coastal Plain, except the northern portions, and the *South* are almost synonomous. The Cotton Belt, however, does include small portions of other physical regions. In part of the (*a*) Georgia-Carolina Piedmont, cotton is grown; Tennessee Valley fiber matures on parts of (*b*) the Ridge and Valley subregion and (*c*) the Appalachian Plateau; and (*d*) cotton grows on the southern Great Plains in western Oklahoma and Texas. All these areas show little if any departure from nearly level to gently rolling plains.

Soils. With the exception of the high plains of western Oklahoma and Texas, all soils are pedalfers of the red and yellow earth class. For several reasons they are not, in general, as fertile as Corn Belt soils.

1. Pleistocene glaciation did not reach south of St. Louis, and Cotton Belt soils received no contribution like that given to the Corn Belt by the Ice Age.

2. Natural vegetation in most of the Cotton Belt is forest; tall and short grasses covered much of the Corn Belt when early explorers reached the region. Grasses contribute more to natural soil fertility in middle latitudes than do forests.

3. Winters are cold enough in the Corn Belt to freeze the ground, a freezing which lessens soil leaching; temperatures in the Cotton Belt are relatively high almost the entire year and ground is frozen for but short periods, if at all.

4. The temperature of the precipitation averages higher in the Cotton Belt than in the Corn Belt, and the leaching power of warm water is greater than that of cold water; furthermore, danger from soil erosion is high where thunderstorm rainfall is most frequent, as it is in the Cotton Belt. Thus, many physical factors are less favorable for soil fertility in the Cotton Belt than in the Corn Belt. However, corn and cotton are both soil robbers, and commercial fertilizer is purchased in large quantities in both regions.

The Cotton Belt has an advantage over the Corn Belt in proximity to fertilizer. Florida phosphates are well located for supplying the eastern section of the Cotton Belt; and the western part lies near the large potash deposits of Carlsbad, New Mexico. No natural nitrates are available in the United States, but recent power developments in the South give encouragement for increasing supplies of synthetic nitrogen.

Vegetation. When the sixteenth century Spanish explorers, notably Ponce de Leon and De Soto, first penetrated the area now known as the Cotton Belt, they encountered a virgin forest of what is frequently called southern pine. Southern pine is sometimes called yellow pine because of the yellowish color of the wood, or hard pine because its wood is generally hard in comparison with that of other American trees which make up the softwood group. Southern pine is famous for its great strength in comparison to that of many other coniferous trees.

Interspersed among the conifers were hardwoods, such as oak and gum. Natural grasslands, probably a result of edaphic conditions, occupied parts of Alabama and Texas; but these prairies form a small per cent of the subregion's vegetation.

Conifers occur on sandy soils, which suggests that these trees can tolerate soil infertility better than the broadleafs. The latter are more likely to occupy the clay soils.

Cotton Growing Regions (Fig. 3). Several changes [1] have taken place in Cotton Belt crop patterns in the past few decades. Acreage reductions have obliterated the old Cotton Belt; but yield increases have offset acreage decreases and gross cotton income is about what it was 30 years ago. However, cotton is no longer the dominant source of farm income; 30 years ago it accounted for approximately 50 per cent of income, whereas in the early 1950's its percentage had dropped to 25.

Merle Prunty, Jr., lists seven cotton regions which now produce nearly two-thirds of the crop within counties representing less than 10 per cent of the land area of eleven cotton producing states. These include (*a*) the Georgia-Carolina inner coastal plain; (*b*) the Georgia-Carolina Piedmont; (*c*) the Tennessee Valley in northern Alabama; (*d*) the Mississippi alluvial valley; (*e*) the northern Black Waxy Prairies of Texas; (*f*) the south Texas coastal plains, a discontinuous region; and (*g*) the high plains of western Oklahoma and Texas. [2]

Farms in the seven regions are larger than the average for the South; soils are more fertile, and slope land is less; all these factors encourage mechanization and will continue to do so.

In each of the cotton regions, cotton occupies less than half the farm land; in fact, more land may be devoted to each of two or more other crops. The choice of crops, other than cotton, is not the same among the several regions. In the west Texas High Plains, a three-crop pattern includes cotton, grain sorghum, and hay forage for beef cattle. Beef cattle, and the growing of hay to feed them, are important in every one of the regions; but the third item of the crop pattern may be different. In the Mississippi alluvial valley, it is soybeans, except in central Arkansas where it is rice; in northern Alabama, it is corn or soybeans; the Piedmont produces winter small grains; the Georgia and south Carolina Inner Coastal Plain produce

---

[1] For a short historical survey of local and world changes affecting Cotton Belt economy, see Earl B. Shaw, *World Economic Geography,* John Wiley and Sons, 1955, pp. 395–399.

[2] Merle Prunty, Jr., "Recent Quantitative Changes in the Cotton Regions of Southeastern States," *Economic Geography,* July 1951.

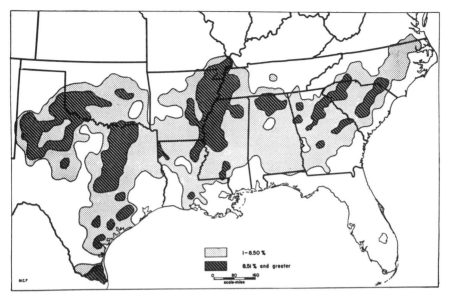

Fig. 3. Cotton Regions of the South. Today there are seven cotton regions: (1) The Georgia-Carolina inner coastal plain, (2) the Georgia-Carolina Piedmont, (3) the Tennessee Valley in northern Alabama, (4) the Mississippi alluvial valley, (5) the northern Black Waxy Prairies of Texas, (6) the south Texas coastal plains, a discontinuous region, and (7) the high plains of western Oklahoma and Texas. Percentages show relation of cotton acreage harvested to total land area. (Courtesy *Economic Geography* and Merle Prunty, Jr.)

corn and peanuts; but North Carolina produces tobacco on the same plain; and on the Black Waxy Prairies of Texas, corn, legume seed, and peanuts, along with cattle and cotton, are raised. Thus, instead of a similar crop pattern all over the Cotton Belt, different sections specialize in diversified crops that best suit their individual needs. Diversification is the rule, but field plans vary from place to place.

Although mechanization (Fig. 4) has increased rapidly, there is still much room for improvement. In 1950, at least 3,500,000 acres in Mississippi, Alabama, and Georgia alone were devoted to feeding work stock. If this land were in pasture it could support a million beef cows and their calves. Farm hands may criticize mechanization as taking jobs from the farm workers. In reality, farm machinery is increasing partly because there is not enough agricultural labor. Workers have gone to factory jobs in the North, or to manufacturing plants in the South.

Rotation systems capitalizing on legumes are utilized throughout the South to an extent not even remotely anticipated a quarter of a century ago. Research to produce still better cotton continues at experiment stations and commercial seed farms. Fertilizer—the South pays half of the country's fertilizer bill—farm specialization, and mechanization all point toward more

Fig. 4.   The Cotton Picking Machine.   At harvest time, machines move down the rows method-ically plucking cotton from bolls and blowing it into cage-like hoppers behind drivers.   Since mechanized agriculture needs fewer men, many workers are migrating to industrial centers. (Courtesy Standard Oil Company, New Jersey.)

intensive cultivation; and cotton yields are likely to rise rather than fall on the same or a lesser acreage.

Diversification: Crops Other Than Cotton.   Corn covers more acreage than cotton, but land use for other crops has lowered corn land almost 25 per cent since 1938.   However, per acre yields are increasing because better hybrids are used, with more carefully followed rotation schemes.   The South is still a grain and feed importer, so that local markets easily absorb the large percentage of the corn crop which is sold.   Hogging down corn is increasing each year.

In value, tobacco is second only to cotton, and its producing regions have been more or less stable in location for years.   Seaboard regions of southern Georgia, north-central Florida, the Carolinas, and south-central Virginia produce flue-cured cigarette tobacco; southern Maryland markets a fire-cured product of lower quality; and central and western Kentucky and north-central Tennessee grow the burley type.   (Not all of these areas are in the Cotton Belt.)   Strict government control of price and acreage, a man-made factor, has stabilized tobacco's regional boundaries more than those for any other crop.   It is even difficult for a newcomer to start raising tobacco unless he purchases land formerly under acreage and support prices; this is a good example of political regional determinism.

Peanuts are third in value among Southern cash crops, and the South has changed the former import status of the United States to that of an export one. Increased demand for vegetable oils, encouraged by two world wars, has been the dominant stimulant for the expansion. But the use of the crop for nuts, hay, hog feed, and for many other purposes has also increased demand. Southwest Georgia, southeast Alabama, and northern Florida produce more than half of the nation's peanuts.

War demand for vegetable oils is also a reason for more than doubling the 1940 soybean plantings. Soybeans cover large areas in the alluvial upper Mississippi Valley and in northeastern North Carolina. Acreages will likely increase in other parts of the South. Double-cropping is possible since growing season requirements are only 100 to 110 days.

A trend towards greater production of market vegetables occurs in several small specialized areas including, south-central Louisiana, northwestern Tennessee, southwest Mississippi, south-central Georgia, the central coast of South Carolina, northwest Arkansas, and northeast Tennessee-southwest Virginia. Factors favoring truck crop specialization include railroad agents interested in expanding freight cargo on constantly improving transport facilities; agricultural extension work, especially improving plant varieties; opportunities for sale in frozen and canned foods; and small farms with a large labor force.

Tree crops have been important for a long while and their production will probably expand. These include peaches, for which Georgia is famous, pecans, tung nuts, and many others. The South has many advantages for truck crops and tree crops. These include a long growing season and 30 to 60 inches of dependable precipitation; since crops can be planted earlier in the year than those farther north, Southern crops reach the early spring market sooner; tree crops prevent soil erosion, a fact of importance where precipitation is heavier than that in the North; labor is less costly than that of the North. Danger of glutted markets is the major factor limiting expansion in both tree and truck crops.

Diversification: Livestock. Production of livestock, especially through an expansion of grazing, represents one of the greatest changes in the South's land occupance in recent years. Many conditions have contributed to the growth of the beef industry. The boll weevil caused a reduction in cotton acreage; the economic depression of the 1930's, with resultant low cotton prices, caused abandonment of some cotton fields to grass; in 1933, the first cotton delimitation program brought acreage changes to feed and forage; soil conservation payments gave inducements for legumes, hay-forage, and permanent pasture; beef prices and labor shortages during World War II stimulated attention to cattle and grazing land; mechanization freed acreage, formerly used for raising feed, for work stock; high-yielding feed, forage, and grass crops have been introduced; farm education programs are increasing; urbanization, increase in manufacturing, diversification—all have increased the South's per capita income and demand for beef.

The South has many advantages for livestock. Climate minimizes shelter costs and year-round grazing reduces purchases of winter feed. Climate also makes advisable the use of beef breeds less susceptible to the high sun and tick hazards than cattle originating in the cooler climates. Cross breeding with India's Brahman bulls proceeds rapidly. The King Ranch in Texas has developed Santa Gertrudis cattle, the first truly American breed; animals used in the original cross were the English Durham or Shorthorn and the Indian Brahman or Zebu. Beef cattle production currently consists almost entirely of feeder cattle and those fattened on grass and hay. It seems clear that the South can probably raise such grades of beef at lower unit costs than can other large livestock areas.

Dairy animals also have increased, but they are not nearly so widespread as those grown for beef. Expansion has taken place mainly around urban centers, which provide a good local market. Winter grazing, ample water supply, and little need for winter shedding give regional advantages for dairying. The main drawback is the lack of a dairy breed which will retain high milk-producing qualities in the hot humid climate characteristic of most of the region during a long period of the year. In spite of recent growth, the industry does not satisfy regional demand; and the South seems destined to continue as a dairy products importer for some time to come.

Sheep raising is not likely to expand significantly except in the dry western portions or on the cool uplands. Like dairy cattle, sheep do not thrive in a hot humid climate.

With a diversification program including hybrid corn, increased peanut production, and larger acreages in clover, swine growing will likely increase and improve. Feed and shelter costs are lower than in the North, but these advantages are offset by greater susceptibility to diseases.

Sales of poultry [3] products have increased significantly. Much of the poultry is raised for the family table, but there are a few specialized areas, including northwestern Virginia, the Upper Chattahoochee Valley in Georgia, northwestern Arkansas, and the Guadalupe-San Marcos Valley of Texas. Poultry farms, like tobacco farms, are highly specialized and utilize a small acreage intensively. [4]

Forest Industries. Trees, one of the South's most valuable resources, cover more than half of the region. Exclusive of western Texas and Oklahoma, over 55 per cent is in forest—a little more than 30 per cent of the

[3] In 1957, Georgia's gross income from broilers was greater than that for any other agricultural commodity. The state shipped more than 261,000,000 birds to market—151,000,000 more than second-ranking Arkansas.

[4] Much of the material on crop diversification and livestock is based upon Merle Prunty, Jr., "Land Occupance in the Southeast: Landmarks and Forecast," *Geographical Review*, July 1952.

national total. About 40 per cent of the nation's commercial forest is in the South, and half of the country's privately owned commercial forest. Public ownership is less significant than elsewhere; roughly 86 per cent of the forests are privately owned, and about 40 per cent are on farms. There are some 1,650,000 small-forest landowners, whose holdings average 75 forested acres. Pulp and paper companies own vast tracts of forest land, especially on the coastal plain east of the Mississippi.

Percentage of area in forest in certain parts of the South is so great that, by almost any reasonable measure, they must be considered forest regions. One region occupies most of the Appalachian Highland from northern Georgia through South and North Carolina and eastern Tennessee to northwestern Virginia. Another extends from southeastern South Carolina through most of southeastern and south-central Georgia and encompasses Florida north of the peninsula. This very large region, site of the naval stores industry, contains county after county with more than 90 per cent of the area in forest. Southwestern Alabama and southern Mississippi constitute a third region. Another extends from central Louisiana into eastern Texas (this region includes nearly half of Louisiana). Southern Arkansas is another, as are the Ouachita and Boston Mountains in Oklahoma and Arkansas. Throughout these regions, roughly 80 per cent of total area is in forest. Smaller areal proportions characterize the Cumberland Plateau forest of Alabama, Tennessee, and Kentucky.

Cutting in the South has gone through the same three general stages that have characterized action in all of the country's forests. When Europeans first came to what is now the Cotton Belt, forest was something to get rid of to make way for farms, and forest mining was the manner of exploitation. Next, the forest miners moved in to exploit the trees for various commercial purposes, with little thought of any conservation. Within the last few decades, when forest cutting exceeded tree growth, the South and the whole nation awakened to what is happening to the country's forests. Even in 1944, total drain on the South's forests exceeded growth by at least 2 per cent; that year, Southern forests were producing roughly 42 per cent of the nation's lumber and timber, 53 per cent of its fuel wood, 44 per cent of its pulp; and virtually all of its naval stores.

In recent years, something is being done about forest depletion. Planting is taking place on areas with inadequate stands. Georgia alone set out 45 million seedlings in 1950, and even these failed to meet the demand. Most trees are machine planted; and, as machines have become more numerous, seedling demand has increased rapidly.

One of the greatest changes in Southern forest utilization of recent years is reflected in construction of new pulp and paper mills. By 1951 there were at least 670 paper and paperboard plants in the South, including a mammoth newsprint plant at Childersburg, Alabama. In 1950, these plants produced gross volume worth more than $2,000,000,000; within the last five months of 1951, construction of a half dozen large new plants was announced.

Manufacturing (Fig. 16, Chapter 8).   Forests are one of several raw materials utilized for various types of manufacturing.   Besides newsprint plants at Lufkin, Texas, and Childersburg, Alabama, based upon southern pine, other plants use Southern hardwoods for many purposes, such as rayon-pulp made by International Paper Corporation at Natchez, Mississippi.   Rome, Georgia, has a multimillion dollar paperboard plant.   Plywood and furniture are made at Memphis, where even the plywood waste is saved to make cattle feed and alcohol.   Pensacola, Florida, boasts a mill utilizing waste liquors from paper pulp, liquors that formerly polluted Southern streams.   Tall oil, a material extracted from paper-mill waste liquors, provides a base used in the chemical industries.   Tall oil, furniture, plywood, lumber, newsprint, pulp, kraft paper, naval stores, cellulose for synthetic fibers, these and many other products come from the South's fast-growing trees.

Agriculture also provides raw materials for Southern manufacturing. Fruits and vegetables, particularly on the Gulf Coast and the Florida peninsula, support canning and frozen food factories.   One frozen food invention, the deep freeze, has not been good for Southern fruit and vegetable industries.   Many people in higher latitudes store surplus summer production by this method and lower their purchases from the South.   The large increase in Southern livestock has encouraged packing plants at urban centers, such as Atlanta.   One of the best known products of the South, cotton, contributes much to regional manufacturing.   Nearly a thousand mills, each valued at a million dollars or over, process the cotton fiber and that of its synthetic competitors, competitors which have an agricultural or forestry base.

Other factories change cotton seed into food for man and feed for livestock.   Soybeans and peanuts, like cotton seed, provide vegetable oils and a long list of manufactured articles.   Cigarette factories process locally grown tobacco in Virginia and North Carolina, and cigarette paper is produced from forests on the Blue Ridge Mountains in North Carolina's Ecusta plant.

Minerals and power resources combine with agriculture and forestry to support Southern manufacturing.   At the border of the Piedmont and the Coastal Plain, streams provide hydroelectric power.   Petroleum and natural gas not only provide fuel easy to use and transport, but they also contribute by-products for a growing chemical industry.   Alabama leads the South in coal resources, and uses fuel with nearby iron and limestone to manufacture about 5,000,000 tons of steel annually.

As far as is known, the South has no large resources of uranium, but chemical companies have discovered a uranium by-product in processing large quantities of phosphates from Florida and Tennessee.   A huge atomic energy factory has been built on the Savannah River near Aiken, South Carolina. This billion dollar project is in addition to the Oak Ridge, Tennessee, development.

Southern salt domes attract chemical companies; at McIntosh, Alabama, the Mathieson Chemical Company invested several million dollars in a soda-chlorine factory, powered by Alabama Power's multimillion dollar steam plant nearby. Southern agriculture benefits from the anhydrous-ammonia and ammonium-nitrate plants at Yazoo City, Mississippi. Here is an example of man taking minerals from the air when none are available in the ground. Before the early 1950 Mexican discoveries, half of the world's sulfur came from Louisiana's Gulf Coast. Although most of United States bauxite, base for aluminum, is imported, the South accounts for the entire home production, 95 per cent from Arkansas. Reynolds Metals Corporation has a large aluminum plant in the state, and Aluminum Company of America has expanded its factories in Texas. Other minerals, utilized in manufacturing, include fine clay from Georgia and South Carolina, and North Carolina's mica and feldspar.

Much Northern as well as Southern capital has been invested in Southern industry. Labor is not only cheap, but there are also ample workers available. The increasing size of farms, greater emphasis on the grazing industries, and agricultural mechanization are three of several factors that release farm workers to urban centers.

The attitude of state and local governments is another factor attracting manufacturing to the South. Companies have been given factory sites, aid in building factories, tax concessions, laws favorable to industrial expansion, and other government contributions encouraging investment (Fig. 5).

Man gave another aid to Southern industry in the 1940's when freight rates were placed on a more favorable basis. For a long while, lower Southern labor costs and other industrial advantages were offset by higher freight charges. A Southern manufacturer might be no farther from a potential market in Ohio, for example, that New England competition, but he would pay higher carrying charges. If he wished to supply Southern markets, he also discovered his New England competitor receiving lower freight rates. This advantage of the North and East over the South and West was changed by an Interstate Commerce Commission ruling starting in 1945.

Man has also improved Southern transport by building modern highways; straightening and deepening waterways, especially the Mississippi and the Tennessee; expanding rail routes and adding better rail equipment; and finally by greatly improving air transport. Through the sound national policy of airplane factory dispersal, the South has gained several aircraft manufacturing plants. Fort Worth and Grand Prairie, Texas, produce planes in large numbers.

Small Georgia Town

POPULATION 1500

OFFERS industrial sites plus financial assistance to business executives
who desire to locate in a small Georgia
town with ample supply of intelligent,
willing workers. No unions.

ADEQUATE power and water, natural gas, main line railroads and highways to all points. New motels.

CONFIDENTIAL inquiries invited
and full information will be furnished.
Write to Industry,

Fig. 5. The South Bids for Industry. The above advertisement appeared in a New York paper for Feb. 28, 1956.

The increased number of factories in the South serves as a magnet to draw more factories. Laborers get more spending money, which creates an expanding market demanding more processed goods. Northern manufacturers, such as those producing automobiles, decided it was cheaper to supply the Southern market from branch plants than to feed the market by freight from the parent factories. Although branch factories are moving to large urban centers, such as Atlanta, many Southern factories locate in small towns which offer the social advantage of planned cities. Moreover, the newness of equipment and factories in most Southern industrial plants somewhat overbalances the advantages of an early start enjoyed by Northern competition.

In conclusion, it may be said that in the early 1950's industrial expansion in the South was rising at a rate nearly 50 per cent higher than the national average. Only in one Southern state, Arkansas, was industry increasing at a rate slightly less than the national average. In 1953, three Southern states, Georgia, North Carolina, and Texas, were among fifteen states leading in factory employment. Industry has definitely drawn ahead of agriculture as a major source of income in the South;[5] but both show great potential as a result of physical and man-made environmental factors.

The Humid Subtropical Coast

Location and Boundaries. The Humid Subtropical Coast includes narrow seaward sections of Fenneman's Atlantic Coastal Plain in southeastern North Carolina, eastern South Carolina, southeastern Georgia, all of Florida, the panhandles of Alabama and Mississippi, southern Louisiana, and southeastern Texas, including the lower Rio Grande Valley. In no section does the subregion extend inland as much as 100 miles.

The subregion is bounded on the northeast by the Middle Atlantic Coastal Plain, on the southwest by the southern Great Plains, on the north by the Cotton Belt or the zone of less than 10 inches of autumn rainfall, and on the east and south by the Atlantic Ocean and the Gulf of Mexico.

Surface Features and Climate (Fig. 2). The low-lying plains topography in no place rises more than 500 feet above sea level, and drainage is a major problem. In fact, over half of the 75,000,000 acres of ill-drained land within the United States lies in this subregion. There are tidal marshes, lagoons, barrier beaches, deltas, lakes, bays, and sounds. A wide continental shelf borders almost the entire area.

Precipitation ranges from more than 60 inches in southeast and northwest Florida, southeast Louisiana, and the panhandles of Mississippi and Alabama to approximately 20 inches in the Lower Rio Grande. In most of the subregion, the growing season lasts nine months or over; and in southern Florida an entire year may elapse without frost temperatures. However, Key West is the only station in the United States without a frost record. Latitude and marine location are important influences upon temperatures. Cyclonic storms, both the normal sequence of the westerly wind belt and the tropical hurricanes, influence amount and distribution of precipitation. The rainfall shows an autumn maximum resulting from hurricanes and, generally, a cool season minimum. More thunderstorms occur than in any other section of the United States.

[5] Although the subregion under study is the Cotton Belt, the author has referred to the entire region, the South, in many places. He has also placed a broad interpretation of the South in some cases and extended it into border regions already described.

Vegetation and Soils. Great diversity characterizes the vegetation. On the southern tip of Florida are almost impenetrable mangrove forests; a climax forest of tupelo-gum-bald cypress appears along many streams; broad interstream sections support various species of southern pine; in south-central Florida, as well as on coastal sections of Texas, Georgia, South Carolina, and Louisiana, one may see nothing but broom grass, water grass, marsh grass, and saw grass; a climax of oak-pine occurs in small sections of the subregion. Drainage conditions exert an important influence upon vegetation response (Fig. 6).

The red and yellow pedalfer soils show several differences, resulting largely from vegetation cover, topographic situation, and stream and shore deposition. Along barrier beaches, sands are dominant; in ill-drained sections, bog or muck soils may occur; in deltas, such as that of the Mississippi, a layering of topset, foreset, and bottomset beds occurs. In general, soils show considerable leaching and a relatively low humus content. Successful cropping necessitates large amounts of fertilizer.

Agriculture. Farming shows similarities to and differences from that of the Cotton Belt. A major difference is the small amount of land devoted to cotton; another appears in the large production of rice; still another is the greater emphasis upon truck crops; and finally, a decided

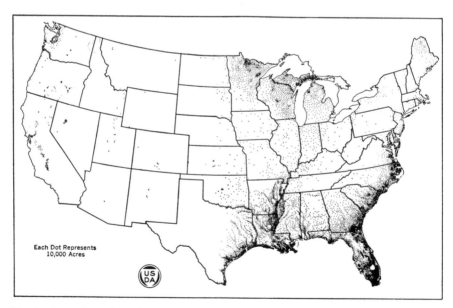

Fig. 6. Approximate Location of Drainable Wet Lands. Many of the undrained lands of the United States lie in the South. The physically drainable area in the United States totals 91,000,000 acres, but it is estimated that only approximately 75,000,000 acres can be drained at a cost that would justify their use for cultivated crops. (Courtesy U. S. Department of Agriculture.)

contrast occurs in the stress upon cane sugar and citrus fruits, which are entirely absent from the Cotton Belt. Probably the greatest similarity appears in the growth of beef cattle and in the trend toward agricultural diversification in both subregions.

Rice (Fig. 7). The production of rice is dependent upon (*a*) high temperatures, especially relatively high mean temperatures during the growing season; (*b*) a dependable supply of fresh water for irrigation; natural rainfall is not enough to mature the rice crop and water is pumped from streams and from wells; (*c*) soils that hold water well because of the tight subsoil through which loss by seepage is small; and (*d*) comparatively level land. These conditions prevail in much of the subregion, especially in southwestern Louisiana and southeastern Texas.

World War II caused a dislocation in world rice economy. The drop in production that occurred in Asia's occupied countries was especially serious for importing lands. At the same time, factors that caused shortages and attendant high prices stimulated production in all countries outside combat areas where physical environment favored rice. In the Western Hemisphere, rice production nearly doubled. In 1947, rice acreage in the United States was twice that for 1940, and the country was the second largest exporter. In 1951, the United States ranked third among rice exporters and shipped 10 per cent of the world total, a larger per cent than that of Indochina.

Rice acreage could double easily if adequate markets were available; but without war-stimulated demand, rice production may decline. United States consumption of about 6 pounds per capita is far less than Oriental consumption. In Japan, for example, the people consume about 300 pounds per capita.

Sugar cane. Two major areas, southern Louisiana and the Florida Everglades, produce sugar cane, a member of the grass family which grows best in a hot humid climate with a twelve-month growing season. Neither area has such a climate, but both produce crops in spite of the frost hazard; a great help is the protective tariff on the big United States market, the largest sugar market in the world.

The Florida peninsula has a climatic advantage over Louisiana. A water boundary on three sides gives a strong marine influence, a great aid in keeping frost away. Moreover, the sugar lands surround Lake Okeechobee, which gives further help in sustaining above-freezing temperatures during the cool season. Louisiana, with a water boundary on only one side and a slightly higher latitude, is more susceptible to frost. By planting cold-resistant varieties, Florida may be able to raise sugar cane for several seasons without replanting, a practice known as ratoon cropping. Louisiana must replant each year. Land is farmed in large acreages, and machines are used to prepare the fields for planting, and to plant, weed, and cut the cane.

Fig. 7. Rice Growing in the South. Production costs on this Texas rice field are less than those of the densely populated Asiatic rice country because American rice growing is almost entirely mechanized. The only hand labor required on this immense rice farm is the breaking of levees with a shovel to permit water drainage. Ground is prepared with tractors, fermented seed is sown from airplanes, and harvesting is done with combines. (Courtesy Beaumont Chamber of Commerce.)

By-products of sugar refining include molasses and the crushed cane stalk, with juice removed, called bagasse. Molasses may be sold for cattle feed or processed for industrial alcohol. Bagasse provides insulating material, pulp, paper, and other items.

Citrus Fruit. Two major producing areas account for almost the entire citrus production, central Florida and the Lower Rio Grande Valley of Texas. Just as Florida has a climatic advantage over Louisiana in the growth of sugar cane, so does the state possess similar advantage over Texas in growing oranges and grapefruit. Nevertheless, Florida lacks the assurance of a frost-free season essential for greatest safety in the citrus industry. In the winter of 1894–95, the Big Freeze killed practically every orange tree in the state, with a total loss of $75,000,000. The 1940 and 1957 freezes brought smaller losses, possibly $20,000,000 each, largely because man has made better adjustments to the physical environment. Instead of selecting flat lands, orange groves are set out in hilly lake-dotted areas, utilizing the moderating effects of water bodies and favorable air drainage. Since serious damage may be caused by the loss of heat due to out-going radiation, fires are started among the fruit trees. The firing of fat pinewood or smudge pots creates a smoke screen, which cuts down earth radiation and heats the grove. Huge fans for stirring the lower air also may be used. Government frost warning stations give advance notice of frost.

Another climatic hazard to Florida and the rest of the Gulf Coast citrus production is the too-frequent occurrence of tropical hurricanes; and in contrast to helpful adjustments that man can make in protecting crops from cold waves, little can be done to minimize tree crop losses when the hurricane strikes. Lack of a hurricane hazard is one advantage that California citrus growers have over Florida producers. But Florida is near the great Eastern market.

Tung Oil. The tung tree came to the United States by way of China, where, according to Marco Polo, the oil from the nuts was used for calking boats and ships. Here in the United States, the quick-drying oil encourages use in paints, varnish, enamel, and lacquer. It also serves in the manufacture of linoleum, oilcloth, printing inks, brake linings, etc.

The deciduous tung tree is extremely sensitive to the physical environment; it requires a rest period of about three months between November maturing of the fruit and March budding. If frost touches the bud or unripe fruit, the results may be damaging to crop and tree. Trees do well on land with gentle slopes providing air and water drainage. Soils that are favorable show good depth, medium texture, both surface and subsoil, and good moisture relations. For high crop yields, commercial fertilizer is advisable. With these critical requirements the area of tung production lies in a narrow belt 50 to 100 miles north of the Gulf of Mexico (Fig. 8).

Mississippi leads in growing tung nuts, with 85,000 tons out of a national total of approximately 150,000 tons in 1953. The value of Mississippi's production was approximately $6,000,000.

Truck Crops. In the marketing of fruits and vegetables it is a well-known fact that producers who reach the market first with their produce are likely to profit most. The Humid Subtropical Coast, and especially Florida, has freedom from frost earliest in the year of any section in the country, except possibly the Southwest. With fear of frost gone early in the year, crops can be planted early, they will mature early, and they can be moved on to the early market. With plantings made at the same time in Florida and California, Florida has an earlier marketing opportunity through proximity to the great Eastern market.

Fruit and vegetable growing may show specialization on one or two crops in one area. There are soil advantages, or climatic advantages, or topographic advantages, or all of them on the physical side; and there may be better opportunities for cooperation in the use of labor, machinery, transport, or other industry factors on the cultural or man-made side. Examples of specialization within the Humid Subtropical Coast are many: celery in Sanford, Florida; strawberries around Plant City, Florida; early potatoes near Hastings, Florida, etc.

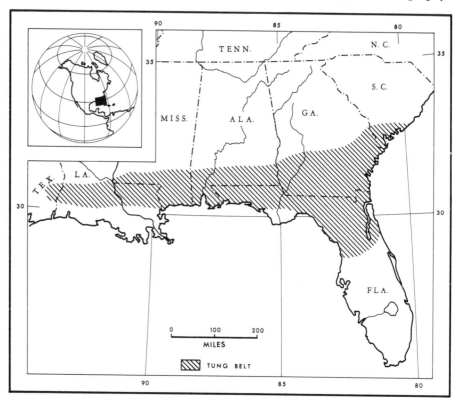

Fig. 8. The Tung Belt. The belt is located in the southern part of the Coastal Plain where mild climate, abundant rainfall, and gently sloping land favor the tung tree. (Drawn after map *Better Crops With Plant Food,* April 1954.)

In most producing areas, cooperation in packing, advertising, marketing, and other phases of the industry is well developed; growers know that cooperative organizations have definite advantages. One great problem faces cooperatives as well as individual growers, the danger of a glutted market. Expansion possibilities are great, but the local Southern markets are limited, and the larger Eastern markets are easily flooded. Canning and freezing have helped remove surpluses, but they fail to remove them completely.

Beef Cattle. The beef cattle industry is expanding on the Humid Subtropical Coast just as it is in the Cotton Belt. Florida, for example, had 1,392,000 animals in 1950, 82 per cent more than in 1940. Cattle have become so numerous that they pose a road hazard to automobiles; and the state, in 1950, passed a law forcing the fencing of cattle ranches. As in the Cotton Belt, considerable emphasis is placed upon feeder cattle, and large numbers move north to the feed lots. However, many of the big packers have local processing plants.

In spite of rapid expansion, cattle raising in Florida, as well as in the entire region, faces many problems. Dipping is advisable to guard against the tick that brings Texas fever. Cattle with Brahman blood are almost a necessity to gain immunity from the high sun and certain diseases and pests peculiar to hot climates. The Brahman or Zebu has sweat glands which better enable it to endure the excessive heat of the long summers.

Winter pasture grasses are vital to the development of the cattle industry, because winter range and the release from heavy winter feeding give the region a great advantage over most other cattle areas. Efforts are being made to develop grasses and legumes to provide these pastures. Such feed, supplemented by sweet potato vine silage, oats, rye, corn, and even root crops such as sweet potatoes, dasheens, and cassava may answer the winter feed problem.

Naval Stores. A name that no longer possesses its original meaning is still applied to one of the South's most important forest products. In early colonial days, wooden ships of the British navy were calked with resinous gum from southern pine; pitch was used for the seams, and tar was applied to the rigging. Tar and pitch were called *naval stores*. For the most part, naval stores are no longer finished commodities, but basic raw materials for hundreds of industrial products. Turpentine, the distilled essence of the gum, is used chiefly as a thinner for paints and in chemicals and pharmaceuticals. Rosin, the bulk residue after distillation, goes into paper, paint, rubber, and many synthetic resins (rosin is the product of the tree, resin is the refined chemical). In recent years, the distillation of wood turpentine and rosin from old stumps (Fig. 9) and the by-products of sulfate woodpulp (as distinct from gum) have accounted for half of the annual United States production of some 33,000,000 gallons of turpentine and 1,000,000,000 pounds of rosin.

Modernization of the naval stores industry came in the 1930's. In 1938, the United States Department of Agriculture Naval Stores Station in Olustee, Florida, started operations in a new steam distillery that increased and improved the rosin yield from crude gum. Processors banded together to build big central stills, using the Olustee method. By 1950, 29 big steam stills had been built, most of them in Georgia, which produces 75 per cent of the United States gum naval stores. Thousands of small landowners who had never had capital to build their own stills were able to sell crude gum for cash; and as turpentine farmers they receive subsidies when prices fall below parity.

Besides the use of steam stills, there have been other improvements in naval stores industry, such as stimulating the flow of gum by applying sul-

Fig. 9. Loading Stumps for Naval Stores. Stumps are being transferred from the truck to a railroad car which will carry them to the processing plant. (Courtesy of the Hercules Powder Company.)

furic acid to the freshly chipped streak on the tree face. With rising labor costs, the producer can survive only by making more gum with less work. Long-range hopes are in scientific reforestation; carefully spaced plantations of high-yielding trees enhance the possibility of mechanization and greatly increase the yield per acre.

Trapping. We might expect trapping to take place in a forest environment, and in most places it does. However, Louisiana sells more furs than any state in the Union, and practically all of them come from the millions of acres of salt marsh lands along the southern coast.

Louisiana trapping is a migratory occupation. Shortly before December 1, many thousands of trappers leave their little farms in the interior or their fishing villages along the coast and move into the salt marsh country. The whole family makes the journey to live in shacks leased from the fur buyer until February 15, the close of the trapping season. During the season, several million skins will be taken by the migrants, with a value of 5 to 10 million dollars. Most of the skins will be muskrat, but trappers also catch otter, mink, skunk, raccoon, and nutria.

All members of the family help in the trapping economy; men remove the pelts, but women may stretch them on wire frames to dry. Skins are collected by local buyers who forward them to the dealer's warehouse in Houma or New Orleans. Here they are sorted, baled, put into cold storage and eventually sent to New York for fabrication. At the end of the season, trappers load their families, their bedding, and furniture and other equipment on dingy fishing boats and pull out of camp for home. After repaying the fur buyer for advances made at the beginning of the season—money supplied for food, rent, and supplies—the migratory trapper may have a few hundred or more than a thousand dollars for the 2½ months work.

Power and Minerals. Certain power and mineral resources of the Humid Subtropical Coast are large in amount and possess some unique methods of exploitation. Immense reserves of petroleum and natural gas (Figs. 10, 11) are found not only in coastal sections but also in the continental shelf. The Fuels Branch, United States Geological Survey, estimated (in 1953) potential reserves on the entire continental shelf of Texas and Louisiana as 13 billion barrels of oil and 65 trillion cubic feet of gas. Drilling for offshore oil (Fig. 12) and gas has been going on for years and several wells are already producing. In 1955, a large percentage of the drilling was

Fig. 10. Laying Pipe for the Transport of Natural Gas. Natural gas is gaining more rapidly than any other major source of heat and power in the United States. Gas is piped hundreds of miles from the South for use in the North. (Courtesy Consolidated Natural Gas.)

Fig. 11. Geophysical Prospecting Causes Waterspouts. Waterspouts dance as a multiple seismic shot, patterned for more accurate readings of underground conditions, is set off in the midst of the Florida Everglades. Throughout the Gulf Coast, prospecting for oil is going on. (Courtesy Standard Oil Company, New Jersey.)

taking place off the Louisiana coast; prospecting off Texas shores is said to be more difficult because of high winds and rough seas.

A political controversy has been raging for nearly a decade between exponents of states' rights for offshore oil and those who believe in federal control. It is a well-known fact that a very strong reason for Eisenhower winning the 1952 Texas vote involved his belief in states' rights for tidewater petroleum. However, with drilling operations extending farther and farther from the three-mile limit, both states' rights and federal factions may share in royalties. In 1957, the issue was still clouded because Texas and Louisiana claim control beyond the generally accepted three-mile limit.

It has been said that an industrial civilization can be measured by its per capita consumption of sulfuric acid; and most of the 4,000,000 tons of sulfur consumed in the United States in 1950 was used in sulfuric acid. Sulfur appears in a newspaper, in the ink used to print the paper, in the steel of a motor car, as well as in its tires, paint, and fuel. Sulfur goes into synthetic textiles, food, the fertilizer which helps grow the food, and the compounds needed to process and package the food. It is used in soap, in drugs, in motion picture film, and in literally hundreds of articles useful for everyday living.

Most United States sulfur reserves (Fig. 13) lie along the Gulf Coast, and the means of exploitation is closely related to the occurrence of the mineral. It occurs in the cap rock overlying salt domes at depths varying from

Fig. 12. Oil Derricks on the Gulf Coast Continental Shelf. Oil exploration in the Gulf of Mexico has been going on for years. It set off the tidelands oil controversy that became an issue of the 1952 presidential election campaign. (Courtesy Standard Oil Company, California.)

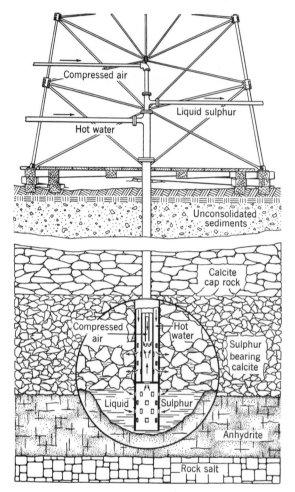

Fig. 13. Sulfur Well in the South. For complete description of Gulf Coast sulfur production see *Modern Sulphur Mining*, 1952, a 32-page booklet with map prepared by Texas Gulf Sulphur Company, 75 East 45th Street, New York, N. Y. (Courtesy Texas Gulf Sulphur Company.)

300 to 2,000 feet, and is brought to the surface by the Frasch process, named for the man who invented it in 1891. The method consists in melting the sulfur while it is underground by pumping heated water to it, and then raising the melted sulfur to the surface where it solidifies in vats. This takes advantage of the fairly low melting point of sulfur, about 240°F.

Another mineral, contributed by sea water, along the Gulf Coast, is magnesium. At Freeport, Texas, for example, Dow Chemical Company separates the four parts of magnesium chloride contained in each thousand parts of sea water. The process is accomplished by letting sea water stand in huge settling tanks containing crushed calcined oyster shells, available along the coast, and other materials useful in chemical separation. Later the magnesium chloride is changed to metallic magnesium by treatment in electrolytic cells.

Open-pit mining is employed to exploit the huge Gulf Coast phosphate deposits (Fig. 14) in Florida. Phosphate is a great advantage to the entire South, whose soils need a great deal of fertilizer for successful crop production.

Avery Island, a low hill rising out of the marsh of southern Louisiana, is an example of another mineral location; for the hill is a thin veneer of earth covering an underground base of solid salt, two miles in diameter and extending to depths of 2,200 feet. The island is an example of a salt dome, a buried plug of salt with roots far beneath the earth's surface.

Salt was discovered here in 1791. It became important during the Civil War at the time of the Union blockade, when 200 to 300 horsedrawn wagons were constantly lined up at the island waiting for 600 men to quarry and bag the salt. Today, salt is recovered at the rate of 100,000 tons a year by the process of shaft mining. International Salt Company has sunk a shaft through the earthen cap of Avery Island to a depth of over 500 feet, where it is possible to wander for an hour in the underground vaults of salt. At the present rate of consumption, it is estimated that all the salt mines of Louisiana and Texas are good for some 300,000 years.

Fig. 14. Florida Phosphate. Open-pit mining methods are used since phosphate occurs at or near the surface. (Courtesy International Minerals and Chemicals Corporation.)

Petroleum, natural gas, sulfur, magnesium, phosphates, and salt are power and mineral resources that give the Gulf Coast a strong support for a prosperous economy.

Manufacturing. Petroleum and natural gas provide useful power resources for manufacturing. A good example is Aluminum Company of America, which was one of the first companies in the world to use natural gas to make aluminum, at Point Comfort, Texas.

The history of natural gas utilization may be of interest. Thirty centuries ago the Chinese drilled for gas, using bamboo drill pipe and hand-wrought iron drill heads. Even a few years ago it was a common sight in the oil fields of the Southwest to see gas fires wasting gas 24 hours a day from the tops of pipes stuck into the ground. In the 1920's the practical use of natural gas came into its own, and today, it provides the fuel for approximately one-fourth of the nation's energy. A man-made factor encouraged this change. New kinds of steel pipe were invented—seamless and welded —which carry the fuel thousands of miles under pressure with a minimum danger of developing leaks. Now a national network of pipe stretches more than 300,000 miles, a much longer distance than that covered by the country's rail lines.

Petroleum has been used for power a long time; and today by-products from oil provide the materials for one of the Gulf Coast's fastest growing industries, the processing of petrochemicals.

The ordinary layman may be unfamiliar with petrochemicals by name. Who but a chemist would know that polybutene is a golden colored sticky material resembling honey, which makes adhesive tape stick and assures dependable electric service; that phthalic anhydride's white slivers, resembling shredded coconut, may be used in paints; that detergent slurry, looking like sour cream, will remove the ring around the bath tub and make glassware shine even in hard water. Natural gas also has uses other than that for power; at Decatur, Alabama, Chemstrand Corporation is making synthetic fibers from natural gas.

The Gulf Coast has no steel factories comparable to those at Birmingham, Alabama; but Houston's tidewater plants had a capacity for manufacturing over a million tons of ingots and steel castings in 1954.

Agriculture as well as mining contributes raw materials for Gulf Coast factories; sugar cane centrals change cane into refined sugar; and rice mills husk the rice as it comes from the fields and start it on its way toward the consumer's table in the form of polished rice, rice flour, rice cereals, etc. Citrus fruits are canned and frozen, and former waste products are now utilized in many ways. Minute Maid Corporation has a plant at Plymouth, Florida, which makes dehydrated pulp for cattle feed. The industry yearly produces over 200,000 tons of cattle feed, 75,000 tons of molasses, a million pounds of essential oils, and other by-products.

Contributions of other Gulf Coast raw materials for manufacturing could be mentioned. Livestock and forests have been described already. Comment also has been made on the mobility of capital and labor as it aids Southern manufacturing, on the correction of inequities on rail rates unfavorable to the South, on the expansion of the relatively small Southern market; and on the favorable attitude of Southern state and local governments toward manufacturing enterprises. All these and other factors provide a healthy base for Gulf Coast manufacturing.

Commerce. Gulf Coast manufacturing and the entire regional economy has received an assist from commerce. Advantages include (*a*) control of the mouth of the Mississippi, which taps a rich interior; (*b*) a location at the southern gateway of North America, a gateway that leads north, northeast, and northwest between the Appalachian and Rocky Mountains over plains topography favorable for rail and road building; (*c*) proximity to Latin America, a region largely in the raw materials stage of industrial development. Use of this proximity has become easier with the completion of the Panama Canal, which shortens distances to west coast South American countries.

Several Southern ports stand high among American trading centers. New Orleans, at the mouth of the great water artery, which drains one of the world's most productive hinterlands, could not help being a great port. In 1950, 70 per cent of the city's business dollars came from trade passing through the port. In the same year, New Orleans was second only to New York in dollar value of cargoes handled; it lead in imports of raw sugar and molasses and stood second in coffee, bananas, jute, and sisal; and fourth in bauxite, which goes to busy aluminum factories. In spite of competition from Galveston and Houston, the city is still a large exporter of cotton, leads in flour export, stands second in shipments of farm machinery, fourth in trucks and buses, and fifth in wheat. Each year, river pilots guide approximately 3,000 ships flying 30 national flags 110 miles up the winding Mississippi to where they may tie up along 4 miles of New Orleans docks. In 1947, shortly after New York received Congressional approval for a foreign trade zone, New Orleans gained similar permission. Now, foreign ships may land their cargoes for rehandling without having to put them through customs. Although trade is the biggest item in its economy, New Orleans is surrounded by a diversified list of industries.

Two other well-known ports are Houston (Fig. 15) and Galveston, Texas. For many years Galveston exceeded the interior city in population and economic growth; but in 1950 Houston was the largest United States city south of St. Louis and Washington, D. C. Part of this growth is a result of the 34-foot channel which now extends 50 miles inland from Galveston Bay to Houston, where the canal terminates in a roomy turning basin. Houston's history started with a stress upon cattle, then cotton, lumber, oil,

Fig. 15. The Port of Houston. Notice the ships along the wharves. The 300-foot wide channel which extends for 50 miles to the Gulf of Mexico is being deepened from 34 feet to 36 feet. (Courtesy Houston Chamber of Commerce.)

and now chemicals. Within a short distance from the city lie 11 per cent of the nation's oil reserves and 11 per cent of its oil production. Although oil refining and the manufacture of oil well equipment are important, local businessmen believe the city's economic future will be influenced most by the rapidly growing chemical industries. Production centers mostly around chemical compounds shipped to other parts of the country for conversion into consumer goods. Houston also manufactures metal goods, steel, cement, and many other products.

Houston excels Galveston in its rapid growth as a rail center. Galveston could hardly hope to equal its rival in rail communications because it is located on an island connected to the mainland by one causeway. Nevertheless, in 1950, Galveston was the nation's largest exporter of cotton, wheat, and sulfur.

Mobile, Alabama, lying 150 miles east of New Orleans, has the best natural harbor on the Gulf Coast, and has grown as fast as Houston in the last decade. Ranking as the number 10 United States port, Mobile ships cotton and lumber, and imports aluminum, among the many commodities handled. Each year, 500,000 tons of sea shells are dredged from the bottom of Mobile Bay. Ideal Cement Company annually pulverizes them into 2,000,000 barrels of chemical lime.

Jacksonville, Florida, is not on the Gulf Coast, but it is a busy port, railroad center, and airport. Black Point, the Atlantic Fleet Air Base; Cecil Field with jet plane facilities; and Mayport, a carrier basin, are all nearby and add to Jacksonville's prosperity. In the 1930's the city was named as the eastern terminus of a trans-Florida canal extending to Port Inglis on the Gulf side of the peninsula. The project actually started with WPA labor, but it failed to get complete Congressional approval and was never completed. Opposition appeared from southern Florida coastal cities, which feared loss of business from a shorter route between Gulf Coast ports and the Eastern seaboard. Fruit and vegetable growers also voiced fears of damage to crops by (a) salt water invasion at the surface of the water table, and (b) a lowering of the water table.

A waterway project of great significance to the region and to the nation is the Intracoastal Canal (Fig. 16), which was conceived at a historic meeting of the Intracoastal Canal Association of Texas and Louisiana, August 8, 1905. The main purpose of the meeting was to sponsor a route that would give all coastal areas direct, cheap communication with coastal deep water ports. Today, a little over a half century later, the canal, 12 feet deep and 125 feet wide at the bottom, extends from Brownsville, Texas, to Florida; and it annually transports approximately 40 million tons of commerce a distance of 7.5 billion ton miles.

Although incomplete during World War II, the canal was of great value to the war effort. While scores of tankers and freighters were being sunk by enemy submarines, not only along the Atlantic Coast, but in the Gulf as well, millions of tons of petroleum, sulfur, and other vital war materials were moving in complete safety in a protected inland waterway virtually within sight of the catastrophes at sea.

Future plans call for construction of an across-Florida barge canal, which will link the Gulf Intracoastal Waterway with the Atlantic Inland Waterway, making a continuous transport artery 2500 miles long; moreover, negotiations are progressing towards further extension along the Mexican coast to Tampico and Vera Cruz.

Besides Jacksonville, Mobile, Galveston, Houston, and New Orleans, the Humid Subtropical Coast has other coastal cities whose rapid growth is encouraged by commerce, manufacturing, and other industries.

Fishing. Fisheries do not have the commercial importance of those on the North Atlantic and North Pacific coasts; but red snapper and grouper are caught in large numbers, with Pensacola, Florida, an important fishing port. Shellfish include oysters and shrimp. Mississippi and Louisiana coastal fisheries account for a large percentage of the oyster catch; Biloxi,

Fig. 16.   The Intracoastal Waterway, Atlantic and Gulf Sections, and Principal Connecting Inland Waterways.   The Intracoastal Waterway has been essential in war and is an important economic asset in peace.   (Courtesy Corps of Engineers, U. S. Army.)

Mississippi, is a leading receiving and sales center.   Shrimp occur all along the Gulf Coast, but Texas fishermen secure the greatest number of these demersal fish.

Another demersal fishery may be found in the waters near Tarpon Springs, Florida.   This city is a leading center for sponge fishing.   Cells of the sponge are filled with a gelatinous substance which is allowed to decay, and afterwards the decayed matter is eliminated by pressure.   The skeletal remains make the commercial sponge.   Divers pull this lowly type of marine creature from the ocean floor; or workers may bring the fish to the surface by using a long hook operated from the deck of a sponge-fishing boat. Sponge-fishing beds have been depleted by disease and overfishing. They may recover if (*a*) the disease hazard is eliminated, and (*b*) if synthetic sponges lower sponge prices to make recovery of the natural variety less profitable.

Sport fishing is described in almost all the tourist literature extolling scenic attractions of Florida, especially, and the rest of the Gulf Coast. The quarry sought may include barracuda, sailfish, shark, and tarpon; very little of the catch is used for food.

Tourism (Fig. 17). The tourist industry, especially in Florida, is big business, and contributes millions of dollars to the regional economy. For many years emphasis was placed almost entirely upon winter attractions,

Fig. 17. Miami Beach. Notice the large number of big hotels along the shoreline. (Courtesy of The City of Miami Beach News Bureau.)

but now large numbers of people go to Florida in the summer as well. Geographically there are good reasons for Florida summers attracting people from the continental interior. Temperatures in the summer continental climate are hotter than they are in peninsular Florida, in spite of latitude differences. Florida's strip of land, almost surrounded by water, brings a strong marine influence and lower thermometer readings than those of the central interior. People who like to swim might even be attracted from the coast of Maine at any time of the year. Waters in Maine are cold, even in the summer, and elderly persons might prefer the warm Gulf Stream waters, which course through the Straits of Florida and along its eastern coast.

No longer can New England tourist agencies point to Florida's hurricane hazard in comparing attractiveness of the two regions. In two decades, 1935–55, the northern area has suffered as much or more from these tropical storms as its southern competitor. Of course, the New Englander can point to mountains, lakes, and forests as well as coastal features to attract the visitor. Florida has no mountains, but lakes, forests, and coastal features are present in abundance. Florida, like New England, is close to areas of dense population with high living standards. These are basic requirements for the successful development of any tourist region. California is farther removed from the densely populated East than either New England or Florida.

Florida has spent millions for hotels, motels, and all kinds of tourist attractions. The expenditure is more than paying off. The state experienced one boom and bust, but the present growth appears to have a stable foundation. Lesser, but growing, expansion of the tourist industry is taking place throughout the rest of the Humid Subtropical Coast region.

The Outlook

The word *change* is a good term to apply to land use in the entire South. As previously indicated, the Cotton Belt is no longer a one-crop region. Corn covers a larger acreage than cotton; fields planted to soybeans are expanding; clovers are no longer confined to the North; and many other crops have been added to the diversified farm pattern. Furthermore, mechanization of agriculture is advancing rapidly, together with higher per acre crop yields.

Fields planted in diversified crops are not the only change in use of the land. Cattle are increasing, both the beef and the dairy breeds; and with a continuance of recent trends in hog and poultry raising, the South may become much more of an active challenge to Northern dominance in swine and poultry production.

Change is also evident in Southern manufacturing. The South may lack the large market of the North, but a diversity of raw materials, ample power facilities, and a climate giving cheaper living costs for labor—all provide a good base for textile manufacturing, for petrochemicals, for iron and steel, for lumber and paper pulp, for meat packing, for canneries, and for many other industries. The South may remain a poor second in manufacturing to the North American Ruhr, but Southern industry promises to continue an already rapid expansion.

Southern forests, a great contributor to manufacturing, may lose acreage to agriculture, but better forest care will maintain present yields.

Petroleum and natural gas both from the land and from the bordering sea will continue to contrbute power resources and other bases for manufacture. The adjoining sea not only furnishes oil and gas, but also provides magnesium, a metallic mineral; and in the near future, offshore sulfur mines may add to the South's world leadership in that important mineral. In addition, the South has large deposits of phosphates, so useful in the maintenance of soil fertility.

Recently change has brought improvements in transportation and an increase in commerce, for which the South has many advantages. Again, change is taking place in the population, especially with significant increases in the towns and cities. All in all, the economy of the South is definitely changing for the better.

Questions, Exercises, and Problems

1. What conditions give a certain unity to the South? Describe the physical boundaries and the physical environment of the Cotton Belt. Compare the soils and vegetation of the South with those of the Corn Belt.

2. Trace the geography of the cotton industry from colonial time to that of the present. Did cotton have anything to do with the race problem in the United States? How do crops other than cotton differ among the seven major cotton regions? Describe the growing of major Cotton Belt crops. What are the advantages and disadvantages of the South for raising livestock? Read Merle Prunty, Jr., all references cited.

3. Describe the forest industries of the South. Describe the growth and variety of manufacturing developments in the South. Compare Southern manufacturing with that of the Eastern Quadrilateral. What has delayed the growth of the labor unions in the South? Why has the South long been an advocate of low tariffs? Will this attitude likely change?

4. Name and describe the major oil and gas fields of the South. Refer to Bureau of Mines, *Mineral Facts and Problems*, Bulletin 556 and to the *Minerals Yearbook*, reference cited.

5. Give the location, boundaries, and physical features of the Humid Subtropical Coast. Describe the growing, harvesting, and marketing of subtropical commericial crops. Compare citrus production with that of California. What advantages does the

Humid Subtropical Coast have for the raising of truck crops? Outline the history and the modern development of naval stores. Describe Gulf Coast trapping. What are the problems of recovering coal, natural gas, and petroleum? Describe the mining of sulfur and the recovery of magnesium. What is the significance of coastal salt domes? Comment on the development of the petrochemical industry; name various products resulting from this industry.

6. Describe Gulf Coast commerce with an emphasis upon New Orleans, Galveston, Houston, Mobile, Jacksonville, and the Intracoastal Canal. Describe Gulf Coast fisheries. Compare the South and New England in their advantages and development of the tourist industry. Outline future trends in the economy of the South. Describe the present distribution of population.

7. What advantages does Cape Canaveral, Florida, possess for a missile base? Name other important military installations in the South.

8. Each of the following cities has about 100,000 people or more in its urban district: Austin; Baton Rouge; Beaumont; Columbus, Georgia; Corpus Christi; Dallas; Fort Worth; Galveston; Houston; Jackson; Jacksonville; Little Rock; Macon; Memphis; Miami; Mobile; Montgomery; New Orleans; St. Petersburg; San Antonio; Savannah; Shreveport; Tampa; Waco.

9. Locate the following cities and indicate the most important economic activities for each: Aiken, Biloxi, Childersburg, Freeport, Decatur, Lufkin, McIntosh, Natchez, Plymouth, Rome, Sanford, Tarpon Springs, Yazoo City.

10. Identify the following: across-Florida barge canal, turning basin, New Orleans foreign trade zone, Avery Island, Frasch process, offshore oil, nutria, Texas fever, smudge pot, ratoon crop, tupelo, Santa Gertrudis, political regional determinism, boll weevil, pink boll worm, Eli Whitney, Olustee, Okeechobee.

SELECTED REFERENCES

Ball, Charles E., "The New Beef Breeds are Rolling," *Farm Journal,* November 1956.

Carson, Robe B., "The Florida Tropics," *Economic Geography,* October 1951, pp. 321–339.

Chapman, H. H., and others, *The Iron and Steel Industries of the South,* University of Alabama Press, 1953.

Colby, D. S., and B. E. Oppegard, "Natural Gas," *Minerals Yearbook,* 1951, U. S. Department of the Interior, pp. 865–892.

Diettrich, Sigismond de R., "Florida's Climatic Extremes: Cold Spells and Freezes," *Economic Geography,* January 1949, pp. 68–74.

Diettrich, Sigismond de R., "Florida's Human Resources," *Geographical Review,* April 1948, pp. 278–288.

Dyer, Donald R., "The Place of Origin of Florida's Population," *Annals of the Association of American Geographers,* December 1952, pp. 283–294.

Fortune, "Muskrat Trapping," November 1949.

Fortune, "They're Still Called Naval Stores," April 1951.

Foscue, Edwin J., "The Ports of Texas and Their Hinterlands," *Journal of Economic and Social Geography,* January 1957, pp. 1–13.

Fulmer, John Leonard, *Agricultural Progress in the Cotton Belt Since 1920,* University of North Carolina Press, 1950.

Hart, John Fraser, "Functions and Occupational Structures of Cities of the American South," *Annals of the Association of American Geographers,* September 1955, pp. 269–286.

Hartwig, Edgar E., "Soybean Production in the Southern States," *Better Crops with Plant Food,* March 1955.

Hoover, Calvin B., and B. U. Ratchford, *Economic Resources and Policies of the South,* Macmillan Co., 1951.

Johnson, B. L., and G. E. Tucker, "Phosphate Rock," *Minerals Yearbook,* 1951, U. S. Department of the Interior, pp. 1053–1066.

Lathrop, H. O., "Distribution and Development of the Beef Cattle Industry of Florida," *Journal of Geography,* April 1951, pp. 133–144.

Laubenfels, D. J. de, "Where Sherman Passed By," *Geographical Review,* July 1957, pp. 381–395.

McKnight, Tom L., The Distribution of Manufacturing in Texas," *Annals of the Association of American Geographers,* December 1957, pp. 370–378.

Montgomery, Frank A., Jr., "The Story of Naval Stores," *Steelways,* May 1952.

Neubrech, W. Leroy, "American Southern Pine," *Trade Promotion Series 191,* U. S. Department of Commerce, 1939.

Palmer, A. W., "Cotton Faces up to New World Problems," *Foreign Agriculture,* June 1950.

Parsons, James J., "Recent Industrial Development in the Gulf South," *Geographical Review,* January 1950, pp. 67–83.

Prunty, Merle, Jr., "Land Occupance in the Southeast: Landmarks and Forecast," *Geographical Review,* July 1952, pp. 439–461.

Prunty, Merle, Jr., "Recent Expansions in the Southern Pulp-Paper Industries," *Economic Geography,* January 1956, pp. 51–57.

Prunty, Merle, Jr., "Recent Quantitative Changes in the Cotton Regions of the Southeastern States," *Economic Geography,* July 1951, pp. 189–208.

Prunty, Merle, Jr., "The Renaissance of the Southern Plantation," *Geographical Review,* October 1955, pp. 459–491.

Rostland, Erhard, "The Myth of a Natural Prairie Belt in Alabama: An Interpretation of Historical Records," *Annals of the Association of American Geographers,* December 1957, pp. 392–411.

Schlesselman, G. W., "The Gulf Coast Oyster Industry of the United States," *Geographical Review,* October 1955, pp. 531–541.

Sitterson, J. Carlyle, *The Cane Sugar Industry in the South, 1753–1950,* University of Kentucky Press, 1953.

Stockes, George A., "Lumbering and Western Louisiana Cultural Landscapes," *Annals of the Association of American Geographers,* September 1957, pp. 250–266.

U. S. Weather Bureau, "Weather and Cotton," *Daily Weather Map,* Oct. 17, 1950, Washington, D. C.

Vance, Rupert B., and Nicholas J. Demerath, editors, *The Urban South,* University of North Carolina Press, 1954.

Vanderford, H. B., "Tung Culture Finds a Place in South Mississippi," *Better Crops With Plant Food,* April 1954.

West Virginia Pulp and Paper Company, *The Managed Pine Forest,* 1958.

Zelinsky, Wilbur, "The Changing South," *Focus,* American Geographical Society, October 1951.

Zelinsky, Wilbur, "The Log House in Georgia," *Geographical Review,* April 1953, pp. 173–193.

II · The Great Plains

(Figure 1)

The Great Plains of the United States and Canada, broad grasslands that extend from north-central Canada to the Rio Grande along the eastern border of the Rockies, form one of the world's most distinctive environments. It is an environment of semi-aridity, low humidity, clear skies, high elevations, broad horizons, and seas of waving grass, where less than two centuries ago, antelope, elk, and bison; prairie dog, gopher, and ground squirrel; coyote, couger, and wolf; Cheyenne, Comanche, and Sioux, and several more of the red man's linguistic stocks, found forage and food, and wild free living.

The white explorer and missionary brought the horse to the Great Plains, and a new era of culture opened up for the Indian; the white fur trader brought firewater, firearms, and metalwares and the Indian further changed his way of life. Then the white man brought cattle and sheep, and the flocks and herds grew to countless thousands with pastoral nomadism and range life flourishing. After that the white man brought the revolver, barbed wire, the plow, and tools for drilling artesian wells; he converted some of the range into crop lands, some of the ranch into fields.

Within a few years the farmer was plowing the same land on which the cowboy rode the range and the covered wagon wound along trails from station to station and from spring to stream to water hole. By the end of the nineteenth century, most of the Indians had disappeared, cowboys were becoming less numerous, and a great agricultural industry was producing grain and meat for the world's industrial workers. Today, in the middle of the twentieth century, the Great Plains provide quantities of grain, livestock, and petroleum to the United States and Canada. Modern technology, modern economy, modern society, have transformed what was once called a part of the Great American Desert into a source of valuable raw materials for man's welfare.

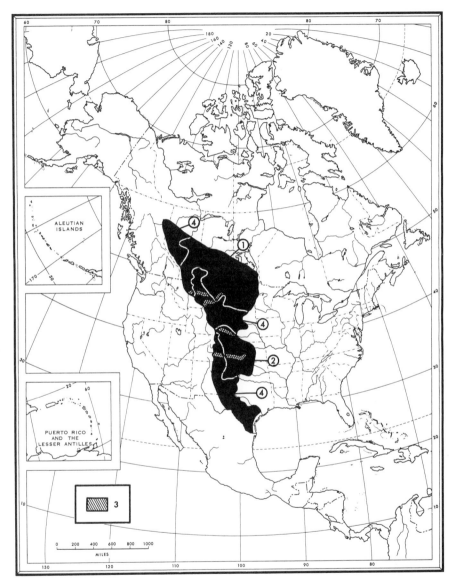

Fig. 1. The Great Plains. The Great Plains may be divided into four subregions: (1) the Spring Wheat Region; (2) the Winter Wheat and Grain Sorghum Region; (3) the Irrigated Crops Region; and (4) the Range Livestock Region. Location of the widely separated parts of the Irrigated Crops Region is highly generalized and some areas do not appear on the map. Note that, in general, grazing lands lie west of the croplands, in the drier climates.

Location and Boundaries. The physiographic province of the Great Plains extends in a north-south direction from the Rio Grande to the Mackenzie [1] Lowland, 30° north to 60° north, or approximately 2,000 miles; from east to west the Plains lie between the Central Lowland and the Rockies, with an average width of about 400 miles.

Physical boundaries are well marked on the north, south, and west, but not on the east. On the north, the province stretches to the Mackenzie Lowland, on the south to the Rio Grande, and on the west to the Rockies. On the east to the far north the Great Plains make contact with the Laurentian Shield. Since glacial debris covers the boundary, there is no sharp change in landscape. However, Laurentian land forms show a little more relief and variety than those of the adjoining Great Plains. In Saskatchewan and North Dakota, the Missouri Coteau, a cuesta, is noticeably higher than the lower land to the east, and makes an acceptable boundary; the eastern border of the Nebraska sand dunes forms a good line of demarcation in that state; and low escarpments in Kansas, Oklahoma, and Texas make a visible contrast between Central Lowland and Great Plains in the south.

Besides slight contrasts in surface features between those of the Great Plains and lands to the east, there are several other boundaries which occur near the Plains eastern physiographic border. These include (*a*) the 20-inch rainfall line; (*b*) the boundary between the natural short-grass country on the west and the tall-grass lands to the east; (*c*) the contact between eastern pedalfers and western pedocal soils; (*d*) the eastern boundary of steppe climate in the United States; (*e*) the western limit of numerous good-sized settlements and relatively dense population in the United States; and (*f*) the boundary between humid agriculture on the east and dry farming and irrigation agriculture on the west.

In this study, an examination of the Canadian section of the Great Plains will stop at the Peace River on the north; but in both the United States and Canada, Great Plains subregions may include small portions of physiographic provinces to the east.

Surface Features. Physiographers divide the huge Great Plains province into many sections. Fenneman, for example, makes ten divisions in the United States. All geographers will agree, however, that Great Plains rock formations are dominantly sedimentary, and include sandstone, limestone, shale, lignite, and conglomerate; and that the strata lie in an approximately horizontal position under a nearly level surface crossed by relatively deep valleys of many east-flowing streams. In a few places on the generally flat Plains, there are domed uplifts such as the Black Hills, on the border

---

[1] Plains topography extends to the Arctic, but A. K. Lobeck separates the Great Plains province from the Mackenzie Lowlands on the north. A. K. Lobeck, *Physiographic Provinces of North America,* The Geographical Press, 1948.

between South Dakota and Wyoming; volcanic intrusions like the Devil's Tower, west of the Black Hills in Wyoming; mesas, many examples of which may be seen in the Raton section of northeastern New Mexico and southeastern Colorado; badlands, like those in Wyoming and South Dakota, especially between the Cheyenne and White River of the latter state; sand dunes, such as those of northern Nebraska. Other well-known features include sinkholes, notably in the Llano Estacado of Texas and the High Plains of Colorado; shallow depressions or blowouts, made by the wind, and wallows made by the buffalo; and a great variety of glacial features poleward from the southern boundary of Pleistocene glaciation.

Although most Plains topography looks nearly level, the surfaces decline gently eastward from an elevation of 5,500 feet at the eastern base of the Rockies, to about 1,500 feet at the western margin of the Central Lowlands, a slope of approximately ten feet per mile.

Climate. As previously indicated, the Great Plains of the United States and southern Canada lie almost entirely within the middle latitude steppe climate. Average rainfall is marginal for humid agriculture even on the eastern border, and entirely too low for that type of farming on the western Plains edges. Precipitation also declines from south to north, with the maximum coming in the summer period; but rainfall efficiency declines from north to south. Cyclic rainfall is characteristic and, with averages marginal for crop agriculture, the dry cycle can bring disaster. It should always be remembered that steppe climates are *risk* climates for agriculture.

Temperatures decline from south to north and seasonal range is high. In the latitudes of North Dakota and Saskatchewan, readings may reach 100°F. or more in the summer and drop far below zero in the winter.

The far interior, or continental, location brings the great seasonal extremes and lowers precipitation. Latitude affects temperature, because of the great north-south extent. All of the area lies within the westerly wind belt at least part of the year; and the characteristic sequence of highs and lows brings precipitation and temperature changes. When a fairly moist winter high lies on the Pacific side of the Rockies, and a low pressure area on the Atlantic side, conditions are encouraging for a chinook over the western Great Plains. This wind is a unique climatic feature in the area between Alberta and Colorado where it favors the cattle industry.

Vegetation and Soils. When settlement of the Great Plains took place in the latter half of the nineteenth century, the white man found vegetation strikingly different from that of Eastern United States. Land from the 98th meridian west to the Rockies was practically treeless. In general, the natural grasses were low growing and shallow rooting because of the low precipitation, ranging from 12 inches in central Montana to 20 inches in western Texas. Grass types were distributed in north-south belts according to the rainfall. In the low Plains, like the prairies to the east, the grass was quite tall and luxuriant. To the west, on the high Plains, grass was short, but the surface was sodded. Farther west, the grass grew in tufts or bunches because the rainfall was too scanty to support continuous growth.

On most of the Great Plains, calcium develops in the soil at depths from 8 to 20 inches, and the occurrence marks the lower boundary of the periodically moist surface soil layer. There is little storage of available soil moisture from year to year, and subsoil is almost permanently dry. Growth of deep-rooted plants, therefore, is almost impossible. The frost-free period varies from about 100 to 200 days, but the growth season of the short grasses seldom exceeds 90 days. Grama grass, which is more characteristic of the north, requires about 100 days to complete its growth and produce seed, and buffalo grass, which is limited to the south, has a much shorter growing season of about 40 days. Moisture is the most important factor limiting growth. The main short grasses at the time of early settlement included grama, galleta, buffalo, and mesquite types.

Great Plains soils, like the grasses, are distributed in north-south belts, with the alignment influenced considerably by precipitation and grass cover. In general, the chernozems lie on the eastern section and the brown-earths on the west, bordering the Rocky Mountains. In between are the dark-brown pedocal soils. All have good structure and are rich in their original mineral constituents, because of the limited amount of leaching. Humus deficiency increases from east to west.

The Spring Wheat Belt

Two well-defined subregions can be noted within the Great Plains physiographic province, the Spring Wheat Belt, and the Winter Wheat and Sorghum Region. These two subregions can be seen best by studying maps of North American wheat and grain sorghum distribution and the map of generalized types of farming in the United States (Fig. 2). On the latter map, the remainder of the Great Plains, besides the two wheat belts, falls under the legend Range Livestock, with islands or ribbons of Irrigated in both Range Livestock and Winter Wheat subregions.

The Spring Wheat subregion includes north-central South Dakota, northwest Minnesota, nearly all of North Dakota, north-central and northeastern Montana, and equatorward sections of Alberta, Manitoba, and Saskatchewan.

On the north, the physical boundary of the Spring Wheat Belt has been variously described as a frost line, a zone of limited transportation too expensive for marketing the crop, an area in which clearing forests from the land discourages grain farming, and a soil line. Probably a combination of these and other factors are involved. The western physical boundary lies along the Rocky Mountains. On the east, in Canada, the Laurentian Shield with

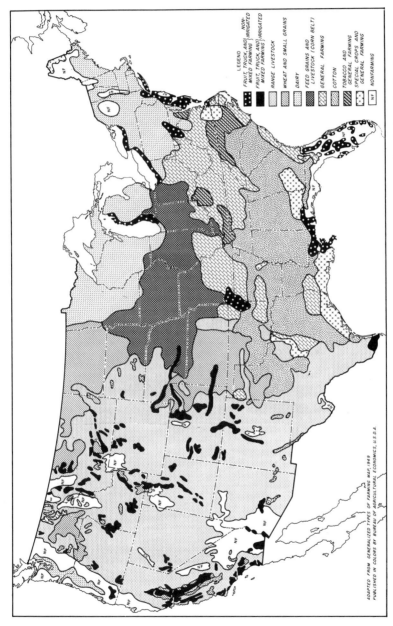

Fig. 2. Generalized Types of Farming in the United States, 1949. Notice the ribbons of irrigated agriculture in the Great Plains. Well-known rivers account for some of these irrigated lands, both in the Great Plains and farther west. Indicate rivers and mountain ranges which contribute irrigation water. (Courtesy U. S. Department of Agriculture.)

many water and bare rock surfaces discourages wheat farming as well as that of other crops. On the southeast, in the United States, land suitable for corn production is given over to the more valuable crop. On the southwest, in the United States, rainfall is insufficient for wheat growing and land is devoted to grazing.

The Environment for Wheat Growing (Fig. 3). The Spring Wheat subregion receives its name because of a climatic environment that compels spring planting for a successful yield. Winters (Fig. 4) are too cold for autumn seeding characteristic of the Winter Wheat Belt to the south. Growing seasons are normally long enough for spring-planted grain to

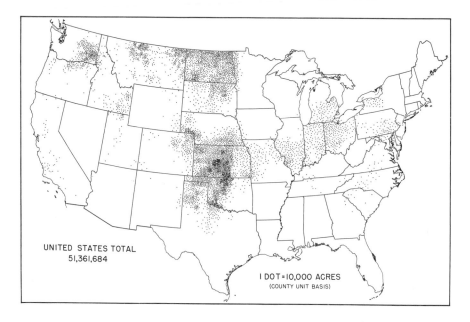

UNITED STATES TOTAL
51,361,684

I DOT=10,000 ACRES
(COUNTY UNIT BASIS)

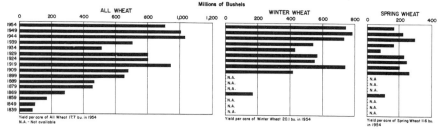

Fig. 3. Wheat Production, 1954, Top; Wheat Production, Winter and Spring Varieties, Bottom. Three great wheat belts stand out on the map: Winter Wheat centered in the Texas Panhandle, Oklahoma, Kansas, and southern Nebraska; Spring Wheat in the Dakotas and Montana; and the Columbia Plateau wheat region of Washington, Oregon, and Idaho. (Courtesy U. S. Department of Commerce, Bureau of the Census.)

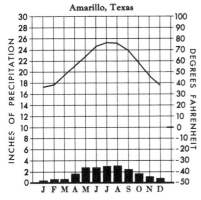
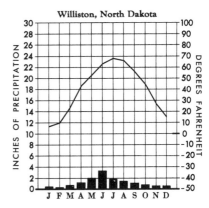

Fig. 4. Climatic Conditions for Winter and Spring Wheat. Amarillo, Texas (35° 13′ N., 101° 49′ W., altitude 3,676 feet), has a mean annual temperature of 56.5° F. and mean annual precipitation of 21.59 inches. Williston, North Dakota (48° 8′ N., 103° 39′ W., altitude 1,878 feet), has a mean annual temperature of 39.6° F., and mean annual precipitation of 14.8 inches. Amarillo, on the southern border of the Winter Wheat Belt, has a mild winter. At Williston, five months of the year have average temperatures below 32° F. This comparison shows why wheat may be planted in the autumn at Amarillo, and must be planted in the spring at Williston.

mature; the cool springs and the summer maximum in precipitation encourage plant growth when total rainfall is sufficient; and autumn usually brings abundant sunshine and low humidity for ripening the crop.

Land forms are suitable for machine cultivation. Pleistocene glaciation aided in leveling the terrain by spreading a huge lake, glacial Lake Agassiz, the ancestor of Lake Winnipeg, over a large section of the surface. Fine lacustrine soils settled in the lake bottom and left a smooth terrain after the ice and lake disappeared; and lake deposits also provided good parent material for the pedocal soils occurring in the region. Edaphic conditions were further aided by the short-grass vegetation that contributed humus during the thousands of years of growth following the glacial recession; and the absence of trees simplified the problem of land clearance for plowing.

The generally favorable physical environment described so far would bring high wheat yields every year if it were not for the cyclic rainfall. A series of wet years follows a series of dry ones, and vice versa. From 1914 to the 1930's, generally adequate precipitation, World War I, strong government encouragement for wheat raising, and the increased use of tractors— all these and other factors accounted for an enormous expansion of wheat acreage throughout both Spring Wheat and Winter Wheat Belts. On the other hand, during the 1930's the rainfall was far below average, and wheat lands and pastures dried up and the always-present wind blew soil from the plowed ground; so much soil blowing occurred, in fact, that a large section of wheat country received the name of the Dust Bowl (Fig. 5). By 1940, the dry cycle was over, a new war, World War II had started, the govern-

Fig. 5. Dustbowl Headlines in Boston. Dust from the Great Plains Dustbowl was carried east by the prevailing westerlies and darkened the midafternoon sun at Boston and Worcester, Massachusetts. (Courtesy *Boston Traveler.*)

ment again encouraged increased wheat production, and wheat farmers were prosperous once more. The second long wet cycle of the twentieth century ended about 1950, and after approximately five years of below-average rainfall, Dust Bowl conditions again returned to the Great Plains.

Dry Farming (Figs. 6, 7). The wheat grower has learned many things about agriculture in this land where rainfall is marginal and cyclic in character. When the early settlers moved in from the humid East, it took them some time and many bitter experiences to learn that humid agricultural practices will not work west of the 100th meridian. Many dry farming techniques were developed before the Dust Bowl of the 1930's, but other new ones have been discovered since then.

On all of the Great Plains, the farmer lets the land lie idle for a while, one year out of three or every other year, in order that sufficient moisture may accumulate in the soil for a successful crop. Even if he lets the ground lie fallow, the farmer is likely to plow the land for several reasons; plowing keeps down weeds which take moisture from the soil; it makes the land more receptive to water storage; and it interrupts evaporation channels which may develop in the soil during periods of dry weather.

The farmer may plow deep furrows along the contours; these will not only store the water for a maximum period, but will prevent runoff at the time the rains come. Trenchlike furrows at right angles to the prevailing wind may also counteract soil blowing. If dust starts to blow badly he may resort to chiseling the land with the Hoeme plow, a device that strikes deep enough to turn up clods that will stabilize the loose soil.

He may select drought-resistant crops such as barley and millet. A useful practice for moisture preservation is called trash farming. All accumulation of refuse after harvest is left on the field until the ground is cropped again. The technique not only protects the land from excessive moisture loss by evaporation, but also will serve as a gigantic sponge to soak up more moisture from each rain. Another moisture preserver is the planting of trees, sometimes called a shelter belt (Fig. 8), to the windward of crops. Such trees create a barrier to the prevailing wind, thus slowing up velocity and causing air to rise over the barrier and to descend beyond the crop zone. In addition, the shelter belt may trap winter snow, which will encourage better tree growth as well as that of the crops. Farmers also plant trees around building plots and feed lots. Plantings like this will save fuel and feed bills. All these dry farming practices have proved helpful to Great Plains agriculture.

Other Crops in the Spring Wheat Region (Fig. 9). Attention to diversification is also proving helpful. Barley, a drought-resistant cereal, can be

Fig. 6. Plowing to Conserve Rainfall. Conservation of rainfall in the furrows between ridges plowed on the contour is practiced on this Oklahoma farm. (Courtesy H. H. Bennett, U. S. Soil Conservation Service.)

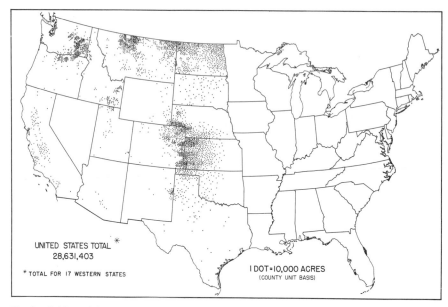

Fig. 7. Cultivated Summer Fallow. Compare this map with the rainfall map of the United States and note relation between low precipitation and dry farming. (Courtesy U. S. Department of Commerce, Bureau of the Census.)

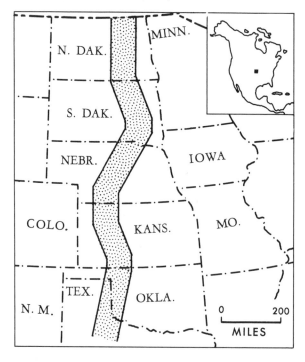

Fig. 8. Shelter Belt on the Great Plains. In the 1930's, drought-resistant seedlings were brought into the Great Plains to start a shelter belt extending from the Canadian border to the Gulf of Mexico. Some of the trees died, but many lived. Great Plains farmers still plant trees; and when the trees mature, crops are planted on the leeward side of the wind barrier. This farming practice cuts down evaporation and conserves soil moisture.

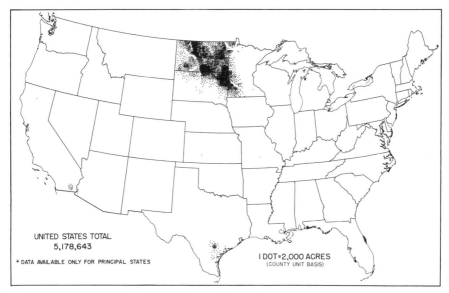

Fig. 9. Flax Threshed. Most flax is grown in the Spring Wheat Region. (Courtesy U. S. Department of Commerce, Bureau of the Census.)

used for fattening hogs in a land where corn growing is more hazardous than wheat raising. Spring wheat climate, with a growing season too short and cool for maize, is not unsuitable for sugar beets; this root crop is the choice of some farmers in the Dakotas, Minnesota, and Montana. Another root crop that normally does well is potatoes. Idaho potatoes, grown a little west of the Spring Wheat area, find a ready market even in eastern United States. Alfalfa provides the farmer a good hay crop in this marginal rainfall area. It may be fed either to beef animals or to dairy cows. In a region so isolated from large urban centers, most dairy products are sold in solids, such as butter and cheese.

The Man-Made Landscape. On the farms, the man-made landscape is different from that of fields and building plots in other regions. Probably the most important difference is in the size of the farms. In the American Dairy Belt, holdings average 120 acres; in the Corn Belt's western portion, 160 acres; but in the Spring Wheat country, farms of less than 320 acres are the exception. Land holdings of many wheat farmers reach a total of several sections, thousands of acres. Here is an example of extensive agriculture; a lower ratio of workers to each 100 acres occurs than in either the Corn Belt or in the American Dairy Region. Mechanization is the rule in plowing, planting, and harvesting. Huge machines, plows, seeders and combines are used.

One of the most distinctive features of the landscape is the grain elevator stored with autumn-ripened grain which pours from spouts to railroad cars alongside.   Little towns with no more than a few hundred people may have as many as a half dozen or more grain elevators standing like tall sentinels overlooking the flat terrain.   These landmarks can be seen for miles when approaching the trading center by motor car or train (Fig. 10).

Although the farmer may have storage for some of his grain, government storage bins, many of them circular and constructed of galvanized material, may be seen in the small towns.   The producer of grain may place his surplus in federal storage on loan or sale basis.   During the harvest season, crops may be so large that they are piled on the ground for a short period, or kept under canvas for a year or more.   Many man-made features shout from the housetops that this is a surplus-grain country.

If the farmers combine cattle raising with grain production, and many of them do, especially in the western part of the Wheat Belt, the cultural pattern shows large acreages of grazing land and corrals and sheds for the

Fig. 10.   Grain Elevators and Drilling Rig.   The drilling rig of an Imperial Oil well, at Smiley, Saskatchewan, dwarfs prairie wheat elevators.   In both Canadian and United States sections of the North American Spring Wheat Region, recent oil discoveries have added new wealth. Imperial Oil brought in the discovery well in Saskatchewan in September 1953.   (Courtesy Saskatoon Board of Trade and Imperial Oil Limited.)

animals. Windmills are built, to take advantage of the almost-constant wind for pumping water. Water for livestock and human use may be obtained from deep wells, many of them reaching the Dakota sandstone (Fig. 11), a water-bearing stratum outcropping over thousands and thousands of square miles on the Rocky Mountains and Black Hills. This stratum underlies large parts of Saskatchewan, the Dakotas, Wyoming, Montana, Kansas, and Nebraska. The first well was drilled into the aquifer in 1882; since that time, more than 15,000 have been drilled.

A three-strand barbed wire fence may enclose the large grain fields and grazing areas, a contrast to the fencing of the Corn Belt. With few swine raised, there is little need of the four- or five-foot stretch of woven wire with a barbed wire strand beneath, both necessary to confine the swine, fed on practically all Corn Belt farms.

Marketing Grain. There is a great amount of grain to be moved to market from the dominantly one-crop Spring Wheat subregion. Neither the Canadian prairie provinces nor wheat growing areas in the United States adjoining have many people. Grain moves east by rail to ports at the western end of the Great Lakes, where most of it continues the journey by water. With the completion of the Great Lakes-St. Lawrence waterway, more grain may move directly to Europe from western harbors of the Interior Seaboard.

Several decades ago, Canada built a railroad from the wheat lands to the Hudson Bay port of Churchill. So far, Hudson Bay ships have carried little grain, in spite of the shorter distance to Europe than by the Great Lakes route. The bay is open for shipping only three months of the year; ice hazards increase insurance rates; a return cargo salable in sparsely populated interior Canada is difficult to find. These are some retarding factors, which offset the advantage of shorter west-east distances to Europe near the top of the world.

Both United States and Canadian parts of the Spring Wheat country have received an economic boon with recent large discoveries of petroleum and natural gas. It has long been known that the prairie provinces and adjoining United States areas are underlain with one of the large North American coal fields. Now oil and gas wells are pouring out a much more profitable resource. Canada's oil prosperity started with the discovery of the Leduc field; and in 1950, the province of Alberta had more than 2,500 producing wells. Alberta's government receipts in that year were far greater than government expenditures, $118,000,000 versus $62,000,000. South of the Leduc field, the rich Williston Basin (Fig. 12) of Saskatchewan and Manitoba extends across the border into the Dakotas and Montana, and promises a great economic future. Pipelines from Canadian oil and gas fields in the Spring Wheat area already extend to the Great Lakes and Pacific Coast ports.

Rainfall

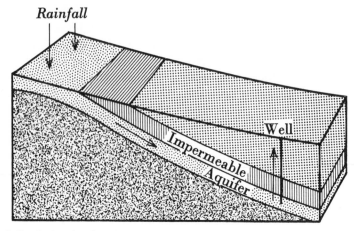

Fig. 11. A Simple Artesian System. A permeable sandstone layer (aquifer) outcrops on the hill to the left and absorbs rainfall, which descends along the sandstone, sealed in beneath a capping layer of impermeable rock. A hole bored down into the aquifer, farther down its slope, becomes an artesian well. For an orientation to the Great Plains artesian conditions, consider the area where rain is falling as Dakota sandstone outcropping on the Rocky Mountains, and the well located in the Dakotas far to the east. (After C. R. Longwell, A. Knopf and R. F. Flint, *Physical Geology,* 3rd ed., John Wiley and Sons, 1948.)

The Winter Wheat and Grain Sorghum Subregion

Location and Boundaries. Large portions of the subregion lie in western and central Kansas, northwestern Oklahoma, eastern Colorado, and the Panhandle of Texas. Small sections occur in southwestern Nebraska, southeastern Wyoming, and east-central New Mexico.

Several factors are responsible for the northern boundary. On the northeast, maize production is possible and corn is the more valuable crop; on the northwest, Nebraska's sandhills and drouth make wheat growing too risky; on the west, wheat raising stops where low rainfall limits dry farming practices; on the south, cotton crowds out wheat because the former is more profitable. The eastern boundary in Kansas corresponds closely to the Flint Hills, a cuesta formation with land forms too rolling for easy machine cultivation. On the southeast, cotton takes over because it will make more money than wheat.

The Environment for Wheat Growing. Surface features approach a flatness similar to that of the Spring Wheat country. The nearly level topography results partly from underlying horizontal strata formed by the accumulaion of sediments in marine waters that swept north from the Gulf of Mexico to the Arctic Ocean. Large sections were mantled by deposition of sand, gravel, and silt, which were deposited by east-flowing streams after the uplift of former sea bottoms. The southern Plains, like those of the north, rise gently to the west about 10 feet per mile; and in many places relief is so monotonously slight that a covered wagon, a cabin, an automobile, or even a horse is conspicuous. In contrast to the northern Great Plains, the southern section has not been glaciated.

Rainfall is a little heavier than that of the north, but more is needed because of higher temperatures and higher rates of evaporation. The milder temperatures of the cool season make possible the planting of wheat in the autumn with little danger of winterkill. Thus, the more southerly latitude of the Winter Wheat country permits fall wheat seeding. Three-fourths of United States wheat is planted in the autumn, and the fraction holds good throughout the world.

Native short grasses are generally similar to those in the Spring Wheat land and so are the soils. However, United States soil maps generally subdivide Great Plains chernozems, dark brown earths, and brown earths into northern and southern chernozems, etc. Slightly different climate and vegetation account for slight contrasts in soil.

Cyclic Rainfall (Fig. 13). The influences of cyclic rainfall in the twentieth century were described briefly in the study of the Spring Wheat subregion. It may be informative to look at influences of rainfall variability upon early settlement of the Great Plains.

Prior to the Civil War, people generally accepted statements of Coro-

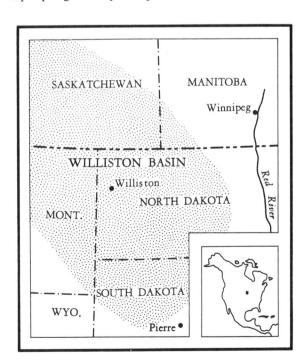

Fig. 12. The Williston Basin. The Williston Basin, which lies in the heart of the Spring Wheat Region, promises to be one of the great petroleum producing areas of the continent.

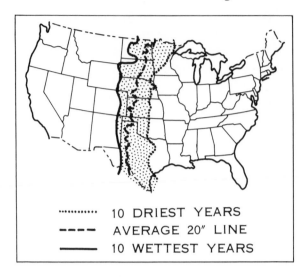

Fig. 13. Changing Position of the 20-Inch Rainfall Line. The average position is about midway between that for the ten wettest years and that for the ten driest years. The dry line shifts far to the east and the wet line shifts far to the west. (After maps, *Climate and Man,* Yearbook of Agriculture, 1941.)

············ 10 DRIEST YEARS
‒ ‒ ‒ ‒   AVERAGE 20″ LINE
‒‒‒‒‒‒   10 WETTEST YEARS

nado, Zebulon M. Pike, John Bradbury, Major S. H. Long, and others that the Great Plains formed a part of the Great American Desert. After the Civil War, the desert conception was abandoned by many students of the Great Plains. Some authorities even decided that the steppe climate, characteristic of the region, was changing to a more humid one. One of the greatest exponents of this theory was Samuel Aughey, head of the Natural Science Department of the University of Nebraska from 1871 to 1883. He believed that "it is the great increase in the absorptive power of the soil, wrought by cultivation, that has caused, and continues to cause an increasing rainfall in the state." Aughey had many followers at the time who believed just as he did.

Other theories for the increase in rainfall during the period, which proved to be only the wet phase of the cyclic rainfall, included the rainy influence of iron rails appearing on the westward extension of the railroads, the favorable effects of telegraph lines upon the condensation of water vapor in the air, and the effect of newly planted trees upon increased precipitation. In 1866, the commissioner of public lands recommended a measure to Congress that would compel Plains pioneers to plant trees on a high percentage of their land, with the view of increasing rainfall in the region. A few years later Congress heeded this suggestion by the act of 1873, which purported to encourage the growth of timber on the prairies.

However, the fiction of man's influence upon increasing the rainfall of the Great Plains was exploded by the coming of a disastrous dry cycle. In the late 1880's and early 1890's came a series of dry years. Crop failure followed crop failure. Want and distress became widespread over the Great Plains. More than 18,000 prairie schooners passed east over the Missouri

River bridge at Omaha in one season—never to return. Caravan after caravan, which had served to bring the pioneer family west, was re-outfitted to carry it away from this land of deception. On many a prairie schooner the owners expressed the bitterness in their hearts as follows:

> In God we trusted,
> In Kansas we busted.[2]

Agricultural Crops. As in the Spring Wheat Belt, the physical environment, with the exception of cyclic rainfall, is generally favorable for large-scale wheat production. Similar dry farming practices are employed, and similar attempts at crop diversification receive emphasis. A rather successful crop addition has appeared, grain sorghum (Figs. 14, 15), especially in the southwest portion of the Winter Wheat Belt, southwest Kansas, western Oklahoma, and the Panhandle of Texas.

The cereal can be used as livestock feed in the form of grain, silage, and hay. Its stalk and root system afford excellent resistance to wind erosion during the winter and early spring, and provide a thick blotter to absorb any precipitation that may fall at that time. In Texas sorghum may

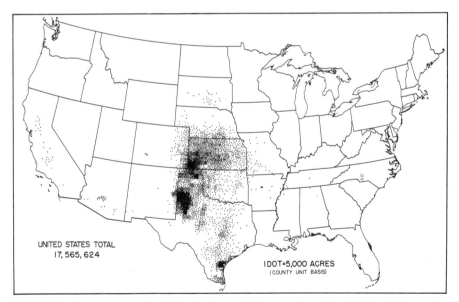

UNITED STATES TOTAL
17,565,624

1 DOT=5,000 ACRES
(COUNTY UNIT BASIS)

Fig. 14. Sorghums, Acreage in 1954. Sorghum's ability to mature with limited rainfall permits large acreage in the southern Great Plains. Notice the correlation with the western part of the Winter Wheat Region. (Courtesy U. S. Department of Commerce, Bureau of the Census.)

[2] Much of the above description is based upon Walter Kollmorgen, "Rainmakers on the Plains," The *Scientific Monthly*, February 1935.

Fig. 15.　Grain Sorghum in the Texas Panhandle.　High-yielding types of grain sorghum which may be harvested with a combine are grown extensively in Oklahoma and Texas.　(Courtesy U. S. Department of Agriculture.)

be planted as late as June and still reach full maturity; and the farmer can use the same machinery, on the expanding acreage of grain sorghum, that he employs for wheat in planting, growing, and harvesting activities.

Grain sorghums are not as high in fat as corn, but they possess a higher percentage of protein.　Poultry do well on the cereal and so do cattle when the grain is supplemented with cottonseed meal or soybean meal.　Besides utilization as a feed for domestic animals, grain sorghums yield sugar, sirup, vegetable oils, starches, and dextrose.　The 1957 grain sorghum crop of the United States amounted to over 500,000,000 bushels, almost double the yield of 1955.

In addition to expanding grain sorghum planting and yields, plant breeders have created new types of wheat yielding approximately 50 per cent more grain than types planted a half century ago.　Yields probably can be increased more, and other crops may be added to give more diversity to farming operations.　The task is not easy, however, for low rainfall and great variability narrow diversified crop opportunities.

As in the Spring Wheat area, farmers may broaden the economic base with livestock, mainly feeder cattle.　Some also have profited from oil; for the Midcontinent oil field stretches across the Winter Wheat Belt.

The Cultural Landscape. The cultural landscape of the Winter Wheat country is quite similar to that of the Spring Wheat area. Land holdings are large; several grain elevators give a distinctive touch to each of the small towns; government storage bins holding farm grain on a loan or sale basis are widespread. During the harvest season, grain may be piled on the ground for lack of storage space; this may occur in spite of the fact that hundreds of cars loaded with wheat have moved to concentrating centers like Kansas City. Windmills, corrals, and cattle sheds suggest a livestock raising phase to the economy, as do large acreages of pasture enclosed in the three-strand barbed wire fence. Plows, tractors, seeders, and combines provide evidence of highly mechanized farming (Figs. 16, 17).

Many combines do custom harvesting throughout the Great Plains region. The federal government encouraged the practice during World War II when materials for all machinery were strictly controlled. Custom operators may own as many as 50 combines, moving them from place to place on trucks; and since combines are equipped with headlights, they may be utilized both night and day. Towards the last of May or the first part of June, a few thousand of the many that harvest Texas grain will move north through Oklahoma, Kansas, Nebraska, South Dakota, and finally into North Dakota and Montana. Harvesting in the latter states takes place in August. On the way back, combine operators may pick up a few contracts for threshing grain sorghums.

Fig. 16. Winter Wheat Harvest. Combines work well on the nearly level Kansas wheat fields. The combine cuts and threshes the grain in one operation. (Courtesy Walter H. Atzenweiler, Agricultural Commissioner, Chamber of Commerce, Kansas City.)

Fig. 17. Cars of Wheat, Kansas City Rail Yards. Railroads have difficulty in moving the grain crop of the Winter Wheat Belt. (Courtesy Walter H. Atzenweiler, Agricultural Commissioner, Chamber of Commerce, Kansas City.)

Range Livestock Subregion

Location and Boundaries. In general, the subregion makes up the western part of the Great Plains physiographic province; in the United States, political portions include southeastern Montana, western South Dakota, eastern Wyoming, western Nebraska, east-central Colorado, eastern New Mexico, and western Texas.

Land is utilized almost entirely for grazing for two main reasons, the most important being insufficient precipitation for dry farming. Land forms and soils provide another reason for eliminating crop agriculture in certain sections such as the Sand Hills of Nebraska, the Black Hills and Badlands of South Dakota and Wyoming, the Edwards Plateau of Texas, the Flint Hills of Kansas, and the Pecos and Raton lands in New Mexico and Texas.

The Grazing Industry.[3] Livestock men on the Great Plains assure them-

[3] For information on historical aspects of the Great Plains grazing industry see Agricultural Year Book, 1948, *Grass,* pp. 21–25.

selves of three basic items for survival, an adequate water supply, winter feed, and a headquarters—ranch house, corrals, sheds, etc.—from which they can operate their own land and, if necessary, lease public lands for additional pasturage.

One of the most important requisites for raising livestock is an adequate water supply. This may be a river, a spring, a reservoir, or even deep wells. The latter are much more numerous than in the early days of ranching, a situation made possible by useful inventions in well drilling machinery. Many wells are pumped by windmills. Winds are active constantly over the wide expanses of flatland supporting low types of vegetation that provide very little wind friction.

If sufficient water is available, the rancher may be able to supplement grass feeding with irrigated crops suitable for fattening animals for market. If water supply is limited, he may sell his livestock to farmers in the Corn Belt, who fatten grass-fed cattle on grain.

The rancher in the southern Great Plains needs little shedding for his animals, although without protection they may suffer damage from an occasional norther. Northern ranchers must protect their animals from winter cold and snow, and must purchase or raise supplemental winter feed for those cattle not marketed before the cold season. Supplemental feed necessity may be lessened by the chinook, already mentioned, which may keep pastures open on many winter days.

If ranches are large and many cattle kept, the rancher may hire a good many cowhands. They are kept busy with such tasks as rounding up animals for branding, which gives better identification; dipping animals in chemically treated water to rid them from ticks—these insects spread disease and ruin the hide; and rounding up cattle for market. On some ranches the cowboy in helicopter supplements the work of the cowboy on the horse. This results from two main causes: (*a*) skilled cowboys are becoming extremely hard to find; and (*b*) the helicopter may do the work of fifteen men on horses. Where the mesquite has grown thick, some cattle may be overlooked without aerial reconnaissance.

Ranches range in size from a few thousand to a half million acres or more. Usually the smaller ranches are found near the humid border of the Great Plains and the larger ones near the desert fringe. Carrying capacity of the range may vary from 10 to 30 acres a cow. On the desert fringe, the number of acres needed to pasture an animal may range from 30 to 50 and, on the desert itself, as many as 75 acres may be necessary. For comparison, one or two acres of grass in the Corn Belt will support a cow.

Sheep ranches are operated about the same as cattle ranches; in fact, sheep and cattle may be pastured on the same ranch. In the north, cattle may be driven to the mountains for summer pasture where they eat grass unavailable during the winter because of snow. Sheep may be moved to and from summer pastures by truck.   Snows probably menace sheep more than cattle, and much care is necessary to keep the animals from drifting with cold winter winds and becoming lost in snow drifts.   Sheep can exist on poorer pastures and less water than cattle, but they are more difficult to handle when disease strikes.   Furthermore, sheep need more protection from wild animals than cattle.   Shearing time shows seasonal adjustments. Animals are shorn in the spring after cold and snow have passed and warm days show summer is on its way.   Wool is a primary product for Great Plains sheepmen, but more and more emphasis is placed upon the sale of lambs for feeding in more humid areas.   Great fluctuations in wool prices make variable returns from year to year.

Angora goats (Fig. 18) are handled like sheep on ranches.   The Edwards Plateau is the goat center of the United States.   Its pasture land, too poor for good sheep and cattle ranching, will support goats, which are browsing animals.   They thrive on good grass, but will do well on bush pas-

Fig. 18.   Angora Goats on the Edwards Plateau.   Texas' Edwards Plateau provides grazing for most of the Angora goats raised in the United States.   (Courtesy Fort Worth Clearing House Association.)

ture where sheep and cattle would starve to death. Goats are raised primarily for mohair, just as they are in Turkey and South Africa, the other two important angora goat regions of the world. In the United States, the market for goat meat is limited because of well-established popular prejudice. No such prejudice is present in countries of the Middle East where living standards are lower.

The Irrigated Subregion

A comparison of the irrigated lands shown on the map of Generalized Types of Farming in the United States (Fig. 2) with a place map of the Great Plains physiographic province will show the following correlations: an irrigated district along the Platte River and its tributaries in Nebraska,[4] Wyoming, and Colorado; a ribbon of irrigation along the Arkansas River in Kansas; and irrigated country in South Dakota bordering the tributaries of the Missouri. These and other watercourses rise in the Rocky Mountains west of the Great Plains, where precipitation is heavier.

The greatest irrigation project of the subregion is the Missouri Valley Administration (MVA). Although the Great Plains do not account for all of the Missouri River drainage basin, the greater fraction lies within the physiographic province. A great deal already has been done on the Pick-Sloan Plan of the Bureau of Reclamation and the Army Corps of Engineers. Broadly speaking the plan calls for (*a*) irrigation, which will be increased

---

[4] Scottsbluff County, Nebraska, which forms a section of the Nebraska Panhandle bordering Wyoming, may be used as an example of the widely separated parts of the Irrigated Subregion. Irrigation was introduced in the early 1890's to augment an annual precipitation of 14 inches. With more water it was possible to get better crops of alfalfa and wild hay for winter feeding of range cattle. The first small irrigation projects were built and maintained by local private capital. After the United States Reclamation Service was established, it built dams across the North Platte in east-central Wyoming and developed a system of canals, some of which serve Scottsbluff County. They have been successful and in an average year as much as 3 acre-feet of water are available to each acre of irrigable land. Original cost of the irrigation system has been assessed against land owners and eventually is to be paid out, with interest, over a 40-year period, after which the water "right" will be "paid up" and only the cost of maintenance and occasional improvements will be assessed.

Although irrigation projects started primarily to assure hay for winter feeding of range livestock, other crops, especially sugar beets, now have become important. Once ample water was available, other conditions of the physical environment proved favorable for sugar beet farming. The growing season averages 140 days; pedocal soils are relatively fertile; terraces along the North Platte approach flatness suitable for machine cultivation; mechanization has reached every phase of sugar beet production. Machines prepare the ground for planting, plant the seed, block out excess plants, weed the fields, spray the crop to prevent insects and disease, and take care of the harvesting. Sugar beet raising ties in well with the cattle industry, for beet pulp and tops are useful for feeding range cattle during the winter period. [The description of Scottsbluff irrigation is based on James E. Rowan, "Mechanization of the Sugar Beet Industry of Scottsbluff County, Nebraska," *Economic Geography*, July 1948.]

from the present 5,000,000 acres to about 10,000,000 acres; (*b*) flood control; (*c*) hydroelectric power; (*d*) navigation; and (*e*) conservation of the land.   Other improvements contemplated include tourist attractions, conservation of fish and wildlife, and more water for domestic use.   Opportunity is also given to help the many thousand Indians, living within the basin, to become self-supporting.

One of several parts of the MVA project is the Colorado-Big Thompson irrigation development already completed.   This provides supplemental water to the western Great Plains around Greeley and Fort Collins, Colorado.   Water from the Colorado River reaches the Big Thompson through the 13-mile Adams tunnel drilled under the Rocky Mountain Continental Divide.

Great Plains Economic Resources

Mineral and Power Resources.   As previously indicated, the Great Plains are rich in power resources, including low-grade coal, petroleum, and natural gas.   North America's greatest coal resources, low grade, lie within the regional boundaries.   Oil and gas fields include Canada's Leduc field, the Williston Basin straddling the international boundary, the Midcontinent, and other fields.   More petroleum will be discovered because the region's geologic environment is favorable.

Potash and phosphates occur in large deposits, the former near the southwest border of the Great Plains at Carlsbad, New Mexico, and the latter in Montana and Wyoming.   Both deposits are far removed from the large share of the nation's farm lands, which could use them to the best advantage.   Metallic minerals, especially gold, occur in the Black Hills, where the well-known Homestake Mining Corporation leads in production.

Manufacturing.   It is doubtful that the Great Plains will ever become a great manufacturing region.   One of industry's most important requirements for successful manufacturing is lacking, a big local market, and distant markets are too far away.   Emphasis is placed upon processing local raw materials and the utilization of cheap power facilities.   Meat packing plants and flour mills are widespread throughout the region.   Petrochemical industries are based upon the presence of large supplies of petroleum and natural gas.   Local oil and gas are also utilized for smelting zinc and other metals in centers like Amarillo in the Texas Panhandle.   Ore moves east from the Rocky Mountains to take advantage of low processing costs which are influenced by cheap fuel.   Pueblo, Colorado, is the largest iron and steel plant west of the Mississippi.   Coal comes from the Raton Mesa in Colorado and iron from Wyoming and Utah.   The industry has developed because of a local market, the great distance from large Eastern steel mills, and the availability of raw materials nearby.   Isolation of the Great Plains probably was a major cause for the location of airplane plants at Wichita, Kansas.

Tourism. Tourist attractions will hardly bring large crowds for several reasons. The region is far removed from dense centers of population; local population density is slight; and the nearby Rockies have much more to offer in scenic quality. However, the region is not devoid of tourist interest. Two of the best attractions are the Black Hills, which received their name from the beautiful forests with which they are covered; and the Carlsbad Caverns, with miles and miles of spectacular underground passages formed by the solution work of ground water.

The Outlook

The Great Plains region has considerable economic diversity, featured by power, grazing, irrigation, minor supplies of minerals, and large-scale grain farming. Progress is possible in every one of these industries if man will cooperate with nature. A major regional drawback in the past has been man's failure to make adjustments to the marginal cyclic rainfall. The economy has shifted from prosperity to adversity and back, something like the following sequence:

During the rainy cycle, the Great Plains became one of the most prosperous regions in the country. The opinion that the climate was changing permanently for the better became widespread. Settlement was stimulated. Land prices rose. Range lands were heavily stocked. Large farms and ranches were subdivided to form smaller grain farms. Crop acreage was expanded on good land and bad. New business enterprises sprang up. New roads and schools were built to serve a growing population and bonds were issued on the inflated land values. New counties were formed, and administration expenses for a given area were almost doubled.

During the dry cycle, crops failed and range pasture and grasses stopped growing. Stock water reservoirs dried up, and cattle were rushed to market to prevent them from starving or dying of thirst. The dust began to blow and black blizzards laid bare the soil down to the furrow bottoms. On Friday, May 11, 1934, the Boston Traveler spread the following words over half of the front page: "Western Dust Cloud Sweeping on Boston"; and dust from the Great Plains actually reached the Atlantic. This dust, locally, was piled in drifts around the farmsteads, and in the fence rows, and it made life unbearable for all the people within a radius of several hundred miles. With dwindling farm income, principal, interest, and taxes became delinquent. Mortgages were foreclosed. The local government found it difficult to raise sufficient revenue to continue operation. Road and school bonds were defaulted and the federal government was called upon to make emergency feed and seed loans, some of which were repaid. Local business enterprises failed. Families left the community, and many of those who stayed went on relief.

The whole region became a land of unrest, and decidedly political unrest. Man has a tendency to blame the government for many of his misfortunes for which the government may be in no way to blame. This is the region which encouraged the Greenback movement of the 1870's, Populism in the 1890's; the Non-partisan League of the 1920's; and it gave strong support to the Townsend Plan. And in the 1950's it petitioned Congress for millions of relief to aid another Dust Bowl.

One thing is certain; there must be better planning to lessen the economic ups and downs resulting from the cyclic rainfall. Maybe the Indian who won an essay contest in Oklahoma can shed some light on what should be done. The contest was based upon two pictures of an abandoned farm in the Dust Bowl. Contestants were invited to express their conclusions.

Out of more than 2,500 essayists, an Indian, whose name was not given, was the winner. He wrote:

Both pictures show white man crazy. Make big tepee, plow hill. Water wash. Wind blow soil, grass all gone. Squaw gone, papoose too. No pig, no corn, no cow, no hay, no pony. Indian no plow land. Keep grass. Buffalo eat. Indian get buffalo. Hide make tepee, mocassins too. Indian no make terrace. No build dam. No give dam. All time eat. No hunt job. No hitchhike. No ask relief. No shoot pig. Great Spirit make grass. Indian no waste anything. Indian no work. White man heap crazy.

QUESTIONS, EXERCISES, AND PROBLEMS

1. Describe the boundaries, location, and other physical features of the Great Plains. Trace the sequence occupancy of the region. What early rainfall theories were advanced by scientist and layman alike? Chart the rainfall of Dodge City, Kansas, for the last 50 or 75 years.

2. What is the difference between spring wheat and winter wheat? What crops, other than wheat, are grown? Indicate the characteristics of dry farming. Comment upon the cultural landscape of the wheat country. What other subregions of Canada besides the Spring Wheat area are suitable for commercial agriculture? How much wheat do each of Canada and the United States produce and export? What routes does it travel to market? Give the geographic advantages and disadvantages of the Hudson Bay Railroad. Sketch the geology of artesian conditions. What do Great Plains wheat, oil, and gas have to do with economic friction between the United States and Canada? Why were the Great Plains an important area for the formation of radical political parties?

3. Describe the grazing industry and show relationships to the environment. Read and stress geographic relationships in "A Sod House," reference cited. Make a study of the MVA and compare the development with that of the TVA. Read carefully Edward Higbee, *American Agriculture,* chapters 14, 15, 16, on Farming on the Great Plains.

4. What power and mineral resources are present? Name and describe the major oil and gas fields. See references already cited. Describe regional manufacturing, tourism, commerce, and other economic activities. Why has manufacturing shown but little development in the Great Plains? Point out major geographic factors that have been important in the location of present manufacturing developments.

5. Each of the following cities has approximately 50,000 people or more in its urban district: Abilene, Amarillo, Calgary, Edmonton, Laredo, Lubbuck, Oklahoma City, Regina, San Angelo, Saskatoon, Wichita, Winnipeg. Name major activities encouraging the growth of each of these population centers. Do the same for Denver, Colorado Springs, Pueblo, and Carlsbad—cities which lie along the border between the Great Plains and the Rocky Mountains. Why are there few large cities in the Great Plains? Describe the distribution of population in the Great Plains.

6. Identify the following: chernozem, steppe, Edwards Plateau, Black Hills, Llano Estacado, Lake Agassiz, Nebraska Sand Hills, Badlands, Raton Mesa, blowout, risk climate, chinook, edaphic, Dust Bowl, Hoeme Plow, shelter belt, combine, Dakota sandstone, Williston Basin, Leduc, Flint Hills, cuesta, Rainmakers of the Plains, dual-purpose sheep, Homestake Mining Corporation, Indian essay, Devil's Tower, suitcase farming.

SELECTED REFERENCES

Allen, L. C., "Sorghums are Eager Beavers," *Country Gentleman,* April 1947.

Bureau of Reclamation, Department of the Interior, *Putting the Missouri to Work,* July 1, 1945.

Calef, Wesley, "The Winter of 1948–49 on the Great Plains," *Annals of the Association of American Geographers,* December 1950, pp. 267–292.

Durand, Loyal, Jr., "The American Centralizer Belt," *Economic Geography,* October 1955, pp. 301–320.

Dutcher, Flora, "A Sod House," *Journal of Geography,* December 1949, pp. 353–361.

Ekblaw, W. E., "The Great Plains," *Economic Geography,* October 1946, p. 230.

Forbes, "Williston's New Crop," Feb. 1, 1952.

Fortune, "A Strategy for Drought," April 1957.

Fortune, "The Missouri Valley," August 1949.

Harrington, Lynn, "Ranch Round-up," *Canadian Geographical Journal,* Vol. 41, 1950, pp. 234–239.

Hart, Henry C., *The Dark Missouri,* The University of Wisconsin Press, 1957.

Henderson, David A., "Corn Belt Cattle Feeding in Eastern Colorado's Irrigated Valleys," *Economic Geography,* October 1949, pp. 364–372.

Hewes, Leslie, and Arthur C. Schmieding, "Risk in the Central Great Plains: Geographical Patterns of Wheat Failure in Nebraska, 1931–1952," *Geographical Review,* July 1956, pp. 375–387.

Hooks, A. J., "Alberta, Nature's Treasure House," *Canadian Geographical Journal,* Vol. 35, 1947, pp. 154–177.

Johnson, Charles W., "Relative Decline of Wheat in the Prairie Provinces of Canada," *Economic Geography,* July 1948, pp. 209–216.

Kollmorgen, Walter, "Rainmakers of the Plains," *Scientific Monthly,* February 1935, pp. 146–152.

Kollmorgen, Walter, and George F. Jenks, "Suitcase Farming in Sully County, South Dakota," *Annals of the Association of American Geographers,* March 1958, pp. 27–40.

Kraenzel, Carl Frederick, *The Great Plains in Transition,* University of Oklahoma Press, 1955.

Life, "The United States Masters the Big Muddy," Aug. 22, 1955.

Miller, E. Willard, "The Hudson Bay Railway Route: A Geographical Reconnaissance," *Journal of Geography,* April 1958, pp. 163–172.

Quartermaster Research and Engineering Center, "Winter Weather Type Frequencies, Northern Great Plains," *Technical Report EP-64,* U. S. Army, Natick, Mass., August 1957.

Stockton, John R., and Stanley A. Arbingast, *Water Requirements Survey: Texas High Plains,* Bureau of Business Research, The University of Texas, 1953.

U. S. Department of Agriculture, *Grass,* Agricultural Yearbook, 1948, pp. 21–25 and pp. 477–540.

Villmow, Jack R., "The Nature and Origin of the Canadian Dry Belt," *Annals of the Association of American Geographers,* June 1956, pp. 211–232.

Wall Street Journal, "Ranchers Fatten More Cattle at Home Using Cheap Grain Sorghums," Feb. 13, 1959, p. 1.

Weaver, J. E., and F. W., Albertson, *Grasslands of the Great Plains: Their Nature and Use,* Johnsen Publishing Co., Lincoln, Neb., 1956.

Wright, Jim, "Co-operative Farming in Saskatchewan," *Canadian Geographical Journal,* Vol. 39, 1949, pp. 68–90.

12 · The Rocky Mountains

(Figures 1, 2)

The Rocky Mountains form the eastern portion of the North American cordillera, which extends from Alaska to Panama. They reach their southern limit along the eastern edge of the Colorado Plateau in north-central New Mexico; and their poleward thrust ends with the Brooks Range just south of Alaska's Arctic plain. The Great Plains lie to the east, and the Colorado Plateau, the Columbia Plateau, and the Basin and Range region lie to the west in continental United States. In Canada, the Fraser, Stikine, and Yukon plateaus form the western boundary; and in Alaska, where the Brooks Range section of the Rockies trends in an east-west direction, the Yukon Plateau borders on the south. The abrupt change in topography between the western edge of the Great Plains and the Rocky Mountains, especially the Canadian Rockies, startles some westbound travelers approaching the highlands by car or train. Mountain outlines lack the more mature, gentle, and rounded forms of the northern Appalachians; and there are many other contrasts between the Rockies and the Appalachians.

The Rockies have a general northwest-southeast trend, whereas that of the Appalachians is northeast-southwest. The length of the Rocky Mountain chain from New Mexico to Alaska is far greater than that of the Appalachians. The highest spot in the eastern mountains, Mount Mitchell, reaches less than 7,000 feet, but hundreds of peaks in the Rockies are more than 10,000 feet high. The Rocky Mountain revolution occurred toward the close of the Mesozoic era, while the Appalachian revolution occurred near the end of Paleozoic time; thus the Appalachians are older than the Rockies. West of the Appalachians, the Central Lowland forms one of the richest farm belts in the United States; west of the Rockies, in the United States, lies the most arid of the country's grazing lands. Although both mountain chains are forested, only the Rockies are high enough to have

315

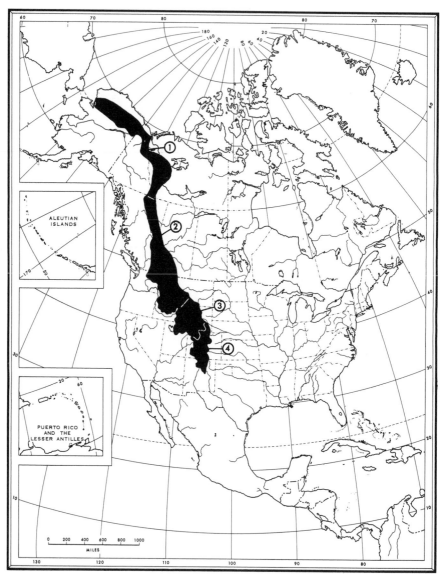

Fig. 1. The Rocky Mountains. The map shows (1) what A. K. Lobeck calls the Arctic Rockies, or the Brooks Range in Alaska and the Mackenzie Mountains in Canada; (2) the Northern Rockies of the United States and Canada; (3) the Central Rockies and the Wyoming Basin; and (4) the Southern Rockies.

mountain pastures above the tree line, where thousands of livestock graze during the summer season. The Rockies are more highly mineralized than the Appalachians, and comprise one of the continent's valuable mining regions.

Rocky Mountains in the United States

In continental United States the Rockies may be divided into four physiographic subregions, the Northern Rockies, the Central Rockies, the Wyoming Basin, and the Southern Rockies.

The Southern Rockies. The Southern Rockies include mountain features of various types. Many of the eastern foothills are hogbacks, nearby are north-south trending anticlinal structures such as the Colorado or Front Range; many parks, examples of which are North, Middle, South, and San Luis, possess the same north-south alignment as mountain ranges which they separate; these parks, primarily of structural origin, and secondarily of alluvial formation, support significant agricultural developments; and finally, irregular mountain knots of igneous origin, such as the San Juan Mountains in southwest Colorado, are noted for minerals.

The Wyoming Basin. The Wyoming Basin, with an area approximating that of New York State, lies to the north of the Southern Rockies, and separates the latter from the Central Rockies. Included within the basin are a number of elevated plains or small basins separated from one another by low mountains. Cinder cones, cuestas, badlands, hogbacks, and plateau escarpments may also be seen. With much less relief than any other Rocky Mountain subregion, the Wyoming Basin could be considered a western embayment of the Great Plains.

The embayment has long been actively utilized by many means of transportation. The Union Pacific, the first transcontinental railroad, passes over the southern part of the basin; closely paralleling the railroad is U. S. route 30, one of the most important, and most heavily traveled, motor roads in the country; and long before U. S. route 30 and the Union Pacific reached the Rockies, the basin became a part of the Oregon Trail and of many other exploratory routes.

The Central Rockies. Anticlinal structure dominates much of the folding in Central Rocky Mountain ranges—ranges such as the Wind River, the Tetons, and the Big Horn; and this structure is responsible for the major mountain trends. Distributed among these anticlines are several intermontane lowlands. One of the largest of these is the Big Horn Basin, an elliptical syncline filled with sedimentary rocks. Big Horn Basin sediments show continuity with those of the Great Plains, and contribute significantly to Rocky Mountain economy. Underground water is available for irrigation, and petroleum and natural gas provide important power resources.

Fig. 2. Structure Section from the Northern Great Plains to the Pacific. This simplified diagrammatic structure section represents the northern margin of the United States from the Pacific Ocean to the Great Plains, and passes through the states of Washington, Idaho, Montana, and North Dakota. Notice the Lewis Overthrust where the Lewis and Clark ranges of the Northern

The Northern Rockies. The Northern Rockies extend northwest from the Yellowstone Park boundary with the Central Rockies far beyond the Canadian-United States border. This is one of many examples showing a lack of correlation between geographical and political boundaries. Folding, block faulting, vulcanism, and dissection by ice and water, all have been active in shaping the Northern Rockies.

In Montana, the great Lewis Overthrust Fault (Fig. 2) has carried already-folded strata east over the western edge of the Great Plains. Again, the Purcell Range, mostly in Canada, is an upthrust block or horst containing several smaller horsts. Downfaulting is present in the Northern Rockies as well as thrust faults and horsts. One of the most conspicuous features of the entire Rocky Mountain system is a structural depression sometimes called the Rocky Mountain Trench. This depression extends from Flathead Lake, in Montana, to the headwaters of the Yukon in Canada, approximately the entire length of the Northern Rockies. Other examples of downfaulting include the Kootenai Valley in Idaho, near the British Columbia border, the Bitter Root Valley in Montana, and the Purcell Trench in the same state.

In Idaho, the Salmon River Mountains are dissected remnants of an old granite batholith; and, in Montana, volcanic action made Butte what has been called the richest hill on earth.

Glaciation has been more active in the Northern Rockies than in mountains farther south. One of the best examples of Alpine glaciation may be seen in Waterton-Glacier International Peace Park, occupying border sections of both Canada and the United States. Active dissection by water may be observed on the main streams and their tributaries throughout the region.

Rocky Mountains in Canada and Alaska

The Rockies in Canada may be divided into two major groups, (*a*) those at the south in eastern British Columbia and western Alberta, and

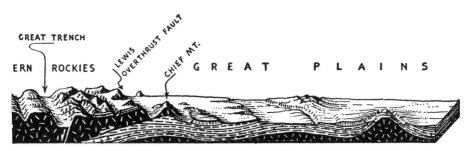

Rockies have been moved east about 15 miles by thrust faulting. Chief Mountain is sometimes called the mountain without roots. (After Wallace W. Atwood, *The Physiographic Provinces of North America,* Ginn and Co.)

(*b*) those at the north on the border of the Yukon and Northwest Territories.

The Southern Group. The southern group includes mountains popularly known as the Canadian Rockies, as well as Canadian portions of the Purcell, Selkirk, and Columbia ranges. Among the Canadian Rockies are some of the most majestic peaks and glaciers to be found anywhere on the continent (Fig. 3). Three passes form the most practicable motor and railroad routes across the Canadian Rockies. The northernmost pass, the Yellowhead in Jasper National Park, has an elevation of 3,700 feet and is used by the Canadian National Railroad. This pass provides the lowest route across the Rockies anywhere on the continent. The Canadian Pacific Railroad utilizes the Kicking Horse Pass and the Crowsnest Pass lying to the south, passes that are also traversed by motor roads.

The Northern Group. The Mackenzie Mountains dominate the northern group and form a gigantic curve about 500 miles long; they possess features similar to those of a sharply dissected plateau. Streams rising in the higher western ridges cut through the eastern paralleling ridges in deep canyons to reach the Mackenzie River. Canada's Mackenzie Mountains are not so high as the British Columbia Canadian Rockies, but many of their bare rock surfaces have remained unexplored by man.

The Alaskan Rockies. The Brooks Range, lying north of the Yukon Plateau in Alaska and Canada, possesses a number of glaciers and is almost completely covered with perennial snow. The remarkable uniformity in summit elevations suggests uplift of an ancient peneplain.

Rocky Mountain Climates

Altitude is the most important climatic influence over most of the Rockies, but the ranges have such a great north-south extent that latitude is also significant. Moreover, the entire physiographic province is influenced by the prevailing westerly winds, in some sections for the entire year and in other areas at least part of the year.

Fig. 3. Valley Glacier in the Canadian Rockies. Tumbling Glacier moves down the side of Mount Robson. Pieces that break off the bottom float in the icy waters of Berg Lake, and give it its name. (Courtesy Canadian National Railways.)

High latitude brings permanent snow on peaks at moderate elevations in the north; in the south, low latitude permits no perennial snow except at extremely high elevations. Western Rockies receive highest precipitation because of exposure to rain-bearing winds. Leeward slopes receive less moisture, and enclosed basins may receive hardly any. Precipitation is not so great as in the Cascade and Sierra Nevada ranges. Wind velocities are stronger as altitude increases, and mountain and valley winds are well developed. Chinooks, characteristic of the western Great Plains, are found in wide open spaces like the Wyoming Basin.

High altitudes bring decreases in pressure and temperature. Temperature decrease with elevation is not uniform, because inversions are remarkably well developed in mountain valleys. Moreover, there are greater differences in diurnal and seasonal temperature ranges in mountain valleys than upon the mountain slopes.

It should also be noted that although thin dry air of the mountains is incapable of absorbing much insolation, mountain soils absorb much more incoming solar heat than do soils of low altitudes. Increase in soil temperatures has a significant effect upon plant growth.

Vegetation and Soils. A climb to the summit of a Rocky Mountain range, will enable a person to pass from one plant zone to another in a relatively short distance. In the Colorado Rockies, lowland vegetation may include greasewood and sagebrush. On the foothills, dwarfed cedars and piñons signal a change in elevation. As altitude increases a continuous forest includes pine and aspen in the lower portion and spruce and fir a little higher up.

Still higher, dwarf cedar, juniper, shrubs, and low flowering plants are characteristic. At loftier elevations is the zone of grasses which occupy all the high alpine benchlands and basins wherever there is sufficient soil. They are luxuriant in summer and furnish pasture for thousands and thousands of livestock. In fact, transhumance is widespread throughout the Rocky Mountain area of the United States. Alpine flora includes an abundance of blossoming plants and large sections of the mountain side are reminiscent of a carefully tended flower garden. All plant forms are stunted by the cool, short growing season which permits little opportunity to grow long stems.

Above the zone of grasses, a variety of lichens on bare rock surfaces are encountered, and even tiny algae may occur on the snow, near mountain summits. Thus, within a short horizontal distance, life forms vary from those of the middle latitude to those of the polar regions. In Canada and Alaska, life forms also vary, but the tree zone, if any, occurs at much lower altitudes.

Soils of the Rocky Mountains are as variable as the vegetation. Where slopes are steep there is little opportunity for normal soil development. In the basins along streams, frequent floods may bring alluvial deposits, which tend to keep soils in a youthful stage. Forested sections may contribute less humus than grassy areas. Precipitation on enclosed basins may be so low that little vegetation develops and soils may be almost devoid of humus, yet retaining their natural mineral constituents.

The Rocky Mountain Barrier

Generally, mountains are considered to be barriers for many of man's activities, especially for transportation; but the barrier quality may be lessened if low-altitude passes are available. Consequently, in the human history of mountains, one of man's first tasks has been to locate all the easy routes and to plan his trails, roads, railroads, air routes, etc., so that they may focus upon and go through the easiest breaks in the highlands.

Most men who discovered the now well-known Rocky Mountain passes were trappers and traders (Fig. 4). In the search for animals to trap and Indian villages where they could trade, they followed mountain streams to their sources. Sources of some streams were near divides, across which headwaters of other stream systems led in an opposite direction. Such is the situation of South Pass, a mountain break which led to Fort Hall, Idaho, and to Salt Lake, Utah, and beyond. South Pass is 20 miles wide, with the sources of the Sweetwater River on the east and Sandy Creek, a tributary of the Green River on the west. Both east and west approaches were easy of ascent and the road was hard and compact. So gradual was the ascent that many travelers could not recognize the actual divide between Atlantic

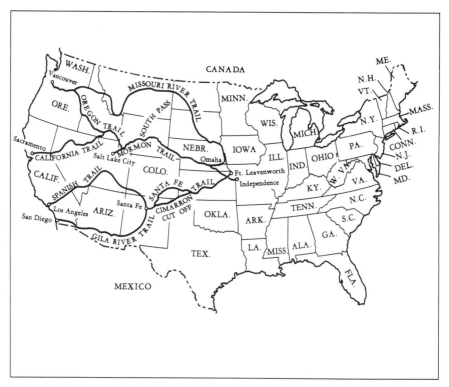

Fig. 4. Famous Western Trails. The early westward-moving pioneers took advantage of the principle that the barrier nature of mountains varies with the height, number, and accessibility of the passes. Travelers crossed the Rockies (1) over the lowest broadest passes; (2) where the mountains narrow; or (3) where the mountains may be bypassed. Many of the old trails follow the same routes, in general, as railroads do today. Names of some states have been omitted to give greater emphasis to the trails.

and Pacific drainage. South Pass, in west-central Wyoming, attained great historical significance as one of the easiest breaks through the Rockies.

Another route useful to traders and trappers was the Lewis and Clark Trail over the Rocky Mountains by way of the Missouri River. A decided advantage of the Missouri route is the fact that it approaches the North American cordillera at one of its narrower sections. Moreover, narrowness permits easier passage of the westerly winds which bring greater precipitation to the northern route than occurs on the Southern Rockies; water supply was sometimes a problem in crossing the Rockies.

For example, the direct approach to Santa Fe, New Mexico, led from Independence, Missouri, along the Arkansas River to the Cimarron Crossing, beginning in Kansas, and thence through Wagon Mound, New Mexico. Although this direct route to Santa Fe had the advantage of avoiding mountainous relief, a long stretch of 70 miles had no water. The mountain route followed the Arkansas into Colorado to Bent's Fort, then south by way of Purgatoire and Timpas rivers over Raton Pass. Water was available all along this route; but it was more indirect and required a greater expenditure of mule power.

The Rocky Mountains are still barriers to modern transport, just as they were to more primitive means of travel in the early 1800's. Only nine railroads (Fig. 5) cross the continent to the Pacific. The route of the Denver and Rio Grande Western illustrates the serious obstacle which mountains can cause to railroad traffic. In 1902, Daniel H. Moffat envisioned a route between Denver and Salt Lake City which would save 175 miles of difficult mountain travel, eight hours for trains moving freight, and six hours for passenger trains; the prospective route would permit transport during winter when travel over the high passes is blocked by snow.

Moffat's vision involved the 6-mile-long Moffat tunnel and the Dotsero cutoff of 38 miles. Thirty-two years elapsed before the Moffat-Dotsero route was officially opened, June 15, 1934; for the project, which involved the expenditure of millions of dollars, faced financial problems as well as the mountain barrier. Today, the tunnel provides a short passageway for trains, telegraph, telephone, and electric power lines, and also carries a pipeline to bring water to the city of Denver, Colorado.

Two other transcontinental railroads, the Santa Fe and the Southern Pacific really do not cross the Rockies, but avoid them completely by taking the southern route. Routes of the Northern Pacific, the Great Northern, and the Chicago, Milwaukee, and St. Paul go through the mountains in Montana, thus taking advantage of the narrower Northern Rockies. The first railroad to cross the continent, the Union Pacific, follows a route over the relatively favorable terrain of the Wyoming Basin which, as previously indicated, separates the Central Rockies from the Northern Rockies. Only two Canadian railroads cross the Rockies, the Canadian Pacific with its

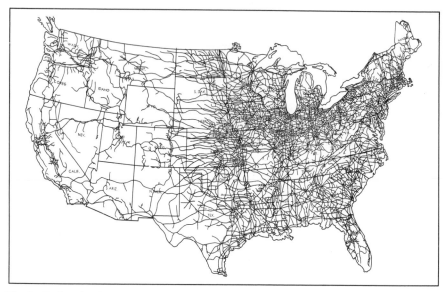

Fig. 5.   Railroads of the United States.   Point out areas in which relief is the most important influence in discouraging railroads. (Courtesy Association of American Railroads.)

western terminus at Vancouver, and the Canadian National, which reaches the Pacific at Prince Rupert.   These two rail lines take advantage of breaks through the Rockies.

Motor transport has found the mountains as much of a barrier as the railroads, and most through traffic uses the Wyoming Basin and routes south of the Rockies to reach the Pacific.   During the summer, however, thousands of motorists use the high passes of Colorado in order to enjoy mountain scenery of surpassing beauty and grandeur, scenery which is unavailable to tourists during winter because roads are blocked with snow. Thirty-four passes in the Colorado Rockies are 10,000 feet or more in altitude; eighteen are 11,000 feet or more; four are 12,000 feet, and one is over 13,000 feet.

Mountainous relief even exerts a barrier influence on air transport. The trouble is not so much with the mountain wall itself as it is with treacherous air currents that result from the rugged terrain.   Aviators have known for a long while that air flow over mountainous terrain may be very erratic, especially when wind velocity is 30 miles an hour or more.   Recently, large amounts of money and time have been spent on mountain wave research (Fig. 6); and from this research it has been learned that when a wave passes the crest of a mountain, the air breaks into a complicated pattern with downdrafts predominating.   An indication of possible intensities can be gained from verified records of sustained downdrafts, and also updrafts, of at least

3,000 feet per minute; other reports are well in excess of this figure. Thus, it behooves the airmen to know how to identify a wave situation, and having identified it to plan flights so as to avoid the wave hazards. Even with these precautions, too many horrible air tragedies occur because of weather perils over mountainous terrain.

Minerals

(Figures 7, 8)

The barrier character of the Rockies is a negative influence on man, but the mountains exert many positive influences as well. Minerals provide one of the region's most important economic resources. Active prospecting for metals began in the Rockies after the Sierra Nevada gold discovery in 1848. Popular opinion held that if mountains in one place contained gold, highlands in another location should contain gold. Popular opinion was correct. Mountains or former mountainous areas are likely to contain minerals for the following reasons. In the first place, mountain building may lift minerals upward from great depths within the earth's crust. Secondly, the same uplift which brings minerals near the surface also lifts the overburden to heights where overlying materials are more easily attacked by agencies of erosion, especially water and ice. Given enough time, these erosive agents will remove much of the overburden from the buried minerals.

Gold was one of the first metals sought in the Rockies just as in the Sierra Nevada Range. It was discovered in 1858, in Colorado, in Cherry

Fig. 6. Mountain Wave Causes Extreme Turbulence. Generalized sketch of air movements on lee side of mountain affected by a mountain wave. (Courtesy U. S. Weather Bureau.)

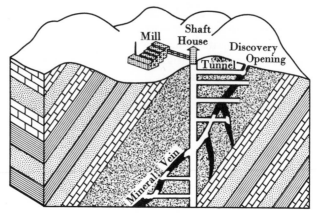

Fig. 7. Shaft Mining. Many Rocky Mountain minerals are exploited by shaft mining. A diagram shows how metal ores are mined deep within the earth. The perpendicular hole is the mine shaft. From the shaft, side tunnels lead to the mineral vein, where the miners dig and blast out the ore. Cars carry the ore along tunnels to the shaft and are lifted to the surface. (After W. W. Atwood.)

Creek near its junction with the South Platte. This site is part of the present location of Denver, and the town received one of its first growth stimuli from local mining activities. After the depletion of Denver's gold reserves, Central City, to the west, became active. But Central City's gold reserves also declined, and by 1900 the majority of Central City's business houses and homes were empty and mining machinery was gathering rust under the collapsing roofs of once-busy mills. The richest mining days were over.

All Rocky Mountain mining areas did not decline at the turn of the century. Butte, Montana, continued operations; and the city is a prosperous mining center today, after nearly 100 years of cyclic mining activity. In 1864, Butte placers were worked for gold. After a few years, gold extraction became less profitable and many miners moved away. About the only major economic activity that remained was dry farming and grazing of livestock on steppe land pastures. Not long after the decline of gold mining, a silver discovery brought a second influx of miners. Population again declined when the best silver deposits were depleted. In the 1870's a rich vein of copper was uncovered, and copper and Butte have been almost synonomous ever since.

Increases and declines in population caused by discovery and exhaustion of gold and silver have continued to occur in Butte during the nearly a century of copper mining. These population changes have been associated with price changes in the metal, the depletion of high-grade reserves, and the invention of new methods of mining and handling of the ore. In the early 1940's, copper prices were down and thousands of miners left Butte. Prophets of gloom predicted that Butte's mining days were over. Their prophecies failed to materialize, however, for with the utilization of block-caving methods, Butte may look forward to several decades of mining in the large resources of low-grade ores.

Butte and the rest of the mining centers in the Northern Rockies mine other metals besides copper. In 1953, the Butte district led in the production of zinc (75,170 short tons), with Montana (80,271 short tons) leading all other states.

Montana did not rank as high in lead mining as in zinc recovery, standing fifth with 19,949 short tons, behind Missouri, Idaho, Washington, and Colorado in the order named. In 1952, Montana ranked third behind Idaho and Utah in the production of silver, 6,138,185 fine ounces. Montana produces a little gold, but stands far behind other Western states in that precious metal. Montana's Butte and Philipsburg districts are ranked among the eleven largest in manganese reserves of the United States; and Montana's Stillwater complex of subgrade chrome is one of the largest reserves of this valuable alloy in the country.

Idaho, another state in the Northern Rockies, also ranks high among mining states. The Coeur d'Alene district (69,885 short tons) is second only to Southeast Missouri in the production of lead; and Idaho (74,610 short tons) ranks next to Missouri in exploiting that metal. Idaho (72,153 short

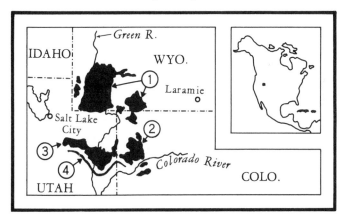

Fig. 8. Rocky Mountain Oil Shale. Three areas of oil shale are (1) the Green River Basin; (2) the Piceance Creek Basin; and (3) the Uinta Basin. Book Cliffs (4) border the oil shale on the south. In countries where gasoline is high, as in Scotland, oil shale has been processed for a century. With relatively cheap petroleum in the United States, the processing of huge reserves of Rocky Mountain oil shale will await lower cost processing or higher priced gasoline. Significant reserves of liquid petroleum and natural gas are also found in the Rocky Mountains. In 1954, oil reserves in thousands of barrels were as follows: for Colorado, 341,398; Montana, 279,573; New Mexico, 1,145,877; and Wyoming, 1,354,263. The figures for natural gas in millions of cubic feet were, Colorado, 1,932,913; Montana, 723,731; New Mexico, 17,240,669; and Wyoming, 2,855,071. All figures from "Mineral Facts and Problems," *Bulletin 556*, Bureau of Mines, 1956. (After map in *Forbes*, April 1, 1957.)

tons) takes second place behind Montana in the mining of zinc, but leads all the states in silver production, with 14,923,165 fine ounces in 1952. Like Montana, Idaho has a low rank in the production of gold, with only 32,997 fine ounces in 1952. Idaho's mercury reserves total about 60,000 seventy-six pound flasks.

Mining is not as significant in the Central Rockies as it is farther north. Park City, Utah, production of lead and zinc has been high in the past, but declined to less than 5,000 short tons for each of the metals in 1953. There is some coal of good quality in southwest Wyoming, and petroleum wells are producing in Wyoming's Big Horn and Wyoming basins.

Although mining is more important in the Southern Rockies than in the Central ranges, it is not so productive as in the Northern Rockies. In the past, names like Cripple Creek, Central City, Creede, Silverton, and many others were associated with rich strikes of gold and silver. Today, Colorado is probably best known for its Climax district, where most of the state's 92 per cent of the world's molybdenum was produced in 1953. Large vanadium reserves are also present in the Southern Rockies along the border between Colorado and Utah. Colorado does not rank high in manganese reserves, but those of the Leadville district total 700,000 tons of metallic manganese. In 1953, Colorado's production of lead (21,754 short tons) and zinc (37,809 tons) placed the state among leading producers.

The Southern Rockies are also important in the production of tungsten and fluorspar, with Colorado second in production of the latter in 1953. Some gold and silver are still produced, with Colorado's total of gold 124,594 fine ounces in 1952; silver production reached 2,813,643 fine ounces in the same year; these figures made Colorado the fifth in rank in both metals, but well behind four other states. Gold and silver mining is very sensitive to federal action on the prices of the precious metals; activity in other mineral production is also affected by government action [1] on the defense program, mineral stock piling, etc.

Mining is a leading industry in the Canadian portion of the Northern Rockies. One of the best-known mines is the Sullivan property near Kimberly, British Columbia. This one mine in the early 1950's yielded annually about 10 per cent of the world's lead, more than 5 per cent of world zinc, and 2 per cent of the world's silver. Production also includes antimony, bismuth, cadmium, copper, and gold.

---

[1] The Leadville district of Colorado has been an important mining area for years, but now its lead and zinc production is surpassed by the output of molybdenum. Climax, Colorado, at 11,000 feet, is a big corporation molybdenum mining town with deep shafts, large smelters, stores, and homes for the workers. The metal is used as an alloy with steel for the manufacture of aircraft, motors, etc. The American Metals-Climax Corporation has had a big government contract for much of the molybdenum for several years, with one in force at present. All the above mineral statistics are taken from *Bulletin 556, Mineral Facts and Problems,* by the staff of the Bureau of Mines, 1956.

Ores of the Sullivan mine and other mines of the Canadian Rockies are smelted and refined at Trail, British Columbia, one of the world's largest non-ferrous metallurgical centers. Power for Trail's industries is developed along the Kootenay River, below Nelson, and along smaller rivers near the smelting plants.

Some years ago, an international controversy developed over fumes from Trail smelters, fumes which were carried by the prevailing winds across the United States border a few miles to the south. These chemicals killed whatever vegetation was growing along their path. The problem was settled amicably when the Canadian mining corporation built a plant to transform the vegetation-killing sulfur dioxide into economically useful sulfuric acid. The Trail smelter also processes phosphates, purchased from Montana reserves, into commercial fertilizer which is sold to local farmers. Expansion in fertilizer production may make it available to farmers on the Canadian prairies.

Mining in Canada's Mackenzie Mountains and Alaska's Brooks Range has been developed but little. If gold, silver, or diamonds are discovered, a rush to these isolated districts will take place, for man will surmount any obstacles to obtain precious metals. However, isolation is likely to keep down exploitation of non-precious varieties of minerals.

Agriculture

(Figure 9)

The early history of mining is closely related to the start of mountain agriculture. Most miners thought little about availability of food and very little about producing it themselves. That attitude, plus the distance from Eastern markets, made farming profitable along the eastern Piedmont and within the parks.[2]

For a while a movement to establish agricultural colonies took place. This practice was pushed by railroads, who sold farms from their land grants to the settlers in the 1860's and 1870's, and by land companies who encouraged several group settlements.

As long as agriculture did not expand beyond the needs of the local market, farmers prospered. But when production brought a surplus, farming was not so attractive. Isolation from the Eastern market was, and still is, a major farm problem.

A few statistics may give information on farming in the 1950's. Five Rocky Mountain states, Idaho, Montana, Wyoming, Colorado, and New

[2] Parks of the Southern Rockies are broad depressions in which trees are either absent or scattered. The nearly-level-floored structural basins receive sedimentary deposits from the high, rugged, and frequently snow-covered mountains surrounding them. North Park is drained by the North Platte; South Park by the South Platte; Middle Park by the Grand River, a tributary of the Colorado; and San Luis Park by the Rio Grande.

Fig. 9. The Colorado-Big Thompson Irrigation Project. One way in which man adjusts to the barrier nature of mountains is by digging tunnels through them. The Colorado-Big Thompson irrigation project brings Colorado River water through the Continental Divide in one of the world's longest tunnels, over 13 miles long. Thus, water falling west of the Rockies is available for Colorado's eastern plains. (Courtesy Gates Rubber Company.)

Mexico make up 353,000,000 acres of land, nearly 20 per cent of contiguous United States. Over half of the Rocky Mountain farms have some irrigation. For example, in Montana 18 per cent of the harvest is on irrigated land and over half of Wyoming's crop is under the ditch. New Mexico has 51 acres irrigated on each farm in contrast to 127 acres for each farm in Montana. In contrast, all of midwest Iowa's crop production is grown without irrigation, depending entirely on adequate, well-distributed precipitation.

Mountain farms average larger than those in the Midwest, 832 acres in Colorado and 2,728 acres in Wyoming. Iowa farms average 178 acres.

In Wyoming, 25 per cent of the land is in farms; Montana, 63 per cent; Iowa, a Corn Belt state, with more of its area in farms than any other state, 95.5 per cent. In Idaho, 27.6 per cent of the farm land is in crops, but the figure for Wyoming is only 5.5 per cent. Iowa has 59 per cent of its total farmland in crops.

Great effort and expense have been involved in Rocky Mountain irrigation facilities. For example, the Gunnison Valley contains a large river, but only a little flat land, whereas the neighboring Uncompahgre Valley contains a small river and an abundance of flat land. To bring the water to the land where it is needed, a tunnel six miles long has been dug through a ridge of mountains so that the water of the Gunnison River is now turned into the Uncompahgre Valley [3] (Fig. 9).

Most farm income is derived from livestock. In the five Rocky Mountain states, 41.2 per cent of the total farm income in 1949 came from crops, and 58 per cent came from livestock products. Much of the irrigation agriculture and dry farming provides feed for animals. Even though Weld County, Colorado, had 8.1 per cent of the national sugar beet acreage in 1949, and even though beets (Fig. 10) are raised primarily for sugar, the beet pulp and tops provide feed for cattle and sheep. Other livestock feed [4] comes from hay fields (Fig. 11) and from oats and barley.

In the 1950's, agriculture was more important than mining in the Southern Rockies, a contrast to the situation a century ago. Increased population gives the local market much more significance than it offered in the 1850's. Moreover, refrigeration and other improvements in long-distance transport encourage the growth of crops with sufficient value to withstand high car-

---

[3] Some may question the advisability of developing more irrigation on high-cost projects. Even now, farm subsidies reach billions of dollars. In short, raising surpluses by subsidy to be paid for by taxation, that already pays for dam building is a practice that has strong advocates *con* as well as *pro*.

[4] In Montana, significant crop and livestock production occurs around Anaconda, Butte, and Helena, where major emphasis is upon growing hay for feeding cattle and sheep. In Idaho, the Boise and Coeur d'Alene agricultural districts produce hay, potatoes, sugar beets, and wheat; livestock raising includes both dairy and beef breeds.

Fig. 10. Sugar Beets. This illustration shows sugar beets ready for harvest. The main roots extend seven feet into the earth and send out smaller side roots. When the beet is pulled from the ground, the small roots remain and add fertility to the soil. Sugar beet production results in two concentrated foods, sugar and meat. After the sugar has been extracted, the entire vegetable portions of the beet are available for feeding purposes. Fattened on these by-products— beet tops, pulp, and molasses—millions of lambs and hundreds of thousands of cattle are sent to the United States markets annually. An average acre of sugar beets produces about 3,500 pounds of pure sugar and 300 pounds of meat. (Courtesy Great Western Sugar Company.)

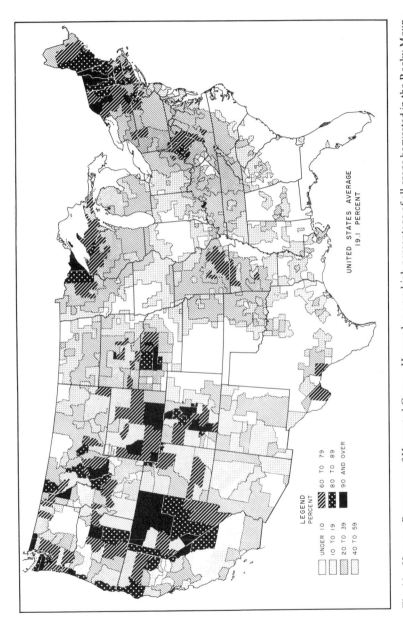

Fig. 11. Hay as a Percentage of Harvested Crops. Hay makes up a high percentage of all crops harvested in the Rocky Mountains, the Intermontane Plateaus, rugged New England, and in the Upper Lake region. Practically all hay in the Rocky Mountains and the Intermontane Plateaus is produced by irrigation. (Courtesy U. S. Department of Commerce, Bureau of the Census.)

rying charges. One such crop is iceberg lettuce, grown in the San Luis park area near Del Norte. At an altitude of about 8,000 feet, temperatures favor a high quality lettuce crop. Other irrigated crops in the valley include alfalfa, field peas, oats, and potatoes. Cattle and sheep are raised and fattened for local and long-distance markets.

Large acreages of nearly level surfaces in the several parks of the Southern Rockies encourage agricultural expansion; but at least two major handicaps dampen optimism for an increase in farm crops. These two are the shortness of the growing season and the long distance from the big Eastern market.

Grazing opportunities are widespread in the Rockies; in fact, the Rocky Mountains are sometimes called the American Switzerland; both Switzerland and the Rocky Mountain states raise cattle, but little emphasis is placed upon dairying in the Rockies. There is a resemblance to Switzerland, however, in the practice of transhumance. In the Rockies, as in the Swiss Alps, cattle and sheep are winter fed in the valleys, but they leave for the uplands as soon as the high sun starts melting the snow from the mountain pastures (Fig. 12). Winter pastures in the valleys may be kept open for many days in the cold season by the warm, snow-melting winds of the chinook (Fig. 13).

Much Rocky Mountain grassland has been overgrazed; this results in increased erosion and a lower quality of plant life. Sheep (Fig. 14) are likely to be the greatest offenders; sharp hoofs damage grasses and the cleft lip permits grazing closer than is possible for cattle. But cattle damage pastures as well as sheep, when the number of cattle on any specific area will not permit grass to maintain itself in a healthy condition.[5]

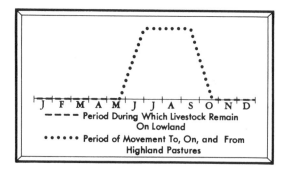

Fig. 12. Mountain and Valley Grazing. Transhumance may be shown diagrammatically as indicated by the above movements of livestock in the Colorado Rockies.

[5] Many cattle are grazed in parklike sections of the national forests. Parts of this timberland provide grazing of a substandard type in which the browse is not the best. Over a long term it may be better to discourage grazing and leave such marginal pasture lands entirely to forest.

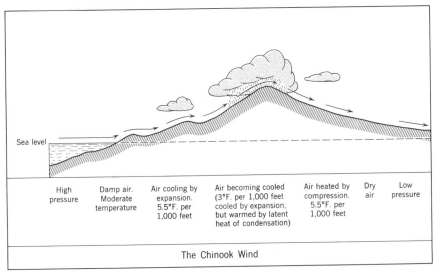

| High pressure | Damp air. Moderate temperature | Air cooling by expansion. 5.5°F. per 1,000 feet | Air becoming cooled (3°F. per 1,000 feet cooled by expansion, but warmed by latent heat of condensation) | Air heated by compression. 5.5°F. per 1,000 feet | Dry air | Low pressure |

The Chinook Wind

Fig. 13. Chinook Wind. The chinook is an economic aid to the cattle industry along the contact zone between the Northern Rockies and the Great Plains. (Courtesy C. E. Koeppe and McKnight and McKnight.)

Forestry

Forestry is not the important industry in the Rocky Mountains that it is in the Pacific Northwest; furthermore, largely because the Northern Rockies have a more humid climate than those to the south, Rocky Mountain forests of northern United States and southern Canada comprise better stands of high-quality trees. Much of the annual cut goes into mine props, railroad ties, and other construction materials for use in the Rocky Mountain region. This situation is influenced by the fact that Rocky Mountain forests are probably the least accessible of any of the important timberlands of the United States. No ocean borders them as it does forests of the Northwest, the Northeast, and the South. Nor are Rocky Mountain forests near any large inland waterway, like timberland contiguous to the Great Lakes. Thus, even if the forest resources were as valuable as the forest lands of the Northwest and South, the distance from the large markets and lack of water transportation would be an important handicap to exploitation.

About 13 per cent of the total forest land of the United States, approximately 63,000,000 acres, is in the Rocky Mountains. Large sections are owned by the federal government, with more than 50 national forests and 8 national parks established in the forest area. As a consequence of government ownership, conservation may be practiced more consistently than with private owners.

Fig. 14. The Shepherd and His Sheep. A flock of sheep in the Northern Rockies are grazing on valley pastures. Note the snow lying in the cirques above the tree line. (Courtesy *Farm Journal.*)

Because of the open character of the forests, especially those of the Southern Rockies, the saw timber stand is relatively light. Probably not more than half the timber can be exploited profitably. Nevertheless, forests are an important regional asset because (*a*) they supply local needs for forest products; (*b*) they protect rugged land from erosion; and (*c*) they encourage a more consistent runoff to supply the constant demands for irrigation.

Tourism

(Figure 3)

Colorado, Montana, and Wyoming list the tourist industry among their first three income producers, and in New Mexico it ranks first. Insofar as scenic attractions are concerned, their number is legion; some of the most spectacular are listed and briefly described below.

Southern Rockies. West of Canon City, Colorado, the Arkansas River issues from the V-shaped Royal Gorge that the stream has cut into the

Pre-Cambrian granitic core of the Rocky Mountain Front Range to a depth of approximately 2,000 feet.

Lake San Cristobal in the Gunnison River, near the north margin of the San Juan Mountains, was formed by disintegrated volcanic material which moved down a tributary valley and completely blocked the Gunnison. In time, a narrow lake outlet was established at the margin of the Great Slumgullion Mud Flow.

The Needle and Grenadier Mountains are monadnocks which have sharp pinnacle-like features in the San Juan Ranges. The slopes of many of them defy the boldest mountain climbers.

West of Colorado Springs and near Manitou, the upturned red beds at the eastern base of the Rocky Mountains have been weathered and eroded into a number of fantastic forms. Vertical walls of upturned sandstone, with narrow gateways through them rise to a height of 50 to 60 feet. As the winds, the rains, and the temperature changes have helped forward fragments of the rock material to the neighboring streams, holes have been worn out of the upturned strata, huge masses have been left as balanced rocks, mushrooms or toadstool-like forms have been weathered out where the layers offered a difference in resistance, and many sharp pinnacles have been left standing. Here in the Garden of the Gods, formations show some resemblance to statesmen, seals, bears, camels, etc.

In the heart of the Sawatch Range in central Colorado, not far from Redcliff, an impressive mountain rises to 13,966 feet. On the northeast side of this granitic peak, the joint planes and fissures are so arranged that the snow, which becomes lodged there, forms a great white cross hundreds of feet in length, from which the Mountain of the Holy Cross takes its name.

Rocky Mountain National Park, containing more than 400 square miles of the Front Range, lies about 50 miles northwest of Denver. In this picturesque area with Longs Peak, 14,255 feet high, topping many others which rise over 12,000 feet, there are tiny remnants of glaciers, many large catchment basins that formerly contained ice, a large number of lakes, long U-shaped troughs which were deepened and widened during the Ice Age by alpine glaciers, and a full assortment of moraines.

Central Rockies. If any one wishes to see glacial cirques and glacially scoured U-shaped valleys, he can find no better examples in the United States than in the Bighorn Range of the Central Rockies. Cirque walls, nearly vertical, reach heights of 1,000 to 1,500 feet. The Central Rockies also include the spectacular abrupt western wall of the Wasatch Range, and the flat-topped anticlinal Uinta Mountains, the largest east-west range in the United States, 150 miles of peaks and crests more than 12,000 feet high.

Most of Yellowstone Park, the oldest and largest national park in the United States, is located in the Central Rockies of northwestern Wyoming. Here may be seen an extensive lava plateau; several volcanic peaks; a beautiful display of hot spring terraces; a remarkable group of active geysers and geyser cones; the canyon of the Yellowstone River; a petrified forest; boiling mud in pools called paint pots; Yellowstone Lake, the highest large lake in America, 140 square miles and 300 feet deep; and spectacular Yellowstone Falls, where the river drops more than 300 feet over a vertical mass of hard fresh lava.

Northern Rockies. In Alberta and Montana, to the north and south of the international boundary line, Waterton-Glacier International Peace Park occupies about 2,000 square miles of magnificent mountain scenery. There are more than 75 glaciers, over 200 mountain lakes, and a huge sculptured mountain mass with cirques, sharp peaks, deep U-shaped canyons, and large thrust faults.

The biggest Canadian park, Jasper National Park, contains 4,200 square miles on Alberta's east slope of the Rockies. There are glaciers, perennial snow fields, Maligne Lake and hundreds of other lakes, hot springs, and deep canyons such as the one at Fiddle Creek, through which flows a roaring stream 200 feet below its rim. At places, the walls of this canyon are only 20 feet apart.

Among the many other Rocky Mountain parks, Banff, Yoho, Glacier, and Kootenay have been established because of their special scenic and scientific values. Alberta's Banff Park includes 2,585 square miles of mountain landscape and the celebrated Lake Louise. Yoho, Glacier, and Kootenay parks are in southeastern British Columbia. Each contains between 500 and 600 square miles of rugged mountain scenery, with numerous glaciers, snow fields, waterfalls, and mountain lakes. In the Yoho Valley one of the waterfalls is over 1,200 feet high.[6]

The scenic features just described attract millions of visitors. They come in the winter as well as in summer. In winter they ski at such spots as Sun Valley, Idaho, in the Saw Tooth Range, or at Jackson Hole, where powdery snow and the cold dry climate are ideal for sports. In summer, they come for sightseeing, fishing, hunting, mountain climbing, and for many other reasons. And yet the number of tourists visiting the Rockies each year is not so large as the number visiting mountain and shore country in eastern United States where scenery is far less spectacular. In 1950, visitors spent nearly $85,000,000 in Wyoming, an area of nearly 100,000 square miles. In the same year, tourists spent nearly a billion dollars in New England, an area of approximately 60,000 square miles. Here we see the application of a basic principle in tourism. The development of a profitable tourist industry depends not only upon scenic attractions but also on proximity to dense centers of population with high living standards.

---

[6] Much of the above description is based upon W. W. Atwood, *The Physiographic Provinces of North America,* Ginn and Co., 1940.

Summary and Conclusions

Many characteristics make the Rocky Mountains stand out as a geographic region. Altitude is higher than that of plains on the east and north, and plateaus on the west and south. Thus, the Rockies have always been a most serious barrier to all types of transport, to man on foot, on horseback, in covered wagon, in motorcar, on railroads, and on planes.

But in spite of, and partly because of, the barrier nature of the land forms, a variety of economic activities have developed. The high mountains wring moisture from prevailing westerly winds, especially in the form of winter snow, whose melt water supplies numerous irrigation projects. Mountain rain and snow plus steep valley walls provide suitable conditions for dams, used not only for irrigation farming but for water power. Mountain building, which provided a barrier region for all kinds of transport, encouraged the formation of minerals; these form the bases for numerous mining centers.

Cool moist climates of the high mountains aid the growth of forests, useful for many wood products; these climates also stimulate growth of high mountain grasses to supply feed for thousands of livestock in the summer time. However, mountain terrain and the consequent isolation make forest exploitation difficult; and isolation from the densely populated East and the less densely populated Pacific Coast, weakens tourism whose main attraction is the spectacular mountain scenery of the barrier region.

Thus, both the high mountain environment and man's activities so closely related to the mountains make the Rockies stand out as a geographic region—a region that will continue to stress and expand its mining, grazing, irrigation farming, forestry, and tourism.

QUESTIONS, EXERCISES, AND PROBLEMS

1. With a good atlas at hand, study the major mountain ranges that make up the Rocky Mountain system. Describe the geologic processes involved in the formation of the Rockies. Sketch a vegetation profile from valley lowland to mountain top.

2. Describe the barrier nature of the Rockies with reference to all types of transportation. Trace the main routes which were followed by early travelers en route to the West Coast. Why are minerals likely to be found in most mountains or in former mountainous lands? Indicate the major mining centers and the minerals produced at each center. Should the mining industry be subsidized by price supports like those which apply to farm commodities? Describe mining and population changes in Butte.

3. How was early mining related to agriculture? Compare Rocky Mountain states with Iowa as to size of their farms, percentage of land in farms, and farm land in crops. Describe Rocky Mountain livestock raising. Is there any similarity between the livestock industry of Switzerland and that of the Rockies?

4. Comment on the power resources of the Rocky Mountains. Make a study of the oil shale and the possibility of utilization in the near future.

5. Describe the forests and forest exploitation of the Rockies. Compare forestry activities with those of the South, New England, and the Northwest. Describe prominent geologic features found in Rocky Mountain national parks. Compare opportunities for tourism in the Rockies with those in New England. Comment upon regional manufacturing and commerce. What types of manufacturing are found and what are the bases for them?

6. Each of the following cities has approximately 10,000 people or more in its urban district: Anaconda, Bozeman, Butte, Coeur d'Alene, Helena, Kalispell, Missoula, Rock Springs, Santa Fe, Trail. Name major activities encouraging the growth of each population center. Notice the small number of cities and the small size of the urban centers. Explain. Describe the distribution of population in the Rockies.

7. Identify the following: syncline, faulting, anticline, undifferentiated soils, cordillera, placer, stamp mill, block caving, Rocky Mountain parks (a physiographic feature), transhumance, hogback, Lewis Overthrust, U-shaped valley, horst, batholith, Moffat Tunnel, mountain wave, Uncompahgre Valley, Sun Valley, Lake Louise, Fiddle Creek, Sawatch Range, Garden of the Gods, Wyoming Basin, Bighorn Basin, Kootenay Valley, Bitter Root Valley, Purcell Trench, Rocky Mountain Trench, Salmon River Mountains, South Pass, Central City, Climax.

SELECTED REFERENCES

Atwood, Wallace W., *The Physiographic Provinces of North America,* Ginn and Co., 1940, pp. 281–353.

Atwood, W. W., and W. W. Atwood, Jr., "A Working Hypothesis for the Physiographic History of the Rocky Mountain Region," *Bulletin of the Geological Society of America,* Vol. 49, 1938, pp. 957–980.

Bostock, H. S., "Physiography of the Canadian Cordillera, with Special Reference to the Area North of the Fifty-Fifth Parallel," *Geological Survey, Memoir 247,* Department of Mines and Resources, Canada, 1948.

Bowman, Isaiah, *Forest Physiography,* John Wiley and Sons, 1911, pp. 298–386.

Brown, Ralph H., *Historical Geography of the United States,* Harcourt, Brace and Co., 1948, pp. 442–452 and 455–459.

Calef, Wesley, "Problems of Grazing Administration in the Basins of Southern Wyoming," *Economic Geography,* April 1952, pp. 122–127.

Critchfield, Howard J., "Land Use Levels in Boundary County, Idaho," *Economic Geography,* July 1948, pp. 201–208.

Due, John F., "The Carson and Colorado Railroad," *Economic Geography,* July 1951, pp. 251–267.

Foscue, Edwin J., and Louis O. Quam, *Estes Park: Resort in the Rockies,* Southern Methodist University Press, Dallas, 1949.

Garwood, John D., "An Analysis of Post-war Industrial Migration to Utah and Colorado," *Economic Geography,* January 1953, pp. 79–88.

Hartley, F. L., and C. S. Brinegar, "Oil Shale and Bituminous Sand," *Scientific Monthly,* June 1957, pp. 275–289.

Haystead, Ladd, and Gilbert C. Fite, *The Agricultural Regions of the United States,* University of Oklahoma Press, 1955, pp. 218–232.

Hoffmeister, Harold A., "Middle Park and the Colorado-Big Thompson Diversion Project," *Economic Geography,* July 1947, pp. 220–231.

Ives, Ronald L., "Frequency and Physical Effects of Chinook Winds in the Colorado High Plains Region," *Annals of the Association of American Geographers,* December 1950, pp. 293–327.

Lackey, Earl B., "Mountain Passes in the Colorado Rockies," *Economic Geography,* July 1949, pp. 211–215.

Sampson, A. W., *Range Management: Principles and Practices,* John Wiley and Sons, 1952.

Stead, Robert J. C., "The Yellowhead Pass-Canadian Rockies," *Canadian Geographical Journal,* Vol. 36, 1948, pp. 51–65.

U. S. Department of the Interior, *Minerals Yearbook,* 1951, Copper, pp. 521–556; Lead, pp. 738–759; Molybdenum, pp. 856–864; Zinc, pp. 1319–1344.

U. S. Weather Bureau, "The Mountain Wave—What It Means to the Pilot," *Daily Weather Map,* Washington, D. C., March 2, 1955.

U. S. Weather Bureau, "Weather and Livestock," *Daily Weather Map,* Washington, D. C., March 10, 1953.

U. S. Weather Bureau, "Weather and Sheep," *Daily Weather Map,* Washington, D. C., March 16, 1955.

13 · The Intermontane Plateaus

(Figure 1)

The Intermontane Plateaus make up a huge, sparsely populated region whose economic value is not commensurate with its size. Over many parts, the terrain is too rugged for cultivated crops. But the limiting geographic factor for farming and dense forests is not topography. It is aridity. In the Great Plains, natural precipitation is marginal for growing crops; in most of the plateau country, agriculture is impossible without irrigation, and water for crops or for any other purpose is scarce.

Greater aridity is only one of several geographic factors that set off the region from areas surrounding it. As the regional name implies, many of the land forms may be classified as significant elevations with a maximum amount of summit level—plateaus. Nearly all the lands along the region's eastern border are high, with a minimum amount of summit level, that is, the Rocky Mountains; although the Great Plains, which are lower, lie to the southeast. Land forms to the west also differ from the Intermontane Plateaus. In the United States, the high Sierra Nevada and Cascade ranges form the western boundary; and in Canada and Alaska the plateaus are cut off from the Pacific by coastal ranges.

Not only are regional land forms and climates different from surrounding areas, but so is much of the vegetation; for the Intermontane Plateaus include the desert lands of North America, and also the continent's largest area of interior drainage. Most of the perennial streams—many are intermittent—that cross the region are of an exotic variety, having their sources in other regions.

As a result of the desert and steppe climates, soils retain most of their mineral constituents and, because of limited vegetation, contain only small amounts of humus.

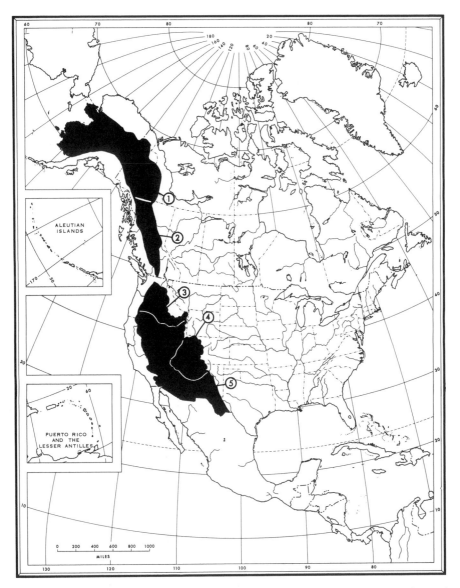

Fig. 1. The Intermontane Plateaus. This is one of Anglo-America's largest regions, and one of the most sparsely populated areas. A continuation of the region, not shown on the map, extends into bordering Mexico. Anglo-American subregions include (1) the Yukon Plateau; (2) the plateaus of British Columbia; (3) the Columbia Plateau; (4) the Colorado Plateaus; and (5) the Basin and Range country.

In a region as large as the Intermontane Plateaus, a better understanding of major and minor physiographic provinces may be obtained by dividing it into subregions. Thus, the United States portion may be broken up into three sections; the Basin and Range country; the Colorado Plateaus; and the Columbia Plateau. The Canadian-Alaskan portion falls into two main parts, the plateaus of British Columbia and the Yukon Plateau of Yukon Territory and Alaska.

Physiographic Divisions

The Basin and Range Province (Fig. 2). The Basin and Range physiographic province lies east of the Sierra Nevada, San Bernardino, and San Gabriel Mountains and includes an eastern strip of California, all of Nevada, western Utah, southwestern Arizona, southern New Mexico, and southwestern Texas. The total area makes up approximately 10 per cent of continental United States.

Uniformity in land forms is characteristic of the entire area. Everywhere rugged parallel ranges are separated by long, wide, smooth-floored alluvial basins. However, enough contrast is present within the region to suggest four subdivisions, the Great Basin, the Sonoran Desert, the Salton Trough, and the Mexican Highland.

The Colorado Plateaus. The Colorado Plateaus comprise approximately 130,000 square miles, an area a little larger than New Mexico, or about twice the size of New England. These high tablelands are bounded on the east and north by the Rocky Mountains, on the west by the Great Basin, and on the south by the Mexican Highland.

The plateaus possess two distinct characteristics, which make them stand out as a separate subregion: (*a*) generally horizontal sedimentary rocks cover the region; these were upraised with a minimum of deformation after deposition by the sea; and (*b*) plateau surfaces are trenched by deep canyons. Canyon cutting has been aided by the rapid downward erosion of master streams, by great differences in erosional resistance of the strata, by an arid climate, and by scarcity of vegetation.

Although the plateaus show uniformity in the physical features just mentioned, certain differences do exist. As a consequence, the Colorado Plateaus may be subdivided into six parts: the Grand Canyon section, the High Plateaus of Utah, the Uinta Basin, the Canyon Lands of southeastern Utah and the adjoining section of Colorado, the Navajo section of northeastern Arizona and nearby New Mexico, and the Datil section of east-central Arizona and west-central New Mexico.

The Columbia Plateaus. The Columbia Plateaus include a large variety of physical features whose bases of unity lie in their common association

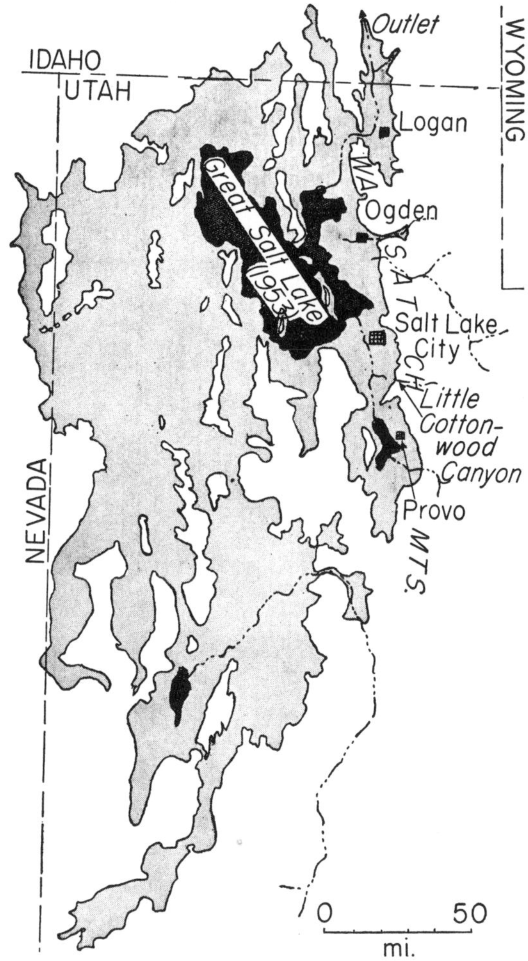

Fig. 2. Great Salt Lake and Lake Bonneville. The Great Basin has more permanent or semipermanent lakes in the north than in the south; these lakes receive their water from mountain streams coursing down the Sierra Nevada and Wasatch ranges. During Pleistocene time, Lake Bonneville, the ancestor of Great Salt Lake, and Lake Lahontan, ancestor of the lakes and playas of west-central Nevada, were much larger than their remnants today. (Source: C. R. Longwell and R. F. Flint, *Introduction to Physical Geology*, John Wiley and Sons, 1955.)

with widespread sheets of basaltic lava. These basaltic flows cover more than 200,000 square miles, an area larger than California, and one of the largest stretches of volcanic rock in the world.

Surface features include small plateaus both level and tilted, hills, eroded slopes, rugged mountains, broad valleys, basins, upfolded ridges, and flat plains. Thus, it is not surprising that Otis Freeman has chosen the name "Columbia Intermontane Province" for Fenneman's "Columbia Plateaus." Freeman divides the province into four subdivisions: the Columbia Basin, the Central Highlands, the High Lava Plains, and the Owyhee Upland (Fig. 3).

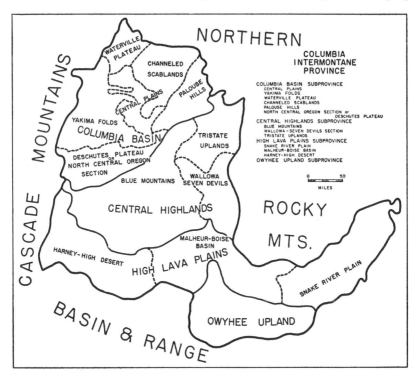

Fig. 3. Physiographic Subdivisions of the Columbia Intermontane Province. Otis Freeman makes four major subdivisions and twelve minor subdivisions of the Columbia Intermontane Province. (Source: Otis W. Freeman, Howard H. Martin, *The Pacific Northwest,* 2nd ed., John Wiley and Sons, 1954.)

The Plateaus of British Columbia.[1]   British Columbia's intermontane subregion extends north of the Okanogan Mountains for approximately 500 miles.   In northern British Columbia, a complex of mountain ranges connects the Rocky Mountains with the Coast Ranges and separates the British Columbia Plateaus from the Yukon Plateau.   The former, which include the Fraser and Stikine Plateaus, are much more dissected than portions of the Intermontane Plateaus found in the United States.   Erosion has been accomplished by both water and ice.   The Fraser River has developed an extensive drainage system.

The Yukon Plateau.   Much of the Yukon Plateau lies in Yukon Territory, with British Columbia to the south, and Alaska, into which the plateau

---

[1] It is suggested that students be given assigned readings in the books of W. W. Atwood, Isaiah Bowman, Otis W. Freeman, Howard H. Martin, and Nevin Fenneman, most of whose works are listed at the close of the chapter.   Such an assignment will give better student understanding of the somewhat complicated physiography of the Intermontane Plateaus, the Rocky Mountains, and the Pacific Borderlands.

continues to the north and west. The Canadian Yukon rises to approximately 6,000 feet, and is made up largely of ancient metamorphic rocks. Elevations in the Alaskan portion range from 2,000 to 4,000 feet. Long-continued erosion has brought about much peneplanation.

Climates in the United States Plateaus (Fig. 4). The diversity of land forms gives rise to a patchy distribution of climates and vegetation. Mountain, plateau, and lowland cause local modifications of the generally dry continental climate. A major cause for aridity is the location in the rain-shadow of the mountain barrier to the west. With the exception of small areas in the uplands, precipitation is everywhere less than 20 inches; it is mostly below 10 inches; Nevada, the most arid of states, has an average mean annual of less than 9 inches. More rainfall occurs in the northern part because of the greater frequency of general storms and the lesser effectiveness of the mountain barrier. The real American desert is in southeastern California, southwestern Arizona, and western Nevada.

Much winter precipitation comes in the form of snow, more in the north than in the south and more on higher elevations than upon lowlands. Snow is rare in the far southwest except on the mountains. Active evaporation causes rapid disappearance of moisture.

Precipitation varies with different stations. In the north, the maximum may come in late winter or spring. In the south, the primary maximum usually comes in late summer with a secondary maximum in the winter. The far southwest has the lowest number of days with rain and the fewest hours

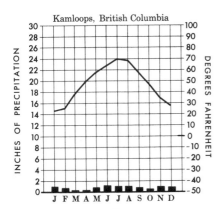
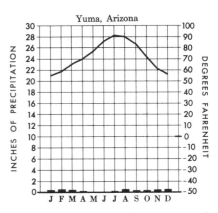

Fig. 4. Kamloops, British Columbia (50° 42′ N., 120° 22′ W.; altitude 1,193 feet; mean annual temp. 47° F.; mean annual precip. 10.1 inches); Yuma, Arizona (32° 41′ N., 114° 37′ W.; altitude 141 feet; mean annual temp. 72° F.; mean annual precip. 3.1 inches). Kamloops has a steppe, BS, climate; that of Yuma may be classified as desert, BW. With much lower temperature, rainfall efficiency is greater in Kamloops than in Yuma; moreover, Kamloops rainfall is three times that of Yuma. However, irrigation is necessary at both places for dependable cultivated crop agriculture.

of cloud cover. Hotels in some southwestern cities advertise free room and board for any day without sunshine.

Temperatures, like rainfall, are influenced by land forms. The minimums are largely a matter of local topographic control and of air drainage. Killing frost dates vary as much as the minimum temperatures. Summers in the southern lowlands are long and intensely hot, but low humidity makes high temperatures endurable. Southern winters are comparatively mild, dry, and bracing. Northern summers are cooler than those of the south and winters are colder. Dry stimulating air, an abundance of sunshine, large diurnal ranges of temperature—these are dominant characteristics of the plateau climates as a whole.

Climates in Canadian and Alaskan Plateaus. Everywhere in the Intermontane Plateaus Region, mountains as barriers and altitude are important climatic controls; but in the Canadian and Alaskan sections, high latitude may be of greater importance. It limits crops in the Fraser Plateau to hardy fruits such as apples and cherries and to cold- and drought-resistant cereals; in the Yukon, the low winter temperatures and short frost-free season make any kind of agriculture hazardous. As in the United States, precipitation and temperature vary with altitude. Marine influences are at a minimum because of location in the lee of the Coast Ranges.

Vegetation. The diversity of plateau climates, which are influenced largely by diversity in land forms and latitudes, causes great diversity in plant cover. Soil may also exert an influence on differences in vegetation. For example, in the Southwest, sagebrush occurs on deep alluvial non-saline soils of Utah, Nevada, and in California east of the Sierras; but where lands are extremely hot and dry, and where alkali appears near the surface, sagebrush gives way to greasewood and shadscale. On the salt flats, halophytic vegetation takes over completely, a situation easily noted around the borders of Great Salt Lake.

In southeastern Arizona, a desert grassland varying from compact sod to open single-spaced clumps of grass makes rapid growth following the rainy periods of both summer and winter. This grazing land lies at elevations of 3,000 to 4,500 feet, between the desert below and the chaparral above. Large grass areas also occur at 5,000 to 7,000 feet on the plateaus of central and northern Arizona, below the piñon-juniper or yellow pine forests with which they make contact and form an understory vegetation. Because of lower temperatures, the vegetation is more varied, and it resembles the grassland just east of the Rocky Mountains. Originally these plateau grasslands were good range lands, but large sections have been overgrazed.

The needle-leaved or piñon-juniper woodland is widespread, with best development between 5,000 and 7,000 feet, elevations intermediate between the occurrence of mountain forests and desert shrubs. The woodland occurs about 500 feet lower on north-facing slopes than on the south-facing ones.

Yellow pine is best developed between 6,000 and 7,500 feet in Utah and from 7,000 to 8,500 feet in Arizona; and Douglas fir forms a distinct zone above the yellow pine forest. Lodgepole pine is dominant at elevations of 9,000 to 10,000 feet in Utah. Subalpine forests form the highest forests, at elevations of 9,500 feet to 11,500 feet on south-facing slopes, but they may occur as low as 7,500 feet on north-facing slopes. Englemann spruce and alpine fir are the most important subalpine trees in Arizona and Utah, and, in southern Arizona, corkbark fir and bristlecone pine are significant. The upper limit of tree growth is commonly a matter of lack of soil or available soil moisture and/or severe wind action rather than low temperatures. At the upper timberline the trees are elfin or prostrate.

In the Columbia Plateaus, sagebrush is characteristic throughout southern Idaho and over the greater portion of Oregon east of the Cascade Mountains. Although not so plentiful as the sagebrush, bunch grass is dispersed almost as widely. Small streams are fringed with a scattered growth of willow, birch, and wild cherry. With an increase in elevation, the juniper makes its appearance, and beyond the lower limit of the juniper are thickets and groves of mountain mahogany. At still higher elevations, yet within the range of the mountain mahogany, the pine appears and reaches up to elevations of 8,000 and 10,000 feet.

Latitude becomes an important influence on vegetation in the plateaus of British Columbia. Here, the cooler temperatures, with a consequent lessening of evaporation, permit a more widespread occurrence of forest. In the Yukon, the growing season is so short that forests give way to tundra mosses and dwarf shrubs, except along the margins of streams.

Soils. As far as row crops are concerned, most soils are of little significance. No matter how fertile or infertile they may be, low rainfall eliminates crops, except where water is available for irrigation. Features characteristic of mature intermontane soils include low humus content and minor leaching of soil minerals.

In the Great Basin, gray desert soils are dominant; these are a response to low rainfall, hot summers, and cold winters. Narrow valleys of alluvial soils are scattered throughout Nevada, and may be used for alfalfa and grasses without irrigation. Extensive areas with saline soils may be classified as poor desert pasture. Shallow residual soils, useful only for sheep pasture, occur on broad expanses of mountainous lands.

On the Sonoran Desert region, important agricultural soils are those, such as the Gila, which occupy the narrow valleys accessible to water. Many soils of the Arizona mountains and valleys and the Colorado Plateaus of Utah and Arizona, receive intermediate rainfall, which results in more humus and a darker color.

Soil management in the Southwest may involve many of the following practices: irrigation, drainage, alkali reclamation, erosion control, leveling of land, terracing of land, blasting of hardpan, subsoiling, application of such soil amendments as lime or gypsum, the use of organic matter and organic fertilizers, the use of commercial fertilizers, and land clearing of trees and brush.

In general, soils of the Columbia Plateau possess greater than average fertility because of the parent material, rich basaltic lava. Most of these soils are pedocals belonging to the sierozem, brown, chestnut, chernozem, and other groups. For example, the Palouse soil is a typical chernozem, with dark brown, friable, and granular silt loam surface soil. The subsoil is a tough, brown to yellowish-brown clay loam, underlain by yellowish-brown silty clay loam, generally non-calcareous except in lower depths. Palouse soil and similar soils are mainly in the 14- to 25-inch rainfall belt of the Columbia Basin wheat section in eastern Washington, northern Idaho, and northeastern Oregon.

Much of the flat surface of the Fraser Plateau in southern British Columbia was made by volcanic flows resembling those of the Columbia Basin south of the border. Trenchlike valleys of streams such as the Fraser, Thompson, and Okanogan are bordered by alluvial and glacial terraces. Soils of the valley floors, the terraces, and the flatlands between valleys are useful for irrigated agriculture or for grazing.

In the Canadian and Alaskan Yukon, soils have little influence on agricultural production. Long cold winters, short growing seasons, danger of frost almost every month of the year, and isolation from market are agricultural handicaps too great for successful farming, regardless of soil conditions.

Farming in the Basin and Range Country and the Colorado Plateaus

Irrigation Agriculture, Historical. Water has been a problem to the indigenous sedentary Indians, the Mormons, and present-day farmers. Hundreds of years ago, Indians were practicing irrigation farming along the streams of what is now Arizona, New Mexico, and southern Utah. They dug ditches and laterals to distribute the water for their crops of corn, beans, and melons, which grew well when moisture was added to the unleached desert soils.

In 1847, the Mormons established the first large Anglo-American irrigation settlements in the United States, along the western base of the Wasatch Mountains. Conditions encouraged irrigation agriculture. Rivers originated in the high Wasatch ranges where precipitation was greater than in the lower lands, and much moisture fell in the form of snow. Thus, the streams flowed perennially and carried water in July and August, the critical period when water is most needed. No serious engineering problems were involved in diverting water to the low-lying alluvial land which slopes, terracelike, to the mountain front.

Mormon settlements were not confined to lands along the western base of the Wasatch Mountains; on the contrary, the industrious Mormon farmers sought springs and streams for irrigation far from the original Salt Lake oasis; and by 1880, hundreds of Mormon settlements were scattered over what is now Arizona, Nevada, and California. Remote outposts, referred to as missions, resembled the early Spanish frontier missions in that they were planned to convert Indians to Christianity and to serve as nuclei for white settlements.

Settlement sites were chosen by the trial and error method. Luxuriant vegetation often tempted the settlers to select lands at too great an altitude, where frosts prohibited successful agriculture, with the result that many towns were moved downstream. Again, selections were made too far from stream sources, and as a means of insuring a greater water supply, towns were moved upstream. Lands charged with alkali were often selected and later abandoned. It was found, however, that harmful salts could often be leached out by successive irrigations previous to the planting of crops.

Many of the streams increased in volume after the settlement of the country. Settlers reacted to this situation like farmers in the Great Plains. They reasoned fallaciously that rainfall follows the plow—that by improving and irrigating the land, more water is evaporated into the air to return in increased precipitation. The real causes for the increased stream flow were temporary increase in rainfall and changes in the drainage basin brought about by man.

Irrigation Agriculture, Present-Day (Fig. 5; Fig. 2, Chapter 11). It has been said that Utah is an oasis on the western side of the Wasatch Mountains. In 1950, the Mormon state had 1,166,972 acres of irrigated land, approximately 2 per cent of the total land area; comparative figures for Arizona show 979,114 acres irrigated, 1.2 per cent of the total land area; for Nevada, 722,896 acres irrigated, or approximately 1 per cent of total land area; and for New Mexico, 577,767 acres in irrigated crop land or less than 1 per cent of total land area.

The above figures show that a very small per cent of total land area is irrigated. Lack of sufficient water is the major cause, but a lesser cause is the fact that water flows through lands that are inhospitable to any crop, or else is separated from good crop lands by mountains, alkali sinks, or sterile basalt. The problem today is still as it was at the time of the Mormon settlements and during the days of early Indian irrigation—availability of water and how to get it to the good land. But now there are other problems that did not disturb the Mormons and the Indians.

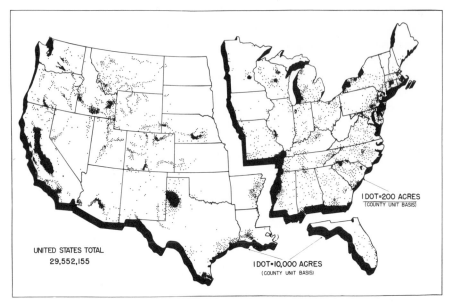

Fig. 5. Irrigated Land in Farms. In most of the West, irrigation is absolutely necessary for successful cultivated agriculture; in the East, supplementary irrigation makes cultivated agriculture profitable with several types of crops. (Courtesy U. S. Department of Commerce, Bureau of Census.)

One of the worst irrigation problems of the arid Southwest is the constantly lowering water table. In Arizona, where approximately half of the irrigated land receives water from deep wells, average pumping lift in Pinal and Maricopa counties has changed from 62 feet in 1939 to 134 feet in 1949. A Senate subcommittee reported early in 1945 that Arizona's "ground water table had reached a point where irrigation may become uneconomic due to the high cost of pumping water."

Another water problem involves the question of prior rights for urban or rural use. In 1913, Los Angeles won a water battle with the Owens Valley farmers under the doctrine of the most important use of the water. In 1949, another bitter fued developed, this time between California and Arizona. The feud was based upon two differing irrigation philosophies: (*a*) city dwellers have the first call on irrigation water; and (*b*) farmers have the first call on irrigation water. City dwellers argue that industry will attract more workers, who will provide a larger market for products of irrigated farms. The farmers fear that there may not be sufficient water for both. Maybe the time will come soon when cheap processing of sea water into fresh water will minimize such controversies. (See "Gains Made in Desalting Sea Water," *New York Times,* June 15, 1958, Financial Section, p. 1.)

A major problem of the Western states is the allocation of Colorado

River water. In 1922, a compact known as the Santa Fe Agreement was drawn up between Upper Basin states, Colorado, New Mexico, Utah, and Wyoming, and the three states of the Lower Basin, Arizona, California, and Nevada. After the agreement was signed, the Upper Basin states did not settle allocations among themselves until late in the 1940's. Among the Lower Basin states, California and Arizona had not adjusted their difficulties completely by 1959. Settlement concerning Colorado River water between Mexico and the United States was achieved in 1945.

Major irrigation lands of the Colorado Plateaus and the Basin and Range country include the Colorado Delta of southern California and Arizona; the Gila and Salt River valleys of Arizona; the Rio Grande Valley of New Mexico; tributaries of the Green River in Utah; and the Humboldt, Carson, Truckee, and Walker rivers of Nevada. Crops occupying most of the irrigated land include hay, cotton, sugar beets, fruits and nuts, and vegetables.

Hay (Fig. 6) is the most important field crop, with alfalfa dominating

Fig. 6. Livestock Corral, Haystacks, and Irrigated Hay Ground. In Douglas County, Nevada, as in all Intermontane Plateau grazing country, corrals and buildings are constructed near a water supply. (Courtesy U. S. Department of Agriculture.)

the acreage; the plant has a moderate salt tolerance and will grow on a variety of soils, with a preference for deep loam having good water penetration. Alfalfa is produced for hay, seed, alfalfa meal, pasture, and as a legume for soil improvement.

Only in Arizona does cotton acreage exceed that for hay; in 1950, Arizona cotton brought in 43 per cent of all farm and ranch income. Both American-Egyptian cotton and upland varieties are grown. Mechanization is widespread on cotton farms.

Because of high yields on dry land and a high feeding value for livestock, barley is the most popular small grain. Fall planting of barley is possible in southern areas, but the severe winters of Nevada and Utah necessitate spring planting. The crop is produced primarily without irrigation, but some acreages are irrigated. Only in Utah does wheat exceed it in acreage.

In Utah, sugar beets are a major irrigated crop. Beet culture is well adapted to regions of long warm growing seasons with rain unlikely during harvest. The high alkali tolerance of the plant enables production on soils not suited for many other crops. Frequently sugar beets are grown in rotation with alfalfa, small grains, and truck crops. Beet growers are usually under contract with sugar corporations having refineries in the producing area, as long hauls and lengthy storage of the beets are not desirable.

Commercially, Utah produces several deciduous tree fruits and some berries, but only a small quantity of grapes and nuts, and no citrus. The commercial fruit acreage is practically all irrigated and closely restricted to locations with favorable climatic and soil conditions, frost hazard being an especially important consideration. Over three-fourths of the acreage is in the north central part of the state on gravelly soils not well adapted to general crops; large areas of such soils occur on the Provo bench in Utah County and on the bench lands of the Wasatch Mountains, extending northward almost to the state line. Although truck farms are concentrated in the same area, all are on a quite different type of soil.

In Arizona, fruit was the source of about 2 per cent of farm products value in 1949, most of it citrus. Citrus orchards in southern Arizona face the same frost dangers as those in California, Texas, and Florida, for no place but Key West in continental United States has a frost-free record. Besides citrus crops, a few grapes, deciduous tree fruits, and nuts—nearly all improved pecans—are produced.

Growing conditions for vegetables are generally favorable in valleys of the Basin and Range country and the Colorado Plateaus. In the southern sections, climatic conditions permit production during the cool season; for example, daily temperatures that average in the low or middle 60's are most favorable for solid heading of lettuce. Therefore, growers in Arizona and in the Imperial Valley of California raise lettuce for marketing during the winter months. Irrigation allows steady vegetable growth in spite of the lack of rainfall, and low rainfall reduces foliage diseases caused by bacteria and fungi. Sandy loams are available for vegetables needing loose soil for root expansion.

Vegetables are grown for the fresh market, for canning, and for seed. Utah has a greater acreage for processing than for fresh marketing. Peas and tomatoes constitute the bulk of these plantings. On the other hand, California and Arizona produce primarily for the fresh market.

Labor supply for vegetable growing is usually plentiful, much of it coming from nearby Mexico. Major farm problems include the long distance from Middle West and Eastern markets, and the danger of surpluses. Increases in United States population and in living standards, as well as improvements in canning and freezing processes are factors favoring the industry.

Livestock (Figs. 7, 8). Livestock contributes more to the economy of some Southwestern states than irrigation agriculture. For example, cattle and sheep account for more than three-fourths of Nevada's farm income. In fact, the entire state is a stock ranching area with operations carried on in the most extensive manner, perhaps more so than in any other state in the nation. The largest part of Utah's farm income also comes from livestock.

Cattle and sheep are grazed on ranches and ranges in both the Basin and Range country and on the Colorado Plateaus. In the north, year-round grazing is not possible as it is in the south. Because of the northern area's higher latitude, more shelter is necessary to protect the animals from cold and snow. Elko, Nevada, has recorded a minimum winter temperature of $-42°$F. More supplementary winter feeding in the north is also necessary. Sometimes even all precautions against winter are inadequate. Operation Haylift saved many cattle during the winter of 1949 when extreme cold and more than two feet of snow struck the country. The snow drifted badly and covered grass and sage brush pastures. Near Fallon, Nevada, for example, Flying Boxcars swept low over the ranches and dropped many tons of hay.

During the summer, especially in the north, cattle and sheep are driven or trucked to the highlands where they remain three to five months to take advantage of upland pastures covered by snow throughout the winter. Thus, transhumance is a characteristic practice (Fig. 9).

Most cattle ranchers prefer the Hereford cattle, which seem well adjusted to Western grazing lands. Many sheep belong to wool type breeds such as the Rambouillet; but some breeders believe a cross between wool animals and the mutton sheep is best for the industry. The use of the same

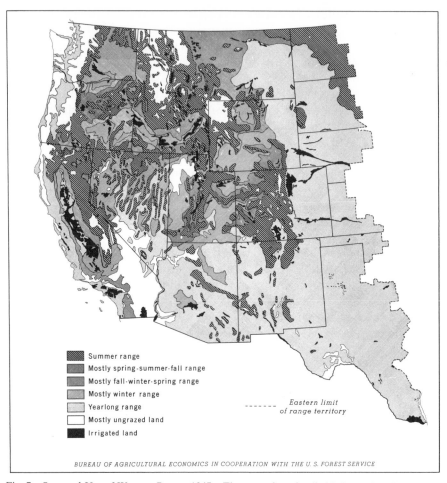

Fig. 7. Seasonal Use of Western Range, 1947. The map gives detailed information about grazing and irrigation areas. (Courtesy U. S. Department of Agriculture, Bureau of Agricultural Economics.)

range by sheep and cattle is a general practice. In Utah, numerous herds are made up of a few cattle or sheep from many farmers and herding is handled on a community basis.

Sheep raising has declined over the last decade or more. Several reasons account for this. (*a*) Pastures are needed for wintering sheep, and sheep have not fared well in competition for pasture land, which also may be used for field crops and for beef and dairy animals; (*b*) good workers for herding sheep are hard to obtain and returns on investments for sheep herders, shearing, etc., are not commensurate with returns on investments in labor employed with cattle; (*c*) cash outlay for operating a sheep ranch

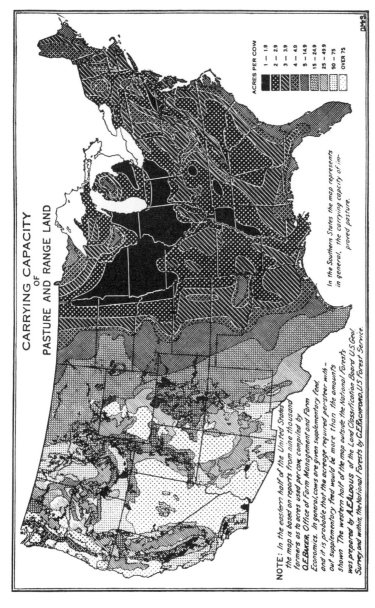

CARRYING CAPACITY
OF
PASTURE AND RANGE LAND

ACRES PER COW

1 — 1.9
2 — 2.9
3 — 3.9
4 — 4.9
5 — 14.9
15 — 24.9
25 — 49.9
50 — 75
OVER 75

In the Southern States the map represents
in general, the carrying capacity of improved pasture.

NOTE: In the eastern half of the United States
the map is based on reports from nine thousand
farmers as to acres used per cow, compiled by
O.E.BAKER, Office of Farm Management and Farm
Economics. In general, cows are given supplementary feed,
and it is probable that the acreage required per steer with -
out supplementary feed would be more than the amounts
shown. The western half of the map outside the National Forests
was prepared by A.E.ALDOUS of the Land Classification Board U.S.Geol.
Survey and within, the National Forests by C.E.RACHFORD, U.S.Forest Service.

Fig. 8. Carrying Capacity of Pasture and Range Land. Notice the contrast between the carrying capacity of Iowa land and that of Nevada. Explain. (Courtesy U. S. Department of Agriculture.)

Fig. 9.   Unloading Sheep on Highland Pastures.   Trucking sheep to and from highland pastures has now largely replaced the practice of driving the animals to and from the uplands.   Water is also trucked to the sheep while in the highlands.   This practice is beneficial both to the range and to the sheep.   The animals obtain adequate clean water and the range can be grazed more uniformly.   Recent improvements in Intermontane Plateau roads have made possible the modernization of transhumance.   (Courtesy U. S. Department of Agriculture.)

has increased 300 per cent since prewar days, whereas comparable expenses on cattle ranches have increased but 200 per cent; (*d*) the lessening of public lands available for upland summer grazing has adversely affected the range sheep industry; and (*e*) prices for wool during the last decade have not encouraged sheep raising.

Handling large numbers of livestock on any ranch necessitates a good many workers; they are needed to locate strays; to keep pumps and other water supply equipment in good order; to salt the animals; to maintain fencing; to assist with branding and dipping; and to perform other tasks associated with livestock production.

The heart of the ranch is near a dependable water supply, a well, a spring, or a stream, without which livestock raising would be impossible. The owner's or manager's house, workers' quarters, animal sheds, dipping tanks, corral, etc., are all located near water.

In the Southwest, there are fully as many problems associated with the livestock industry as with irrigation.   Too many livestock and poor management have depleted ranges and necessitate more supplemental feeding. Feed may consist of irrigated lowland pastures, hay, sugar beet pulp and tops, cottonseed cake, molasses, barley, etc.

Overstocking of ranges has changed the character of the natural plant life for the worse and has hastened the ravages of erosion.   An invasion of mesquite, cacti, and low-value shrubs has occurred on lowland pastures, and brush continues to invade range country on lower mountain slopes. A poisonous weed, *Halogeton glomeratus,* has spread almost entirely over the state of Nevada, as well as on to contiguous parts of California, Oregon, Idaho, Utah, and elsewhere. Sheep eating the spongy leaves of the purple stemmed bush will die within a few hours.

Overstocked ranges and overgrazing have created economic difficulties for the Navajo, the largest tribe of Indians in the United States. In the high, brilliantly colored plateaus of northeastern Arizona, southeastern Utah, and northwestern New Mexico, more than 60,000 Navajos make a living by raising sheep (Fig. 10)—Navajos account for nearly one-half of Arizona's sheep—working on silver and turquoise ornaments, weaving blankets, working on the railroads, and once in a while assisting on movie location.

Many think of the Indian as a vanishing race, but this is not true. When the Navajo tribe moved onto the reservation in 1868, there were fewer than 20,000 people; now there are more than 60,000, in spite of an infant death rate several times that of the population of the United States as a whole. The increase in population and a corresponding increase in the number of sheep have created a bad pasture situation. Navajos need far more pasture if they are to continue their major occupation in this isolated country.

Fig. 10. Navajo Women with Their Sheep. Grazing Sheep has long been an important industry among the Navajos. (Courtesy Milton Snow, U. S. Indian Service.)

Some Indian families still live in one-room huts called hogans. Thick circular walls keep out the oppressive heat of the summer sun and the raw winter cold of the high plateau. A family may live in a hogan until nearby grazing is depleted and then build another hut near better pastures. Navajo sheep generally are not as good quality as those on the larger ranches.

The recent discoveries of uranium and oil on Navajo lands may change the economic difficulties of the Indian. The Four Corners, where Colorado, Utah, New Mexico, and Arizona meet is the scene of the Paradox Basin oil strike, which holds great promise as an oil producing field. Moreover, this area is one of the richest uranium regions in the United States, perhaps in the world.

Farming on the Columbia Plateau

Many characteristics of agriculture are similar to those of the Basin and Range country and the Colorado Plateaus, but enough dissimilarities exist to merit special consideration. Like all sections of the Intermontane Region, the Columbia Plateau has a dry climate. Rainfall is nowhere sufficient for dependable humid agriculture. It ranges from under 10 inches to 25 inches over all sections except in the rugged Blue Mountains; but unfavorable relief gives no opportunity to profit by above-average rainfall. Dry farming, irrigation agriculture, and raising livestock feature farm activities. A specific example of each type of land use will be described.

Dry Farming. The dissected Palouse Plateau has been utilized for dry farming for more than a half century. Soils are derived from volcanic ash, and the characteristic hilly topography ranges from 1,200 feet above sea level at the southwest to 2,800 feet in the east. Southwest slopes have a gentle gradient, whereas north and east slopes are much steeper.

The Palouse country has long been a leading wheat producer (Fig. 3). Huge plows, planters, and combines go around the hills to plow, plant, and harvest the crop. Machinery moves along the contours to prevent disastrous soil erosion, for relief on any 160 acres may range from 100 to 200 feet. Continued planting to wheat has depleted soil in several areas; so much so that in the early 1950's seed peas became an active competitor of small grain. All farming activities are planned to make the most effective use of precipitation; and dry farming methods such as those described on p. 294 are characteristic.

Irrigation Agriculture. Almost every student of North American geography knows of the Grand Coulee Dam (Fig. 11) on the Columbia River in northwestern United States. The term *coulee* is derived from a French word meaning chasm; and Grand Coulee refers to such a depression eroded by the Columbia during the last ice age. In the period of Pleistocene cold, about 50,000 years ago, ice blocked the Columbia at the present dam site.

Fig. 11. Grand Coulee Dam. Aerial view looking over the Grand Coulee Dam shows pumping plant, discharge pipes, feeder canal, north dam, and lake forming in the Upper Grand Coulee equalizing reservoir. (Courtesy Bureau of Reclamation.)

As a result of glacial blocking, the river was compelled to cut a new course, a part of which is known as the Grand Coulee, a gorge 800 to 1,000 feet deep, 27 miles long, and 2 to 5 miles wide. After the ice melted, the river resumed its preglacial course and abandoned the Grand Coulee and other parts of the ice age route to the sea. Today, water from the 150-mile-long Lake Roosevelt, formed by the dam, is lifted into the old coulee, the floor of which is 280 feet higher than Lake Roosevelt.

The lifting operation requires several pumps, the largest ever built. Each pump pushes water through 12-foot pipes over the sharply rising southwest shore of the Grand Coulee Dam into a feeder canal, whence the water flows into the storage dam provided by nature. To drive the pumps requires motors with 65,000 horse power each. And to drive the motors there is power from many dynamos at the dam, each capable of 108,000 kilowatts. From the lake in the old coulee an intricate network of canals, siphons, and lateral ditches feeds water to farm land formerly supporting sagebrush and other desert vegetation.

Besides water supplied by the Columbia at the Grand Coulee, other streams contribute moisture for irrigation agriculture. These include the Snake, Spokane, Wenatchee, Hood, Okanogan, Yakima, and other tributaries of the Columbia. A description of crops and crop practices in the Yakima Valley will serve as an example of regional irrigation farming.

The Yakima drainage basin includes an area of approximately 6,000 square miles, three-fourths the size of Massachusetts. About 9 per cent of the land is irrigated and planted to fruits and open field crops.

Commercial fruit raising did not start until 1895, although irrigation farming began as early as 1867. In the late 1940's (Fig. 12), apples led the fruit crops with 40 per cent of the acreage; pears occupied 20 per cent of the fruit land, peaches 15 per cent, and the remainder was devoted to bing cherries, apricots, prunes, plums, etc.

Factors encouraging production include water from melting snows on mountains to the north, east, and west; mountains that block cold winter winds from the interior; sufficient relief for air drainage protection from frost; much sunshine resulting from leeward-side-of-mountain location in the belt of the westerlies (the average annual rainfall is only 8 inches); a growing season of approximately 190 days; cool autumn nights which ripen and color apples, the leading fruit crop; a minimum of late spring frosts; rich volcanic soils; and well-developed cooperative associations.

Future trends in Yakima Valley fruit farming include less emphasis on apple growing and greater attention to soft fruit, larger sales to canneries and to processors of frozen fruit, larger individual holdings of fruit land, and continued use of seasonal and migratory workers.

During the last two decades, open field and specialty crops continue to occupy an increasing acreage of Yakima Valley land. These crops tend to expand in valley lowlands where danger of spring frosts limits the planting of fruits susceptible to such a climatic hazard. Row crops include potatoes, sugar beets, corn, and commercial vegetables. Fields of small grain and alfalfa appear on many farms, and acreage of asparagus, hops, and grapes is expanding. Hops (Fig. 13), with little green flowers shaped like pine cones, are used for beer. Grapes have an advantage over certain other fruits because they blossom late in the spring and suffer less frost damage.

Fig. 12. Apple Blossom time. Apples are a major crop in the Yakima Valley, Washington. (Courtesy Yakima Chamber of Commerce.)

Livestock. Alfalfa hay, beet pulp and tops, stubble from fields of grain, and valley pastures—all grown in irrigated valleys—provide winter feed for increasing numbers of transhumants. Herds of sheep are driven or shipped to mountain pastures in the spring and come back to Yakima and to other irrigated valleys for winter feeding. A few dairy animals dot the valley farm landscape, but beef cattle are relatively unimportant.[2]

Where irrigation water is not available and rainfall is insufficient for dry farming, stock raising becomes a major agricultural activity. Grazing is dominant on the Harney-High Desert of Oregon, the drier parts of the Snake River country, and the Owyhee Uplands. The sparse population is a decided contrast to the densely populated intensive farming districts of

[2] Much of the material on the Yakima Valley is based on two articles by Richard M. Highsmith, Jr., and Elbert E. Miller, "Geography of the Fruit Industry of the Yakima Valley, Washington," *Economic Geography,* October 1949; and "Open Field Farming in the Yakima Valley, Washington," *Economic Geography,* January 1952.

Fig. 13. Growing Hops in the Yakima Valley, Washington. Vines are being loaded on trucks to be hauled to a stationary picking machine. (Courtesy Yakima Chamber of Commerce.)

the Yakima and other valleys; but few people are needed to produce live-stock on the wide open spaces of the dry steppe lands.

Plateau Farming in British Columbia

(Figure 14)

Dry farming, irrigation agriculture, and livestock raising are character-istic of British Columbia's intermontane country just as they are in Wash-ington across the international boundary. However, dry farming of wheat is less important on the Fraser Plateau than on the Columbia Plateau, and so is irrigation agriculture. The latter shows greatest development in the Canadian portion of the Okanogan Valley, which extends for 140 miles from the Canadian-United States boundary to Shuswap Lake.

The southern part of the Okanogan Valley averages two miles in width, but it broadens to more than twelve miles in the north. A large number of lakes occupy the lowland floor and many terraces occur along the valley walls. Around the southern shores of Lake Okanogan, temperatures are mild enough for growing peaches, and the most important production takes place on the Penticton terraces. The apple, which is hardier than the peach, continues to feature irrigation farming farther north. The low rainfall of the valley, an annual of less than 15 inches, a complete absence of fog, and a high percentage of possible sunshine, all limit fungi attack and favor fruit with brightly colored skin. Land suitable for irrigation has never been a problem, but sufficient water has always been a major obstacle to expansion. Specialized crops, such as cantaloupes, tomatoes, and cucumbers, feature irrigated agriculture of the Oliver-Osoyoos district.

Besides the relatively large acreages under the ditch in the Okanogan Valley, smaller developments occur in the Middle Thompson, Nicola, Middle Fraser, Lower North Thompson, and Kettle valleys. In the Middle Fraser Valley, from Quesnel to Lilooet, the chief irrigation crop is alfalfa for winter feeding of livestock. In summer, cattle and sheep are driven to the highland pastures. Thus, transhumance is characteristic of the Fraser Plateau just as it is on the Columbia Plateau to the south.

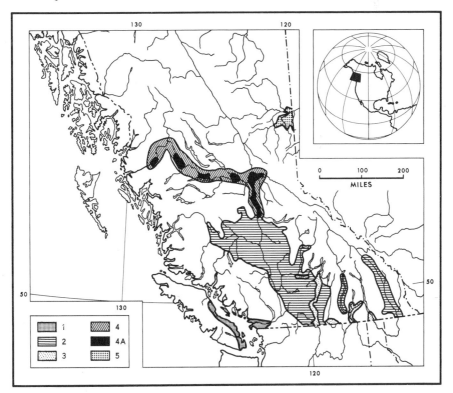

Fig. 14. Agricultural Regions of British Columbia. The map shows (1) dairying on the southwest coast; (2) ranching in the southern interior; (3) fruit in the southern valleys; (4) mixed farming in central British Columbia; (4A) present farm land in central British Columbia; and (5) grain in the Peace River area. (Source: After map 11, *British Columbia Geography Manual*, 1954.)

Farming on the Yukon Plateau

Fairbanks and the Tanana Valley are typical of interior Alaska on the Yukon Plateau; they are the warmest parts of the state in summer and probably the coldest in winter. For the period 1932–47 inclusive, the highest temperature recorded at Fairbanks was 99°F. and the lowest was −65°F. During the growing months, beginning with May, the normal temperature shows a steady rise, reaching its peak in July. The growing season for hardy plants, such as grains and grasses, averages 123 days on the south-facing slopes. For tender plants, such as potatoes, the growing season averages 105 days. On the valley floor, the growing period is several days less.

Total precipitation ranges from 8.5 inches to 16 inches, with approximately half coming during the growing season. This is enough for cereal crops in view of the relatively low temperatures and the favorable evaporation-precipitation ratio. During the growing season, the long daylight contributes to the rapid growth of plants. Earth in the Tanana Valley is frozen to varying depths with some lenses or blocks of ice of various sizes. When the natural vegetation cover is disturbed by clearing the land, summer thawing may be deep enough to melt the ice blocks mentioned above; as a result, the surface area may sink. Because of such sinkings, a number of fields in the vicinity of Fairbanks have become too hummocky and rough for cultivation. Soils developed from stream alluvium are low in organic matter, and deficient in nitrogen and phosphate. A few dairy herds feed on oats and peas grown for hay; garbage from the nearby military base is fed to hogs and chickens; potatoes are the chief cash crop.

Economic handicaps for Yukon agriculture, and that for Alaska in general, are as serious as those of the physical environment. These handicaps include (*a*) expensive labor and equipment—clearing land costs from $100 to $200 per acre; (*b*) high cost of transporting crops to local markets; (*c*) inefficient marketing practices; (*d*) the lure of high industrial wages tempts farmers to leave the land; (*e*) high clearing and development costs keep would-be farmers from agricultural investment; and (*f*) danger of overproduction for Alaska's market of only 200,000 people on the huge area of 586,000 square miles throttles any significant expansion; for any surplus, with added transport costs to outside markets, could not hope to meet competition from better located producing areas.

The Mineral Industries

The Basin and Range Country and the Colorado Plateaus. Mountain building processes, important agencies in the formation of metallic minerals, have been active in the Intermontane Plateaus where mineral occurrence is widespread and in considerable variety. In the early days, gold and silver were metals sought by nearly every prospector, and one of the most famous early finds was that of the Comstock Lode in 1859. Gold was exploited first, but within a few years silver became the most important product from the mine.

The town of Virginia City, Nevada, whose prosperity was based on the profits of the Comstock Lode, illustrates the ephemeral nature of the mining industry as well as the great fluctuation in population for towns whose economy depends almost entirely upon the exploitation of local minerals. The town was located near the Humboldt River route to California and close to Mormon irrigation settlements raising food crops for miners and for travelers moving farther west. Virginia City had a population of 15,000 in 1863, but by 1900, when silver and gold were exhausted, most of the people had moved out. There was nothing else for them to do in a desert environment unfit for farming, forestry, manufacturing, or commerce. As a result of the exodus, homes were vacant, stamp mills were in ruin, and roads as well as streets were in disrepair.

The population figures for the entire state of Nevada also show a fluctuation similar to that of Virginia City. Much of the state's income results from the exploitation of minerals. With new discoveries of minerals and high prices for metals, population increases; but population declines when mines are depleted and demand for minerals is slack. In 1860, Nevada had 7,000 people; 1870—42,000; 1800—63,000; 1900—42,000; 1910—82,000; 1930—91,000; and in 1950—180,000.

New mining ventures from 1860 to 1870 brought a rapid increase in population; increase was less rapid from 1870 to 1880; between 1880 and 1900 several mines were exhausted, and with no important mineral finds there was a sharp drop in population. Since 1900, expanding mineral exploitation, together with other industries, has brought a slow expansion in population. But the entire state only has about as many people as Worcester, Massachusetts.

In the United States section of the Intermontane Plateaus, mining of gold and silver is no longer as important as it was during the early settlement days. In fact, a variety of other minerals, chiefly copper, lead, zinc, and uranium have become of much greater significance.

San Pedro Valley in southwest Arizona will illustrate the change in plateau mining economy. Beneath San Pedro's floor lie 500 million tons of copper ore, one of the largest proved deposits in the United States. Copper men long have known the ore existed, but its low metallic content made it uneconomical to mine. Recently the government offered guaranteed prices for the output of San Pedro copper and molybdenum until 1962, an offer that will make the exploitation of even low-grade ore profitable.

Production started in 1956 and will reach an output of 140,000,000 pounds of refined copper and 6,000,000 pounds of molybdenum when the mines are working at capacity.   This will boost United States production of the former metal 8 per cent and that of the latter 11 per cent.

Sage, mesquite, and candelabra-like cactus had to be cleared before mine and town builders could go to work.   Copper ore occurs at depths of approximately 2,000 feet and shaft mining is necessary.   Shafts have been drilled, blasted, and cleared; and the horizontal grizzly and haulage drifts (tunnels in which the miners work and carry away the ore) have been dug out below the ore to be mined.   San Pedro copper is mined by the block caving method; upward chutes are driven from the drifts into the ore body, leaving pillars to support the ore; as the pillars are blasted away, the ore falls of its own weight down the chutes through the grizzlies to the mine cars below.   The rocky overburden will fall too, eventually changing the topography of the whole area.

In addition to sinking mine shafts and constructing the necessary mine equipment, a thousand houses have been built at San Manuel in San Pedro Valley, and a cheaper housing project is going up in nearby Mammoth, a ghost town left by early gold and silver miners.   The ghost town of Tiger, situated close to Mammoth, is being razed completely to make way for the new mining operation.   Here is an example of the rise and fall of mining for precious metals, followed in the same area by mining for a low-grade deposit of non-precious metal, copper.   A big corporation, San Manuel Copper Corporation, a subsidiary of Magma Copper Corporation, is willing to take the risk on the low-grade ore when supported by government subsidy.   San Manuel has a 50-year life expectancy before becoming a copper ghost town similar to the precious-metal ghost towns which preceded it. Perhaps another profitable metal will be discovered after the copper is depleted.

Many of the great copper deposits of the Intermontane Plateaus occur near the surface, and open-pit mining, rather than shaft mining similar to that at San Manuel, is possible.   The open-pit excavation at Ruth, Nevada, is approximately a mile long, three-fourths of a mile wide, and 700 feet deep. To climb from the bottom to the rim of the pit, mine trains loaded with copper ore go around and around the huge hole for a distance of about four miles.

During the last five decades, ore trains have carried away more than a billion tons of copper ore and waste from the mine at Bingham, Utah. Concentric benching has deepened the open pit to about 2,000 feet and removed ore valued at over a billion dollars.   In terms of recoverable copper, Utah's Bingham region (Fig. 15) led the principal copper mining districts in the United States in 1953, with 268,511 short tons.   Arizona's Morenci district was second, with 123,789 short tons; other districts, including the Globe-Miami, Ajo, Ray, Bisbee, Pioneer, and Eureka, brought Arizona's

Fig. 15. Copper Mine. The occurrence of copper ore near the surface makes open-pit mining possible at Bingham Canyon, Utah. Nearly 2,000 feet separate upper and lower terraces. (Courtesy of Kennecott Copper Corporation.)

1953 total close to 400,000 short tons. Nevada's Ely district accounted for 60,557 short tons, and New Mexico's Central district produced 69,869 short tons in the same year.

The Intermontane Plateaus produce many other minerals besides copper. In 1952, Utah was the United States second producer of silver, with 7,194,109 fine ounces; this total was about half the amount produced by first place Idaho of the Rocky Mountain region. Arizona stood fourth with 4,701,330 fine ounces. Utah was also second in United States production of gold (435,507 fine ounces) in 1952, a little behind South Dakota in the Great Plains region. Nevada and Arizona ranked sixth and seventh, far down the line.

Utah was second again in lead production in 1953, with 41,522 short tons, nearly three times as much as the total for Arizona, Nevada, and New Mexico, and over half as much as first place Idaho in the Rocky Mountain region. Utah, Arizona, and New Mexico ranked fifth, sixth, and seventh among United States producers of zinc, with Nevada mining very little of the metal.

Manganese, molybdenum, and vanadium are also produced in the states of the Colorado Plateaus and Basin and Range country. Significant reserves of manganese are found in Arizona, with much smaller deposits in Nevada. Utah, Arizona, and Nevada rank second, third, and fifth, respectively, far behind Colorado, the first producer of molybdenum. Arizona, Utah, and Nevada are all major producers of vanadium, although each state produces only a small tonnage.

Iron occurs in every one of the Intermontane Plateau states, but the largest deposits—and of high metallic content too—are located in southwest Utah's Iron County. Carbon County in east-central Utah accounts for over half of the Intermontane Plateaus coal production. This good quality coal is much better than the subbituminous deposit near Gallup, New Mexico.[3]

Oil potential (Figs. 16, 17) in the Colorado Plateaus and Basin and Range country looks promising. In 1956, geologists were optimistic about the Paradox Basin in the Four Corners area, so called because it surrounds the intersection of Colorado, Utah, Arizona, and New Mexico.[4] As previously indicated, much of the oil land is held by the Navajo Indians. Nevada boasts two producing wells which have come in since 1953, both southwest of Ely. Enormous reserves of oil shale also are present in the Intermontane Plateaus; no cheap means of processing gasoline from the

[3] Statistics are taken from "Mineral Facts and Problems," *Bulletin* 556, by the staff of the Bureau of Mines, 1956.

[4] Statistics on reserves of petroleum and natural gas for New Mexico and Colorado were given with Fig. 8, Chapter 12. These and other states include parts of the Rocky Mountains as well as parts of the Intermontane Plateaus.

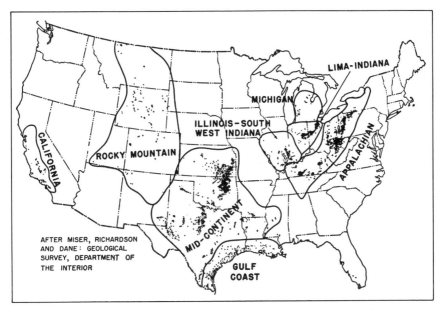

Fig. 16. Oil Fields of the United States. Learn the names and general locations of the major oil fields of the United States. (Courtesy U. S. Bureau of Mines.)

shale has been discovered, and until crude oil reserves drop much lower than they are now, very little power is likely to result from use of the oily stone.

Power in considerable quantity, however, may be obtained from uranium. In fact, it was in Montrose County, along southwest Colorado's border, that one of the earliest finds of radioactive ore was made. From here, in 1898, several tons of uranium-bearing ore were shipped to Paris, where they were used by Madame Curie in the extraction of the element radium.

About 50 years later, in 1948, the United States government gave impetus to uranium production by offering to purchase ore, to pay attractive prices for it, and to continue the procedure for several years to come. The result has been a great uranium prospecting rush with geiger counters clicking all over the Intermontane Plateaus. Prospectors include individuals working for themselves as well as geologists working for gas, petroleum, and other mining corporations. The approximate center of production in 1952 was near Moab, Utah, where a geologist, Charles Steen, discovered an ore body valued at more than $100,000,000. Largely because of production of uranium in the Intermontane Plateaus, the United States ranks high among uranium producing countries.

Non-metallic minerals include potash. Small quantities come from

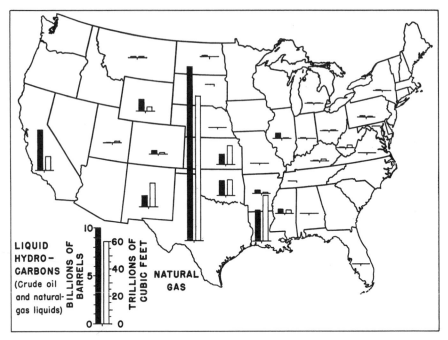

Fig. 17.   Estimates of Proved Reserves of Liquid Hydrocarbons and Natural Gas by States, as of December 31, 1953.   Notice the resources of oil and gas in the South.   (Courtesy U. S. Bureau of Mines.)

Salduro, on the border between Utah and Nevada, and Searles Lake, in the Mojave Desert; but the greatest United States potash reserve is at Carlsbad, New Mexico, on the western edge of the Great Plains physiographic province.   The largest United States deposit of phosphate rock, many times bigger than that of the Southeast, occurs partly in the Rocky Mountain region and partly in the Intermontane Plateaus.   Five states possess this valuable resource, Montana, Idaho, Wyoming, Utah, and Nevada. Most of the West's small production goes to local farm lands with delivery costs much lower than those for across-the-continent shipments.

One of the easiest non-metallic minerals to exploit is the salt occurring in and around Great Salt Lake.   Salt water is pumped into diked ponds; the water evaporates in the dry plateau climate, and the salt remains in the diked enclosures.   Most of the salt, like the regionally produced phosphates, is marketed in the West, where it has an advantage in transport costs over that mined in the East.   Salt is produced both for human and livestock consumption.

In any consideration of the mining industry, some important principles may be stressed.   Minerals once removed from the earth are irreplaceable within human time.   It is true that volcanoes may give off heated gases that include such minerals as lead and iron. But the amounts are too small to be of economic significance to this generation. It is also a fact that minerals like iron can be used over and over again. Mineral technology has made it possible for blast furnace use of as much as 50 per cent scrap iron mixed with ore fresh from the mine. But coal, petroleum, and natural gas, so-called minerals, serve for fuel but once. And, in general, the statement is true that *mining is a robber industry*.

With this in mind, the attitude of an investor in a mining company towards returns from his investment may be different from the outlook of a person investing in an agricultural enterprise. Dividends on mineral properties are returns of a part of the principal; for part of the mineral body is removed each year, never to be replaced. Dividends on agriculture are no part of the principal, for farming, if conducted wisely, can continue for ages with the raw materials of the original land.

A railroad leading to a mining property located in a desert environment will be of little value once the mineral is exhausted. San Manuel is located in the desert and serves as a good example. Tracks have been laid 7 miles across the rugged barren hills from mine to smelter, and another stretch of rails 29 miles long runs from the smelter site to the Southern Pacific's spur line to Hayden. In contrast, the railroad leading to Bingham, Utah, also serves the rich Salt Lake irrigation district; consequently, when Bingham copper is exhausted, the railroad to the general locality will not be devoid of cargo; on the contrary, agricultural shipments may continue indefinitely as long as farm lands and irrigation water receive proper attention.

Mining in the Columbia Plateau and Intermontane Plateaus of Canada and Alaska. The remaining subregions of the Intermontane Plateaus have not the proven reserves nor the production of minerals characteristic of southwest United States.

Minerals of the Columbia Plateau include ores of gold quartz in the Blue Mountains and the Wallawa district, where two-thirds of Oregon's limited gold mining takes place; a little copper in the Wallawa area; chromite in Wheeler, Grant, and Baker counties of eastern Oregon; minor amounts of platinum in southeast Oregon and eastern Washington; small occurrences of lead, zinc, and silicon near Northport, Washington; large amounts of magnesite near Chewelah of the same state; good clay deposits throughout northwestern United States; high-grade marble in Wallawa, Oregon, and close to Northport, Washington; granite quarries in operation close to Spokane; a variety of saline deposits in north central Washington and south-central Oregon; perlite and pumice in central Oregon; and diatomaceous earth in central Washington and central Oregon. Coal occurs in central Washington, but strong competition from developed water power and cheap imported petroleum limits coal mining.

Most of the Intermontane Plateaus of British Columbia do not appear favorable for minerals, and major production will probably continue from mountain foothills along plateau borders. Gold is mined in the Bridge River Valley, the greatest producer; at Hedley in southern British Columbia; along the Quesnel River near Wells; and at Atlin in the north, where mining has continued for more than 50 years. Gypsum is present at Falkland in the Salmon River Valley; rocks near Hazelton and Tulsequah include ores with lead, zinc, silver, and tungsten; and coal occurs in the Bulkley Valley near Telkwa.

The plateau contributes to one of the continent's greatest water power developments. The Nechako River, an east-flowing tributary of the Fraser, has been dammed at Kenney, 40 miles south of Fort Fraser. This dam reverses the direction of flow to the west through a chain of lakes in Tweedsmuir Park, where the water is diverted through a tunnel in the Coast Mountains to a power plant at Kemano. The Kemano Power provides energy for one of the world's greatest aluminum plants at Kitimat on the Pacific Coast. More water power is available from the Stikine and Skeena rivers, but development is unlikely because headwaters of these streams contain great salmon spawning grounds.

Most students of Alaskan geography have heard of the gold stampede to the Klondike, a tributary of the Yukon which flows the entire length of the Yukon Plateau. Alaska possesses nearly all of the more than 30 minerals listed by the United States as strategic or critical. Some of these occur in significant quantity, and the entire list may be present, because less than one per cent of the state has received detailed geological study, and only about half has been covered by geological reconnaissance mapping. In the 70 years, 1880–1950, Alaskan mineral production has amounted to more than a billion dollars.

On the Yukon Plateau, gold-bearing intrusive rocks occur near Fairbanks, and huge dredges (Fig. 18) are active extracting gold a few miles from that city. In the Canadian Yukon near Mayo, ore-bearing rocks are exploited for silver, lead, tungsten, and copper. Ore containing chrome, nickel, and platinum occurs at Livengood, Alaska, and may prove of commercial importance.

Alaska's greatest coal deposits lie within the Yukon Plateau in the Healy River Valley, accessible to the railroad. Alaskan production amounts to about a half million tons annually, all consumed within the state; for comparison, the United States coal mines furnish about 500,000,000 tons a year. A much heavier Alaskan tonnage can be produced and the state may be supplying Oriental markets in the future.

In the past, only high-value, low-volume metals such as gold, silver, platinum, etc., have reached outside markets from the Yukon Plateau because transport and labor costs are exceedingly high in this isolated region.

Fig. 18. Gold Dredge in Alaska. A gold dredge like this one in the Yukon Valley, Alaska, may cost more than half a million dollars, but it can profitably work gravel containing only 10 to 20 cents' worth of gold per cubic yard. (Source: H. Bradford Washburn, Jr.)

Present conditions are likely to continue. Important mineral discoveries will be made, but only those of high value and high metallic content are likely to be developed.

Tourism

(Figure 19)

Tourism has become an important industry. A list of places are of interest to travelers. The Grand Canyon, probably the best known, may be examined from top to bottom and many people visit both north and south rims. Hoover Dam is worth a short visit. The Painted Desert and the Petrified Forest are not more than a day's journey distant and a study of these formations will intrigue many people. If the traveler plans his visit properly, he may witness the annual Inter-tribal Indian Ceremonial at Gallup, New Mexico, usually held in August; and there are many other attractive examples of Indian culture throughout the region. Also, if one wishes to gamble without legal interference he can find excellent facilities at Las Vegas and Reno, Nevada.

During the winter season, places like Tucson, Phoenix, and even Death Valley profit from an influx of tourists. These visitors find the dry air and warm sunshine attractive during the cool months. In the summer, the heat of the southern Intermontane Plateaus is a deterrent to tourist journeys. Travelers avoid the high temperatures of the Death Valley section by the use of night travel. By timing journeys this way, traffic resembles that of camel caravans in the Middle East deserts, where travel in the cooler darkness is customary.

Attractive forests occur in the higher parts of the region. Columbia Plateau lava outcrops along the walls of the Snake River and in many other parts of the upland; such scenery is of especial interest to geology students and to the layman as well. The Grand Coulee Dam is worth a day's visit; the traveler should stop at Salt Lake for a float on the salty water that carries about 25 per cent sodium chloride.

Isolated mountain groups occur throughout the region, but they cannot compete with the Rockies to the east and the Cascade, Klamath, Sierra Nevada, and Coast ranges to the west. Sea views such as those available along the West Coast are also absent; but both high mountain and ocean scenery are within short distances of the Intermontane Plateaus, and many tourists see all of these attractions on the same journey.

All in all, the region has many attractions, but it suffers from the disadvantage of the entire West—too great a distance from the bulk of United States population. The Canadian and Alaskan plateaus, lying farthest away from centers of dense population, get by far the smaller number of tourists.

Fig. 19. The Grand Canyon. The Colorado River has worked millions of years to erode the Grand Canyon. (Courtesy Union Pacific Railroad.)

Military Operations

(Figure 20)

Largely because of low economic value and sparse population, huge land areas are useful for military maneuvers. During and since World War II, the dry lakes of California and Nevada have been of great use to the Armed Services. The flat, hard-packed, vegetation-free areas in sparsely populated regions have proved ideal for aircraft landing fields, gunnery ranges, bombing ranges, and for testing such new weapons as guided missiles and atomic bombs.

The most noted of the dry lakes used by the military is Rogers Lake (Muroc), where the Edwards Air Base is located. The lake, which is roughly 13 miles long and 5 miles wide, provides a landing field more than sufficient for all types of aircraft. The bearing strength of the massive clay body (measured as three-fourths of an inch depression for a single wheel loading of 150,000 pounds) can easily support the heaviest aircraft. Its isolated location is ideal for the testing of secret and experimental equipment. At nearby China Lake, the Navy has a similar installation where guided missiles and experimental aircraft are tested. Frenchman's Flat and Yucca Flat in southwestern Nevada have been the sites of experimental tests of atomic bombs and atomic weapons.

Other dry lakes that are being used by the military are Benson Dry Lake, where the Navy maintains a gunnery and bombing range, and Bicycle and Indian Springs Dry Lake, Nevada, where the Air Force has gunnery and bombing ranges. During the war a primary flying school and glider school was in operation at Mesquite (Twentynine Palms) Lake and a gunnery range at Clark Dry Lake. The Palen playa near Desert Center was extensively used by General Patton in the training of armored divisions in desert warfare.

Future Trends

Military operations, tourism, irrigation farming, dry farming, livestock ranching, mining, and forestry [5] at high elevations provide major occupations for the region's economy. Per capita production figures compare well with those of other regions. But aridity and rugged relief keep population so low that total regional production is far less than that for areas with more humid climates and more favorable relief. In conclusion, the Intermontane

[5] No discussion of forest activities preceded this statement, although highland forests were mentioned under the topic of natural vegetation. Forest industries are mainly of local importance. They provide construction material for homes, factories, and mines, but little for shipment outside the region.

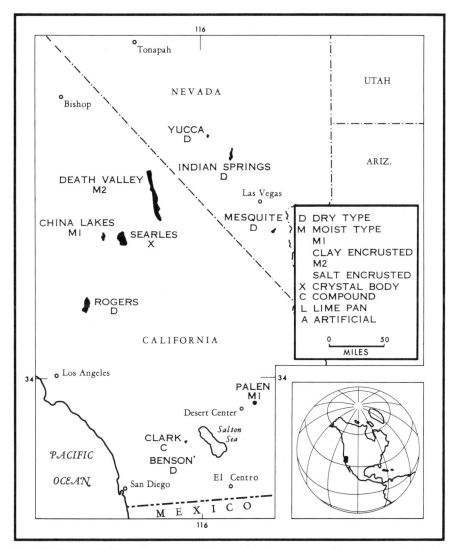

Fig. 20. Playas of Military Importance. Parts of the Intermontane Plateaus are valuable for military maneuvers. (Drawn after map of Quartermaster Research and Development Center, Environmental Protection Research Division, U. S. Army, Natick, Mass.)

Plateaus include enormous expanses of territory, but they support very few people, and it is doubtful that population density will show marked increase in the foreseeable future. The environment offers too little economic reward for the enormous physical challenge it gives to both individual and to the group.

QUESTIONS, EXERCISES, AND PROBLEMS

1. Turn to a good atlas with maps showing surface features clearly and learn the major topographic divisions of the Intermontane Plateaus. Describe the land forms, climates, soils, and vegetation. Read "Southwestern Desert Vegetation," reference cited.

2. Tell of the early Mormon settlements in the Southwest. What percentage of the land is irrigated? What crops are grown? What are the major irrigation problems? How important is grazing? Make a list of major oases developments in the United States portion of the Intermontane Plateaus. Examine reference material on the political geography associated with water scarcity.

3. Indicate the area, population, industries, and problems of the Navajo country. Describe farming on the Palouse Plateau; in the Yakima Valley; in British Columbia; and on the Yukon Plateau. Indicate the geology of the Grand Coulee and its relation to dam building and the distribution of water. Read carefully Edward Higbee, *American Agriculture,* Chapters 8 and 9 for the geography of oases; chapters 10 and 11 on the western range country; and chapter 12 on the Palouse region.

4. What and where are the major mineral and power resources? Point out the relation between mining and population changes. Describe mining practices in the San Pedro Valley. Comment on the use of the Intermontane Plateaus for military activities. Where are manufacturing and forestry carried on? Describe these developments. What are the possibilities for tourism?

5. Each of the following cities has approximately 25,000 people or more in its urban district; Albuquerque, Boise, El Paso, Las Vegas, Ogden, Phoenix, Pocatello, Provo, Reno, Salt Lake City, Spokane, Tucson, Walla Walla, and Yakima. Name major activities encouraging the growth of each population center. Note the small number of cities and the small size of the cities in this huge area. Explain. Comment on the distribution of population in the Intermontane Plateaus.

6. Identify the following: hogan, coulee, laccolith, structural depression, quiescent lava flow, mesa, natural bridge, halophytic vegetation, alluvial fan, geiger counter, ghost town, open pit, chaparral, Lake Roosevelt, Coon Butte, Santa Fe Agreement, Gila, Lake Bonneville, Lake Lahontan, Operation Haylift, Rambouillet, *Halogeton glomeratus,* Harney-High Desert, Owyhee Uplands, Lake Mead, Death Valley, Four Corners, Nechako, Fraser, Okanogan, Virginia City, Klondike, Humboldt, Carson, Owens, Jordan, Mojave, Salton Trough, San·Andreas, Comstock Lode, Bingham, Fairbanks, Gallup, Mammoth, Tiger.

SELECTED REFERENCES

Arizona Highways Commission, *Arizona Highways,* magazine.

Atwood, W. W., *The Physiographic Provinces of North America,* Ginn and Co., 1940, pp. 357–435.

Bernstein, Harry, "Spanish Influence in the United States: Economic Aspects," *Hispanic American Historical Review,* Vol. 18, 1938, pp. 43–65.

Bowman, Isaiah, *Forest Physiography,* John Wiley and Sons, 1911, pp. 256–297.

Brown, Ralph H., *Historical Geography of the United States,* Harcourt, Brace and Co., 1948, pp. 492–500.

Calef, Wesley, "The Salines of Southeastern California," *Economic Geography,* January 1951, pp. 43–64.

Currie, A. W., *Economic Geography of Canada,* Macmillan Co., 1947, pp. 254–275.

Dale, Edward Everett, *The Indians of the Southwest: A Century of Development Under the United States,* University of Oklahoma Press, 1949.

Fisher, E. Franklin, "Alaska and the Alaska Highway," *Journal of Geography,* October 1950, pp. 278–283.

Freeman, Otis W., and Howard H. Martin, editors, *The Pacific Northwest, An Over-All Appreciation,* John Wiley and Sons, 1954, pp. 65–76.

Headquarters Quartermaster Research and Development Command, "A Study of Desert Surface Conditions," *Technical Report EP–53,* U. S. Army, Natick, Mass., April 1957.

Headquarters Quartermaster Research and Development Command, "The Daytime Influence of Irrigation Upon Desert Humidities," *Technical Report EP–35,* U. S. Army, Natick, Mass., May 1956.

Hoffmeister, Harold A., "Alkali Problem of Western United States," *Economic Geography,* Vol. 23, 1947, pp. 1–9.

Hoover, J. W., "Southwestern Desert Vegetation," *Journal of Geography,* April 1935, pp. 148–156.

Joseph, Alice, and others, *The Desert People: A Study of the Papago Indians,* University of Chicago Press, 1949.

Kerr, Donald, "The Physical Basis of Agriculture in British Columbia," *Economic Geography,* July 1952, pp. 229–239.

Leopold, Luna B., "Vegetation of Southwestern Watersheds in the Nineteenth Century," *Geographical Review,* April 1951, pp. 295–316.

Life, "Man Versus Mesquite," Aug. 18, 1952, pp. 69–72.

Miller, E. Willard, "Agricultural Development in Interior Alaska," *Scientific Monthly,* Vol. 73, pp. 245–254, 1951.

Nelson, Ronald A., "Analogs of Yuma Climate in North America," *Research Study Report RER–12,* Headquarters Quartermaster Research and Development Command, U. S. Army, Natick, Mass., January 1957.

New York Times, "Colorado Water," editorial, Jan. 2, 1950.

Percin, Fernand de, and Sigmund J. Falkowski, "Low Temperatures in Alaska," *Technical Report EP–6,* Headquarters Quartermaster Research and Development Command, U. S. Army, Natick, Mass., February 1955.

Research and Development Branch Military Planning Division, "Studies on Clothing for Hot Environments, Death Valley, 1950," *Report 178,* U. S. Army, Natick, Mass., June 1951.

Rockie, W. A., "Snowdrift Erosion in the Palouse," *Geographical Review,* July 1951, pp. 457–463.

Sperry, Omer E., J. W. Dollahite, Judd Morrow, and Garlyn O. Hoffman, "Texas Range Plants Poisonous to Livestock," *Bulletin 796,* Texas Agricultural Experiment Station, 1955.

Thomas, Benjamin E., "The California-Nevada Boundary," *Annals of the Association of American Geographers,* Mach 1952, pp. 51–68.

U. S. Department of Agriculture, "Irrigation Agriculture in the West," *Miscellaneous Publication 670,* Washington, D. C., 1948.

U. S. News and World Report, "Why the Big Boom in the Desert States, Arizona, Nevada, New Mexico," Oct. 11, 1957.

U. S. Weather Bureau, "Weather and Death Valley," *Daily Weather Map,* Washington, D. C., Jan. 31, 1952.

Weir, Thomas R., "The Winter Feeding Period in the Southern Interior Plateau of British Columbia," *Annals of the Association of American Geographers,* June 1954, pp. 194–204.

Zierer, Clifford M., editor, *California and the Southwest,* John Wiley and Sons, 1956, pp. 25–37 and 38–48.

14 · The Pacific Borderlands
Part I

(Figure 1)

The Pacific Borderlands form a long narrow stretch of land along the Pacific Coast of North America, where oceanic influences are so dominant that the region is the only large continental division with a truly marine climate. Moreover, the Pacific not only provides a great physical difference between the region and interior areas, but it also brings economic contrasts between the borderlands and the adjoining Intermontane Plateaus.

For example, accessibility to the ocean provides a valuable fishing industry lacking in inland regions. The sea contributes moisture for luxuriant forests, basis for a major economic activity. Mountains force oceanic winds to rise and give up their moisture, much of it in the form of snow; and a large amount of melting snow in summer provides water for widespread irrigation agriculture; there is much more moisture than is available in the Intermontane Plateaus. Minerals occur in both plateaus and borderlands; but because of the adjoining ocean, the borderlands metals and power resources are far more accessible to world markets. Again, the adjoining ocean not only makes world markets accessible for regional raw materials, but the sea also gives easy access to raw materials unavailable within the region itself. Thus, manufacturing is encouraged, and a growing manufacturing industry along the Pacific Coast is another great difference between land use of Pacific coastal and interior lands. Tourism, commerce, and other regional differences occur, all of which will be described in some detail.

Surface Features

(Figure 2)

The Mountains. Mountains and valleys lie in three approximately parallel elongated belts. On the west, coastal mountains are separated from

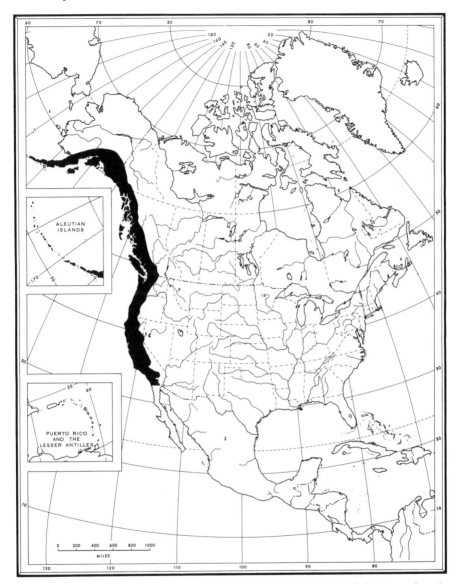

Fig. 1. The Pacific Borderlands. This long, relatively narrow region extends in a general north-south direction along the Pacific Coast for more than 2,000 miles.

an eastern mountain belt by a valley region extending, with slight interruptions, from southern California into the Panhandle of Alaska.

The Coastal Mountains. The coastal mountains may be divided in a north-south direction into three groups: those of California are separated

Fig. 2. Landform Divisions of California. California possesses many different surface features which show considerable diversity in geologic history. The variety of land forms provides a strong influence for contrasts in climatic types. (Source: Clifford M. Zierer, *California and the Southwest,* John Wiley and Sons, 1956.)

from coastal ranges of Oregon and Washington by the Klamath Mountains, lying partly in northern California and partly in southern Oregon; coastal ranges in continental United States north of the Klamath Mountains terminate in the Olympic Highlands just south of the Straits of Juan de Fuca; and north of the straits, coastal ranges continue through the Panhandle of Alaska.

The coastal uplands of California may be divided into four major divisions: the Coast Ranges, the Los Angeles Ranges, the San Diego Ranges, and the Klamath Mountains. The Coast Ranges extend from just north of Cape Mendocino to Point Conception. These mountains display a general northwest-southeast trend, with ridges and valleys paralleling the coast in many places. Where the shoreline changes its general northwest-southeast direction, valleys may open directly on the coast. In places, mountains approach the sea so closely that roads and railroads are forced inland by the bold rocky coast.

The Los Angeles Ranges extend from Point Conception on the north almost to San Diego on the south. General alignment is east-west and the mountains contribute the same trend to a large segment of the southern California coast. Block faulting has been active, and even offshore islands, unusual for the California coast, are the undrowned summits of fault block mountains. The Los Angeles Ranges enclose the Los Angeles Lowland, and form a southern boundary of the Great Valley of California.

The San Diego Ranges, lying south of the Los Angeles Ranges, comprise the northern portion of Fenneman's Lower California Province. These ranges make up a granitic fault block tilted gently toward the west and steeply toward the east. The block resembles the much larger Sierra Nevada fault block both in genesis and in barrier nature toward the interior.

The western portion of the Klamath Mountains lies along the coast, but the uplands also extend inland far enough to join the Sierra Nevada on the southeast and the Cascades on the northeast. Characteristic topographic features include long narrow ridges topped by rounded peaks; marine terraces, which fringe the coast as do those of the Coastal Ranges; and in places bold escarpments approach the Pacific so closely that there is no room for road or railroad.

The coastal highlands of Oregon and Washington fall into three main divisions: Oregon's portion of the Klamath Mountains; the Coast Ranges proper of Oregon and Washington; and Washington's Olympic Highlands.

The Coast Ranges of Washington and Oregon extend from Washington's Chehalis River to Oregon's Coquille River, and inland from the sea to the Willamette-Puget Lowland. The ranges are made up largely of gently folded sedimentary rocks, complicated here and there with intrusive and volcanic materials. Highest elevations reach only about 4,000 feet. Poleward from the Chehalis River is the compact massif, about 60 miles in diameter, known as the Olympic Range. Toward the Olympic's interior, ridges, largely of sedimentary origin, are arranged in a radial pattern with the highest peak, Mount Olympus, reaching nearly 8,000 feet.

That part of the Canadian and Alaskan Pacific Borderlands which corresponds to the elongated north-south topographic belt of Coast Ranges in the United States is the series of islands off the Pacific coast of British Columbia and Alaska, whose bases have been drowned by subsidence; these islands form the outer rim of the Inside Passage.

The Eastern Mountain Belt. The eastern mountain belt of the Pacific Borderlands includes the Sierra Nevada and Cascade ranges of the United States, and the continental Coast Ranges of British Columbia and Alaska.

The Sierra Nevada Range, lying almost entirely within California, extends from about 35° north in the Tehachapi Mountain section to the Feather River, approximately 40° north, and makes up an area of about 31,000 square miles, almost exactly the size of South Carolina. Generally speaking, the range can be characterized as a granitic fault block tilted gently toward the west and dropping off sharply to the east. The southern portion of the Sierra Nevada's eastern escarpment possesses drops of 8,000 to 10,000 feet within horizontal distances of a few miles. Throughout the range, mountain glaciation has been active. Cirques, U-shaped valleys, hanging waterfalls, and other glacial features are common at high elevations; and the most southerly glacier in the United States, Palisade Glacier, occurs at about 37° north.

The Sierra Nevada Range forms a real barrier to east-west travel. Great heights—the range includes the highest mountain in the contiguous United States, Mt. Whitney, 14,496 feet—and the absence of good passes have held railroad and road building to a minimum. Only one railroad crosses the mountains in a distance of 300 miles; and not one road leads over the crest in a stretch of 175 miles. Moreover, both roads and railroads may be blocked with snow during the winter season.

The Cascades are joined to the northern Sierra Nevada by the Klamath Mountains; but unlike the fault-block Sierra Nevada Range, the Cascade Mountains have been built up by numerous lava flows surmounted by large and small volcanic peaks. These include the only active volcano in the contiguous United States, Mount Lassen, whose last eruption was in 1915. Another famous volcanic feature is Crater Lake, which occupies the caldera of an old volcanic cone that lost its top by explosion or subsidence or by both. Glaciation has been active just as in the Sierra Nevada Range, especially above the 5,000 foot level.

Few railroads and roads cross the Cascades. Probably the best cross-mountain route is by way of the antecedent Columbia River which approximately bisects the mountain range along the boundary between Washington and Oregon.

As previously indicated, the Canadian portion of the Pacific Borderlands' eastern mountain belt lies just north of the Cascades and forms the continental division of British Columbia's Coast Ranges. Mountain glaciation has been active; and U-shaped valleys extend westward from coastal mountains, more than 10,000 feet high in places, and terminate in fiords. Several rivers, including the Fraser, Stikine, Skeena, and Nass, cross the 50 to 100 mile wide coastal range to reach the Pacific.

Northwest from the Chilkoot Pass, the Coast Ranges of British Columbia blend with those of Alaska in the Nutzotin Mountains and their extension the Alaskan Range; these two ranges form a great arc paralleling the Gulf of Alaska. The Alaskan Range continues west to the Aleutian Range of the Alaska peninsula and far into the Pacific Ocean. The highest mountain in North America, Mt. McKinley, 20,300 feet, occurs in the Alaskan Range.

Lying closer to the Alaskan coast are the Chugach Range, the St. Elias Range, the Wrangell Range, the Talkeetna Range, and the mountains on the Kenai Peninsula and Kodiak Island.

Pacific Borderlands Valleys. Between the Pacific Borderlands' eastern mountain belt and the coastal mountain belt lies the third major physiographic subregion. This elongated north-south series of lowlands includes the Great Valley of California, the Willamette-Puget Valley, the Inside Passage, a submerged continuation of the Willamette-Puget Lowland, and small valleys, such as the Susitna and Matanuska, near the Pacific coast of Alaska.

Mountains completely surround the Great Valley of California. It is bounded on the east by the lofty Sierra Nevada; on the north by the Klamath Range; on the west by the Coast Ranges; and in the vicinity of Point Conception the west-east trending Los Angeles Ranges approach the Tehachapi, an east-west aligned outlier of the Sierra Nevada, to form the southern boundary of the Great Valley.

The Great Valley includes an area of 21,000 square miles, a little smaller than West Virginia and just about two and one-half times the size of Massachusetts. Geologically, the lowland is a structural depression with the nearly level terrain drained by the Sacramento River in the north and the San Joaquin River in the south. Coalescing alluvial fans spread west from the Sierra Nevada Range, and eastward from the Coast Ranges. The only other interruptions to the nearly level surface, approximately 400 feet above sea level, are a few faulted, folded, and domed structures, such as the petroleum rich Kettleman Hills in the San Joaquin Valley, and the volcanic Marysville Buttes, which interrupt some 80 square miles of the Sacramento plain.

The Willamette-Puget Lowland (Fig. 3) is an alluvial plain about 350 miles long and 50 miles wide which lies north of the Klamath Mountains,

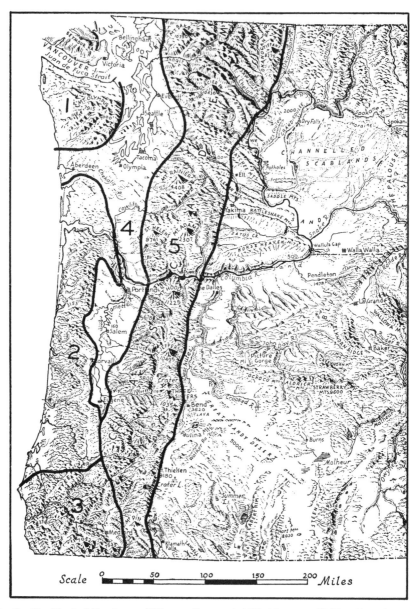

Fig. 3.   The Physical Provinces of Western Oregon and Washington.   (1) The Olympic Mountains; (2) the Coast Range; (3) the Klamath Mountains; (4) the Willamette-Puget Sound Lowland; (5) the Cascade Mountains.   (Source: Otis W. Freeman and Howard H. Martin, *The Pacific Northwest*, John Wiley and Sons, 1956.)

west of the Cascades, and east of the Coast Ranges of Oregon and Washington. Sediments brought down from the Cascades and Coast Ranges cover the lowland's formerly more rugged surface.

The Puget Sound portion of the lowland differs from the Willamette Valley in that the northern area has been glaciated and much of it is covered by the sea. The Willamette section extends from the Cowlitz Valley in the vicinity of Kelso and Longview, Washington, to Eugene, Oregon, a distance of approximately 160 miles. In several places, low hills rise a few hundred feet above the alluvial floor. Well-known examples include Salem, Waldo, Eola, and Amity hills. These are composed of resistant bedrock, mostly sandstone or basalt. Some of the hill land is still wooded, although other portions are cultivated; orchards are common.

The Canadian-Alaskan portion of the Pacific Borderlands lowland physiographic province is the Inside Passage, a submerged continuation of the Willamette-Puget Lowland.

Climates

(Figures 4, 5; also Figure 8, Chapter 1)

The Pacific Borderlands, with the exception of the Sierra Nevada, the Cascades, and the high Canadian-Alaskan Coast Ranges, may be divided into two major climatic regions, largely on the basis of latitude. The California coast and much of the Great Valley poleward to approximately 40°

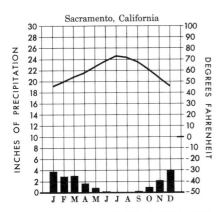
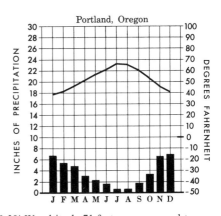

Fig. 4. Sacramento, California (38° 35′ N., 121° 30′ W.; altitude 71 feet; mean annual temp. 57° F.; mean annual precip. 19.4 inches); Portland, Oregon (45° 30′ N., 122° 37′ W.; altitude 57 feet; mean annual temp. 53° F.; mean annual precip. 43.8 inches). Sacramento is a good example of California's Mediterranean, Cs, climate, with winter rain and summer drouth; Portland, Oregon, lying farther north in the West Coast marine, Cb, climate has rainfall distribution similar to that of Sacramento; but the precipitation is more than double that of the California city. Temperatures are also lower in the higher latitude.

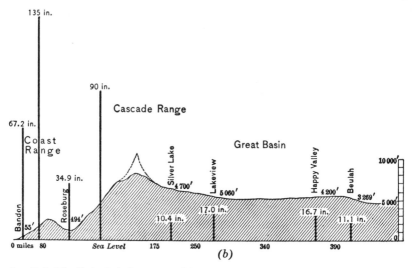

Fig. 5a.   Relief Profile in Relation to Rainfall on the Coast Ranges and the Cascades.   (Source:
Courtesy Edward Higbee, *American Agriculture,* John Wiley and Sons, 1958.)

north have a Mediterranean climate.   North of the 40th parallel, West
Coast marine climates dominate coastal lowlands and interior valleys.

   The Mediterranean, Steppe, and Desert Climates.   The Mediterranean is
sometimes considered a transition climate.   Equatorward lies the desert;
poleward are the humid lands.   Three air mass source regions influence the
climate.   In summer, descending air of the horse latitudes and equatorward-
moving air of the trade winds bring little rain.   Summer months may be hot,
but temperatures are lowered by inblowing winds off the cool California current.   In winter, low pressure storms of the westerly wind belt contribute
most of the precipitation.   Along the immediate coast, frosts are of rare
occurrence—Los Angeles averages less than one day a year with minimum

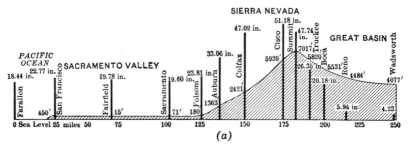

Fig. 5b.   Relation of Relief to Rainfall in the Sierra Nevada.   (Source: Edward Higbee, *American Agriculture,* John Wiley and Sons, 1958.)

temperatures of 32°F. or below. Thunderstorms are uncommon—Los Angeles averages two a year—and snow is unusual.

The central portion of the Great Valley is cut off so completely by mountains that extremely low annual precipitation results. Thus, small steppe and desert sections occur. Summers are hot, winters are mild, and precipitation is light, with practically the entire amount coming during the winter. During this season temperatures may fall to the freezing point at night, and frost sometimes forms. The unbroken sunshine of summer and early autumn is a feature of the region and favors the maturing and curing of fruit, particularly raisin grapes.

The West Coast Marine Climate. The region of West Coast marine climate receives the greatest influence from the adjoining Pacific. Extension into the continent is limited by high mountains such as the Cascades and the Sierra Nevada. Summers are cooler than the average for the latitude, and winters are warmer. This is a natural climatic result of the sea as the dominant control. Brookings, Oregon, at 42° north has a mean annual temperature of 52°F.; Prince Rupert, British Columbia, at 55° north, about 900 miles poleward, has a mean annual of 45°F. The difference in temperatures is only 7°F. On the Pacific Coast there is an average drop of 1° F. for each 130 miles, whereas on the Atlantic Coast the same drop occurs each 60 miles.

In winter, when a favorable pressure gradient is present, cold air will flow west through low gaps in the mountain barrier, such as the Columbia River gorge. There is enough winter cold to keep most vegetation relatively dormant, a contrast to conditions in the Mediterranean climate to the south where growth continues throughout the year.

The distribution of precipitation resembles that of the Mediterranean climate except that summers have low rainfall rather than drought conditions. Both climates show maximum precipitation in the cool season, but total rainfall is much greater in the West Coast marine climate. Winter snow may fall on the coastal lowlands, but it never lasts long. Heavy snow may accumulate on the higher altitudes of the Coast Ranges, the Cascades, and the Sierra Nevada. At Tamarack, Alpine County, elevation 8,000 feet, the average annual snowfall exceeds 500 inches.

Precipitation comes largely from cyclonic storms; and with more storms and better developed ones in winter than in summer, it is easy to account for the winter maximum in precipitation. Very little convectional rain falls, because summer air masses are relatively stable and temperatures are seldom high. Orographic precipitation is important. An abundance of cloud is characteristic, and northwestern United States has the questionable honor of the lowest annual percentage of possible sunny hours. In the mountains especially, a variety of climates may be noted depending upon altitude, exposure, and distance from the coast.

Vegetation

Much of the Pacific Borderlands is covered with forest. Trees occur in relatively consistent stands of Douglas fir, hemlock, lodge pole pine, red cedar, redwood, Sitka spruce, yellow pine, and others. However, not all of the region is covered with trees. Natural grassland and bush vegetation covered California's Great Valley and several of the state's smaller valleys among the Coast Ranges prior to Spanish and American settlement. At that time Oregon's Willamette Valley also had some grass, in contrast to Washington's heavily forested Puget Sound Trough.

The western slope of the Sierra Nevada shows striking relations between climate and distribution of natural vegetation. At the base, climate is so dry that the plain and lower foothills support a grass cover which is green only a few weeks each year. A little higher up, where rainfall increases, dwarf oak, a member of the dry forest, appears with its hard, prickly leaves. At higher altitudes, where there is abundant rain, dry forest gives way to a wet forest of pines, cedar, fir, and giant sequoias. Above the tree line are bushes and grasses. Here, where the temperature is too low for trees, cold-resistant vegetation successfully competes with higher forms of plant life. Within a day's climb a variety of climates and a varying vegetational response are found (Fig. 6).

The influence of temperature and precipitation on vegetation may be noted with changing latitude as well as with changing altitude. South of San Francisco, in progressively lower latitudes, the dry timber line ascends for several hundred miles until the hot dry climate changes to a hot wet one in southern Mexico and Central America. From San Francisco north, in latitudes where cyclonic storms continue throughout the year, rainfall permits forests at sea level; but as latitude increases and temperature decreases, the upper limit of forest growth occurs lower and lower down the mountain side. The cold timber line of 7,000 feet in western Washington becomes lower in the higher latitude of British Columbia, and declines to sea level near Prince William Sound in Alaska (Fig. 7); and the forest disappears entirely a little beyond the sound.

If we look at specific forest units of California, we find more evidence of environmental influences on distribution of vegetation. Redwoods, in some places pure stands and in some places associated with Douglas fir, occur most commonly near stream bottoms along central and northern coasts. Somewhat farther inland and a little higher up, where climate is a little cooler and less moist and foggy, Douglas fir is dominant. Yellow pine grows from sea level to 6,000 feet in the north, and in the south at about 3,000 feet. Lodge pole pine occurs in the Sierra Nevada and in northern California at elevations of about 9,000 feet. A thick snow mantle is vital for red fir, best developed in the Sierra Nevada between 8,000 and 9,000

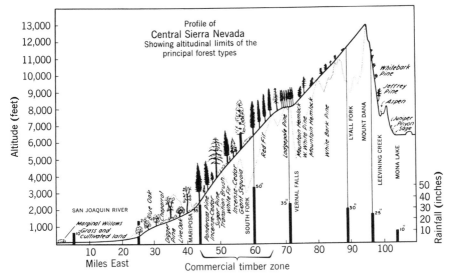

Fig. 6. Vegetation on the Sierra Nevada. Notice that the 10-inch rainfall (annual) at the western base of the mountain discourages tree growth but permits a natural grass vegetation. Higher up, with a 20-inch rainfall, chaparral and other drought-resistant trees crowd out grasses. Still higher, the 35-inch rainfall encourages commercial forests, which reach optimum development at the 50-inch isohyet near 3,500 feet altitude. Thereafter precipitation gradually declines to about 25 inches near the summit, where cold temperatures rather than lack of precipitation discourage tree growth. Notice the 10-inch rainfall near Mono Lake on the eastern (leeward) mountain side, where vegetation is restricted to drought-resistant varieties of piñon and sage. (Source: U. S. Department of Agriculture, Yearbook of Agriculture, *Trees,* 1949, p. 353.)

feet. The snow pack protects seedling growth from snow and ice blast and from the dessicating effects of winter winds; snow melting delays seedling growth until summer, when danger of winterkilling is past.

Subalpine species of white bark fir, lodge pole pine, limber pine, foxtail pine, and mountain hemlock form the highest forests at elevations of 9,500 to 11,500 feet on south-facing slopes, but may occur as low as 7,500 feet on north-facing slopes.

Fig. 7. Latitude, Altitude, and the Upper Tree Line. In a distance of 11° of latitude, from western Washington to Cross Sound near Juneau, Alaska, the upper tree line drops from 7,000 feet to 2,500 feet. A little farther north, it drops to sea level. South of western Washington the upper tree line rises.

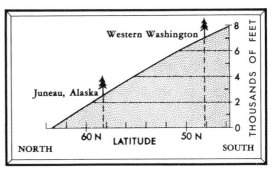

Oregon and Washington Vegetation. Near the coast of Oregon and Washington, forests of hemlock, spruce, and cedar are interspersed with smaller tracts of grass, brush, and cleared land. Inland, the Douglas fir forest predominates, often with an understory of hardwoods, although fires and logging operations have greatly altered its character. In the Klamath Mountains of Oregon, the Douglas fir forest is dominant as in the Coast Range, but the large areas of hardwood, such as oak and madrone, reflect the drier summers of the interior. Chaparral is common. Most of the region now lies in national forests.

In the Olympic Mountains, climatic variations based mainly on altitude and exposure to wind and sun are associated with a diverse pattern of natural vegetation. On the west and southwest, forests of cedar, spruce, and hemlock are common. To the southeast and to the north, large stands of Douglas fir are found in the valley floors and on the adjacent slopes. The higher elevations have large areas of subalpine vegetation, and the highest peaks are devoid of trees.

On the western slopes and lower elevations of the Cascades, the outstanding formation is the Douglas fir forest. In Oregon, this forest originally was a nearly continuous belt varying in altitude from less than 1,000 feet to more than 4,000 feet. In the northern Cascades, the Douglas fir was limited to the floors and lower slopes of the valleys and did not reach the higher ridges. On the higher elevations are forests of pine, spruce, and hemlock, and at the crest is a belt, narrow in the south, wide in the north, that lies above the cold timberline. Here, subalpine forms are common, and some of the higher peaks, because of steep slope and the porosity of the lava, are almost devoid of vegetation.

British Columbia Vegetation. The largest trees and the heaviest stands of Canada's coniferous forests are found in the Pacific Borderlands of British Columbia. The dominant types are western hemlock and western red cedar, with Douglas fir in the south and Sitka spruce in the north. All four of these species, of which the most important commercially is Douglas fir, grow to large size and occasionally are found in stands running up to 100,000 board feet per acre.

Considering the province as a whole, two-thirds of British Columbia is forested—247,000 square miles out of a total area of 359,279 square miles. Of the forested section, 123,218 square miles are productive forest, with 86,253 square miles accessible; and 124,141 square miles are non-productive forested land.

Alaska Vegetation. Alaska may be divided into four vegetation regions: (1) the Pacific coastal area from the British Columbia border to Cook Inlet; (2) the Southwestern Alaska grasslands; (3) the interior plateau and mountains; and (4) the treeless coast of the Arctic and Bering Sea. One and two are included in Alaska's portion of the Pacific Borderlands.

Alaska's Panhandle is covered with conifers to an altitude of approximately 2,000 feet. The conifers include large stands of giant cedar, yellow cedar, Sitka spruce, and western hemlock. Underbrush and herbaceous plants flourish beneath the cone-bearing trees; above the tree zone, alpine flora form the climax vegetation.

The Panhandle includes the Tongass National Forest, an area of approximately 25,000 square miles, whose coastal location and heavy forest near sea level is attracting commercial exploitation. The forest consists of 60 per cent western hemlock and 20 per cent Sitka spruce; the other 20 per cent includes western red cedar, yellow cypress, some lodge pole pine, and a small amount of cottonwood and white birch.

Poleward beyond the Panhandle, low temperatures bring a decline in the upper tree line until it reaches sea level in the vicinity of Cook Inlet. Around Cook Inlet, Prince William Sound, and on the Kenai Peninsula is the Chugach National Forest. It is only about one-third as large as the Tongass, has not as rich timber resources, and is broken up into several distinct units. Forest types are somewhat similar, but on the northern edge several species occur that do not appear in the Tongass. These include white spruce, black spruce, and white birch, species characteristic of Alaska's interior plateau country.

From Cook Inlet west, grasses, some of them several feet high, dominate the natural vegetation of the Pacific coast side of the Alaskan peninsula and the Aleutian Islands beyond. The low temperatures, and especially the high winds, a result of small land area in a wide expanse of ocean close to the Aleutian Low, favor grasses rather than forest. Some stunted bushes and dwarf trees occur, but grass occupies the larger area. Plant growth is encouraged by relatively heavy rainfall; GI's, stationed in the Aleutians, say the precipitation moves horizontally rather than downward.

Soils. Regional soils show great diversity. Little if any soil occurs on steep mountain sides; gentle slopes have better opportunity for developing mature profiles; and soils on relatively flat valley lands may be rejuvenated each year by flooding. Although most soils develop under forest cover, grasses and bushes make their organic contribution in various locations.

In California alone there are over 1,200 soil types. The kind of parent material influences texture, chemical makeup, and other soil characteristics; the amount of rainfall may produce an acid, a neutral, or an alkaline soil; the vegetation determines the amount and character of the organic matter; topography influences soil erosion, deposition, and drainage; and time may determine the type of soil profile.

In southern California, the best soils for agriculture are alluvial soils in the lowlands. These show a relatively favorable humus content and a high retention of original mineral composition. Moreover, since Mediterranean climates are relatively dry, the proximity to stream courses favors necessary irrigation. Deep well water is also more easily available from the porous unconsolidated alluvium.

Most soils in the marine West Coast climate are forest soils; those lying in equatorward portions belong to the gray-brown podzolics and those in the poleward areas may be classified generally as podzols. The latter show weak structure, low humus content, and considerable leaching; the former have good structure, a fair supply of humus, and good quantities of mineral plant food. As in the Mediterranean climatic subdivision, the alluvium in the valleys with moderate rainfall and good drainage provides best opportunities for agriculture. Bog soils may develop on lowlands with heavy rainfall and poor drainage.

Agriculture

California. *The Mission Period.* Because of the great latitudinal extent of the Pacific Borderlands, and the consequent climatic differences, farm crops and practices show considerable contrast; thus, for a better understanding of regional agriculture, each major subdivision will be examined as a unit.

Farming was introduced to California, along with other elements of Spanish colonial life, late in the eighteenth century. In the early days of Spanish colonization, the missions were agricultural centers. Spanish missionaries were well equipped to introduce farming into what is now California. Much of Mexico, whence the colonists came, is dry; horticulture, production of grain under dry farming methods, and the herding of livestock, all well established in Mexico, were easily transplanted into Upper California. The Spaniards had brought from Spain, much of which has a climate similar to that of southern California, tree crops and grains that could flourish in this part of North America. Mission agriculture included extensive grazing of livestock on the ample tracts of land assigned to the missions; grain farming; the production of tree crops such as figs, olives, and grapes; and garden cultivation with the aid of irrigation from the streams of the Coast Ranges. Such an economy represented an efficient use of the physical environment; production was largely for local consumption because transportation and export markets were limited.

The site of each mission was carefully selected with regard to natural advantages, such as soil and slope for irrigation, adequacy of water supply, accessibility and distance from other missions and forts, and the prospects of serving the Indian population.

Livestock raising was a basic industry at all missions and wheat became a universal crop. This is not surprising. Southern California's winter rainy season gives the grain a cool moist growing period, and the almost rainless summers provide a dry sunny ripening period.

Many of the early mission buildings were destroyed by fire and earthquake. A severe earth tremor occurred on December 8, 1812, that affected the whole chain of missions, requiring much new masonry. Fire was also troublesome on roofs covered with local tarlike bituminous material known as tule.

Mexico's declaration of independence in 1821 marked the beginning of mission decline. The trend toward secularization of the missions began with Mexico's independence and became final by legislative act on August 17, 1833. Unrest and turmoil held sway for a decade or more, not ceasing when California became a territory of the United States. The Mexican War brought more chaos, with more than 15,000 Indians dislodged from their mission residences, and church property occupied by ranchers or by the military. The scene was made still worse by indefinite or indefinable land grants with which Mexico had previously rewarded its citizens. Ranchers used these large tracts of land for grazing immense herds of cattle, sheep, and horses; and hides and skins were an important money crop shipped out by sea. It was into this scene of confusion that the tide of Anglo-American gold-seekers and settlers swept after the discovery of gold at Sutter's Mill, January 1848.

The Gold Rush Period. The influx of gold-seekers raised the population of the land west of the Sierra Nevada and south of the Oregon country from 15,000 white persons in 1848 to more than a half million people in 1857. Obviously, an agricultural development providing food for 15,000 people was not adequate for a half million; and for some time the only item of food in plentiful supply was jerked beef. Flour became so scarce that the price of $5 per hundred weight in San Francisco in March 1848 increased to $200 per hundred weight during December of the same year.

In spite of the need for rapid farm expansion, several conditions delayed progress: (*a*) most of the adventurous people who came to the mines had little if any farming background or interest; (*b*) the prospects of making a good strike made mining a relatively more attractive undertaking; (*c*) clouded titles, many of them covering the more desirable agricultural land, delayed or prevented normal farm settlement. In view of the confusion of land titles, an 1854 visitor was led to the humorous remark that "for many years to come, the lawyers will doubtless derive the largest income."

Handicaps slowed farm expansion, but did not stop it. Wheat acreage increased significantly, especially after 1862–64, when a bad drought destroyed thousands of cattle. Many ranchers, however, changed from cattle to sheep, and flocks of these animals increased until they threatened destruction of grassland, bush and forests.

The Modern Farming Period. Intensification of land use, the consequence of continued heavy immigration to California, has involved particularly an increase in the area devoted to fruits, nuts, and vegetables grown for Eastern and foreign markets. Since 1900, California has changed huge fields of grain into thousands of citrus groves, orchards, and vineyards, and has become the largest producer, fresh shipper, processer, and exporter of commercial fruit in the world.

Some credit for the increase in fruit, nut, and vegetable production should be given to the refrigerator car, which was invented by William Davis of Detroit in 1868, and which was greatly improved several years later. Possibilities in the natural environment for expanded vegetable and fruit growing had been known for years, but expansion awaited, among other things, the successful development of fast refrigerator transport that would safeguard perishable products on the way to market. Although refrigerated rail transport was available before the last quarter of the nineteenth century, profitable use of the invention awaited greatly lowered transcontinental freight rates, which came in the early 1890's. Improvements in canning and freezing also have expanded fruit and vegetable acreages. Man's inventiveness may change the landscape of almost any region.

Cooperation is another man-made influence on California's fruit and vegetable expansion. Practically every community has a cooperative packing house where fruit and vegetables may be cleaned, sorted, and packed, and from which they can be shipped to meet market demands. Research has also aided expansion, and federal, state, and private agencies have discovered improved production, processing, storing, transport, and marketing practices.

A steady increase in the use of water has given aid to large crops. From north to south, irrigation increases in importance as the total annual precipitation decreases. But only in dry interior valleys and in southern California does it dominate agriculture to the extent of being absolutely necessary for crop production. Thus, throughout much of the state, irrigation is a supplementary source of water for crops and so is a feature of intensification of agriculture rather than a necessary basis for it.

Aside from its influence upon the climates, the topography of the Pacific Borderlands has had a further effect on agriculture by determining the distribution of the lands smooth enough for tillage, and especially for irrigation. Population and cultivation of the soil are closely associated with the valleys, but the mountains play an important part in valley agriculture. Everywhere they receive more precipitation than valley floors. Mountain runoff goes into valley surface streams and ground water, and thus supplements the scanty rainfall of the lowlands. Development of agriculture has been closely linked with increasingly efficient use of mountain runoff. In the Mission period, agriculture used strictly local water supplies, but these have been inadequate where large aggregations of people are located. Constantly greater amounts of water have been required for cities and for irrigation farming.

Thus far, water supply systems as large as those built by cities have not been built for irrigation. On thousands of farms, water is pumped directly out of the ground for irrigation. Natural summer runoff through streams supplied by melting snow in the Sierra Nevada has provided a further supply. Winter runoff, most of it, has gone to the sea unused. The next step is the storage of the water that has heretofore run off unused in winter and in spring. Already work has begun on the largest of the projects for such storage and distribution of water, the Central Valley project.[1] A well-organized system of dams and canals will represent a long step toward what must be the ultimate goal, namely, as complete a use as is practicable of winter precipitation for crop production during the dry summer.

California Fruit and Nut Crops (Fig. 8). Different valleys lead in producing different fruit and nut crops. Although the San Joaquin Valley is California's largest farming region, fruits and nuts are not so important relatively as they are in less diversified southern California. However, the San Joaquin Valley accounts for over three-fourths of the grapes, two-thirds of the peaches, 15 per cent of the citrus crop, 90 per cent of the figs and nectarines, 50 per cent of the plums, and 40 per cent of the olives. About three-fourths of the San Joaquin orange acreage—almost all in Tulare, Fresno, and Kern counties—is in navels, a variety more tolerant of high temperatures and less susceptible to winter frost than valencias. Apples, prunes, and pears are of little commercial importance.

The Sacramento Valley has more precipitation and lower temperatures than the San Joaquin Valley; as a response, there are more deciduous fruit trees than those of the citrus variety. The Sacramento Valley and the adjoining Sierra Nevada foothills produce less than 10 per cent of California's fruit and nut crop on about 10 per cent of the acreage; but figures for specific crops run higher; they include 40 per cent of the nuts—mostly almonds—25 per cent of the prunes and peaches, 40 per cent of the plums, and 50 per cent of the pears; all figures are percentages of total state acreages.

The central coastal area north of Santa Barbara County has considerably more fruit and nut acreage than the Sacramento Valley, but these crops account for only about the same part of the crop acreage of both regions. Fruit and nut yields are below the state average chiefly because a larger proportion of the acreage is not irrigated. No citrus is grown commercially, but about 45 per cent of the state deciduous tree fruit acreage is found here. This includes 80 per cent of the apple, 75 per cent of the prune, 65 per cent of the apricot, nearly half the pear, and almost half the cherry acreage.

California's fourth major region growing fruits and nuts is southern California—the eight counties south of the Tehachapi Mountains. This area

---

[1] For map and other useful information, see Clifford M. Zierer, editor, *California and the Southwest,* John Wiley and Sons, 1956, pp. 135–145.

Fig. 8. Fruit Growing in a California Valley. Mountain barriers against prevailing westerly winds, active in the winter season, encourage precipitation for irrigating valley lowlands planted to fruit trees and other crops. Note the snow-clad mountains in the background; farmers are vitally interested in this source for irrigation. (Courtesy Keystone View Company.)

accounts for 25 per cent of the state acreage, but fruits and nuts form a more important part of the region's agricultural economy than in the three other major regions—about 40 per cent of the value of harvested crops and 25 per cent of the value of all farm products.

About 65 per cent of the acreage of fruits and nuts is in citrus, which yields about 25 per cent more value per acre than the state average for noncitrus fruits.   Commercial production of avocados and lemons is practically confined to southern California, largely in the coastal valley areas in San Diego, Orange, and Los Angeles counties.   About 60 per cent of the navel oranges of the state, and more than 90 per cent of the valencias are grown in southern California; the latter are highly concentrated in the coastal areas, where the moderate and equable climate favors production of the best quality of fruit with the least risk of frost damage to the winter blossoms.

California Vegetables (Fig. 9).   Like fruit and nut production, most of California's vegetable growing takes place in valleys where level areas and water are available.   Here the soils are usually relatively deep, permitting good dispersion and deep penetration of vegetable roots.   Major producing valleys include the Sacramento, the San Joaquin, and the valleys of the central and southern coast—the same valleys important in the state's fruit and nut industry.

Although vegetables have been grown for local consumption since the early Mission period, sales on the Midwest and Eastern markets awaited

Fig. 9.   California's Agriculture Is Largely Intensive.   Plastic film is laid over strawberry plants to prevent fruit losses from mold rot.   A large number of Japanese workers may be seen on California's fruit and vegetable lands.   Note the nearby oil derricks which suggest another important industry.   (Courtesy Bakelite Company.)

man-made changes, such as improvements in refrigeration, faster train schedules, and dietary education.

California vegetable farmers produce primarily for the fresh market, although growers also plant 10 per cent of the nation's acreage in vegetables for processing. More than 30 commercial varieties are grown, but state leadership is definite in a lesser number. California has approximately half of the country's acreage in asparagus, lettuce, and cauliflower grown for the fresh market; one-third of the acreage in carrots, cantaloupes, and celery; and three-fourths of the nation's acreage in honeydew melons. The state's acreage for processed asparagus, tomatoes, and lima beans also stands high.

Vegetable growing may take place year after year on the same fields with the help of commercial fertilizers, but rotation with field crops also may be followed. The various activities associated with growing vegetables require much labor; machines may aid in such operations as harvesting and topping onions and loading head lettuce into trucks, but most harvesting is done by hand labor; thus, expansion may be limited by supply of workers. Throughout the years, California has depended much on nearby Mexican labor. Foreign labor supplies and seasonality of the crop bring local and international problems.

California Field Crops. Diversity is a word that applies to field crops as well as to the state's vegetables, fruits, and nuts. Hay leads in acreage— half of it alfalfa—followed in order by barley, wheat, cotton, beans, rice, and sugar beets. The importance of hay may be judged from the fact that alfalfa is grown in every county—primarily by irrigation—except San Francisco County, which is entirely a metropolitan area. From one to six cuttings are possible, depending upon the length of the growing season.

Barley displaced wheat in California as the principal small grain crop in 1904 and now has three times the acreage. In 1950, California led all states in barley production and accounted for over one-sixth of the national yield. In the Great Valley, where greatest concentration takes place, barley is planted early enough to permit maximum use of winter rainfall and to avoid excessive summer temperatures and warm weather diseases. Seeding by broadcast or drilling occurs from late October to mid-February.

The southern half of the San Joaquin Valley is the center of California's cotton production, where it is grown entirely by irrigation in the summer. That conditions are suitable for production may be seen by a comparison of acreage yields—770 pounds per acre in 1950, and the average yield for the United States, 236 pounds per acre. Mechanization is a characteristic feature, with most of the picking done by mechanical harvesters. Chemical defoliants are applied by airplane or ground machines to bring about leaf drop before harvest.

About one-seventh of the nation's rice is grown in California, most of it in the southern half of the Sacramento Valley and in the northern and central portions of the San Joaquin Valley. Here, high temperatures, level land, heavy clay soils, and ample water for irrigation all provide a useful physical environment. Rice also may be planted on some alkali soils; large amounts of water needed for rice growth will wash salts from the soil. Rice may be planted by airplane and harvested with combines.

Another crop showing tolerance to certain alkali soils is the sugar beet, always grown by irrigation in California. Mechanization has increased greatly in the last few years, thus lessening the former great dependence on hand labor for tasks such as thinning and weeding.

California Livestock (Fig. 10). California's field crops make up one of several factors responsible for the state's growing livestock industry. Many cattle and lambs are fattened in the Great Valley on beet pulp and molasses, cottonseed concentrates, fibrous barley, and the all-important alfalfa hay.

The foothills surrounding the valley have annual and perennial grasses on which the livestock are dependent. In fact, these rolling grasslands provide the most important range in the state. The problem of range management depends on the proper correlation of the three-fold cycle of vegetation: (*a*) during early winter some supplemental feeding is necessary; (*b*) from

Fig. 10. Feeding Cattle in the Great Valley. Cattle feeding has become an important industry in California. These Herefords are eating the by-products of processed sugarbeets—the beet pulp, leaves, etc. California barley also makes a good ration for fattening livestock. (Courtesy Great Western Sugar Company.)

February to May the green forage is sufficient; (c) during the dry summer the rough herbage contains some carbohydrates, but because it is low in protein, supplements should be added; these supplements come from the field crops of the Great Valley.

California's neighbors provide a third factor aiding the livestock industry. Feeder cattle and lambs move in from the arid lands of Arizona, Nevada, Oregon, and Texas to be fattened in the Great Valley. In this respect there is a similarity between California and the neighboring states on the one hand and the Corn Belt and the Great Plains on the other. Both California and the Corn Belt are livestock fattening areas.

The fourth major factor in California's livestock industry is the large local market for meat that has developed on the Pacific Coast. No section of the United States is growing faster in population, and California may soon boast the largest number of people of any state in the Union.

Oregon and Washington Farming. Although in the pioneer period there was some movement back and forth across the 42nd parallel, the historic boundary between California and the Oregon country, most settlement of the northern territory followed a different course from that in California. Oregon settlement was similar to pioneer settlement in the forested country of eastern United States. Before the influx of immigrants, principal population centers were trading posts of the Hudson's Bay Company. There was the familiar sequence of trapper and Indian trader, missionary, and frontiersman, and finally the pioneer settler staking out his frontier farm on public land. Here, too, relations with the Indians were similar to those that obtained in the pioneer period of the East. There was no civilizing influence to incorporate Indians into a local economic system, such as that exercised by the missions in California; and there was little large-scale preemption of the land to prepare the Oregon country for the settlers who flocked westward over the Oregon Trail at the same time that others were "rolling down the slopes of the Sierra Nevada" into California. In the Oregon country, where the more abundant winter rains maintain a better supply of ground water through the shorter summer-dry season, the crops with which the settlers were familiar in their earlier homes in the Mississippi Valley and the East could be grown more easily than in California.

The Puget Sound Trough. As previously indicated, the Willamette Valley and the Puget Sound Trough lie between the Coast Ranges and the Cascades and are separated from the Great Valley of California by the Klamath Mountains. The Puget Sound Trough, which lies north of the Columbia River, has heavy rainfall and a relatively dense tree cover. Most farms are located on valley flood plains of streams flowing from east to west across the trough, or upon the upland divides which separate rivers draining to the Pacific.

Dairying is the feature industry, with over half of Washington's milk cows and five of the ten leading dairy counties of the Pacific Northwest located in the Puget Sound Trough. A climate similar to that of the best dairy regions of Northwest Europe, large city markets nearby, and agricultural conditions more favorable to intensive use of crop land than to general farming, all combine to favor dairy specialization. Rainfall is sufficient for good pasture and hay crops. If the two summer months of July and August show low precipitation, crop growth suffers little because of the seepage in most alluvial soils used for farming. And the low summer rainfall permits the growing of small grains for fodder, oats especially, thus supplying some supplemental feed; however, some grain and alfalfa are imported, mainly from eastern Washington. About two-thirds of the milk is sold on the local market, but there are also creameries, condenseries, and cheese factories. Partly because clearing the forest land is an expensive process, farms are relatively small.

A typical dairy farm may contain 40 to 50 acres, about half of which is cropped. Part of the crop may be clover, timothy, and rye grass, grown together for meadow or pasture. Oats, which occupies most of the remaining crop land, may be harvested as grain or cut for green feed. Oats is well adapted to the cool moist climate of the Puget Sound area, which leads the Pacific Northwest in the production of this small grain. A potato patch, small orchard, and family garden may make up the rest of the crop land. Stump pastures of low carrying capacity may occupy the remainder of the farm. The well-built dairy barn for 15 or 20 cows will probably be larger than the family dwelling.

Many dairy farmers raise poultry as a side line or as an enterprise of equal importance. In fact, this region is well suited for poultry farms. The industry is an intensive one well adapted to a small acreage. Clearing land is a huge task, uncleared land may be purchased at a relatively low price, large local markets are available, and cooperative marketing is well developed; thus, poultry farmers can start with a relatively low capital outlay, and climatic conditions are generally favorable. So far, Northwestern poultry raisers have not expanded beyond supplying their own regional markets.

Bush fruits and vegetables, raised in significant quantity, are favored by several local conditions. Intensive farming fits in well with small acreages; the large amount of labor necessary for each cultivated acre is available locally from urban districts; nearby markets and processing plants provide easy disposal of crops; and availability of dependable moisture assures high acreage yields. Bush fruits include loganberries, boysenberries, youngberries, raspberries, blackberries, strawberries, etc. The first three were obtained by crossing blackberries and raspberries, and they are named after their respective discoverers.

Willamette Valley. The Willamette Valley differs from the Puget Sound and Coastal areas in several ways. The broad expanse of gently rolling farm land has more fertile soils than all but the best alluviums of the Puget Lowland. Winters are cooler and summers warmer and dryer. Annual precipitation is less and the summer season of natural pasturage is limited to approximately three and one-half months. Many farmers supplement natural rainfall with irrigation; this lengthens the pasture season to six or seven months and increases the hay crop.

General farming is much more common than in the Puget Sound region. Farm landscapes are featured by dairy animals, fields of small grain, hay, bush crops, nut crops including filberts and walnuts, fruits such as cherries and prunes, and other crops. Many diversified farms have a wood lot to supply fuel and fence posts. Dairying is important because it provides a regular cash income, furnishes an outlet for farm grown hay and grain, utilizes available pasture, furnishes manures to improve the soil, and distributes farm labor evenly throughout the year. More than 80 per cent of all crop land is in pasture, hay, and grains such as wheat, oats, barley, and corn—crops basic to dairying. Farms are generally larger than in the Puget Sound section with an average of nearly a quarter section of land for dairy farms. Half of the farm may be devoted to crops and the remainder to brushy pasture.

In the early 1950's, the Willamette Valley produced approximately half of America's hops on about 22,000 acres. Cut flowers, flower seeds, and bulbs are grown in both the Puget Sound and Willamette lowlands. The leading bulb crops are lilies, gladioli, narcissi, irises, tulips, and dahlias. In the Nooksack Valley, north of Bellingham, flower bulb production is carried on by descendants of immigrants from Holland. Curry County, Oregon, ranks high in the production of Easter lilies and Puyallup, Washington, is a center for daffodils.

Most English walnuts and filberts of the Northwest are grown in the Willamette Valley, especially in the northern part, where they rank next to prunes in acreage. However, there are more prune trees than all other fruit trees combined. Most of the crop goes to canneries and driers. Summers less dry than those of the Mediterranean climate of southern California make artificial drying necessary.

Coastal Oregon and Washington. Dairying dominates land use on the narrow fringe of lowland in Oregon and Washington between the Coast Range and the sea. The cool temperatures and heavy rainfall favor the growth of grasses, but discourage the ripening of grain. Nearly every farm keeps cows, the percentage of dairy farms being higher than in any other section of the Northwest. In fact, the livestock industry might be called pasture dairying because so many practices are adjusted to the advantages and limitations of the environment.

For example, cows freshen in the spring for peak production of milk during the long pasture season, and milk production slackens during the coolest season to economize on hay and grains. Much hay and practically all feed grains are imported. Silos are built to store the lush spring grass. As in the Puget Sound area, farms contain large acreages of uncleared or rough mountain land, with only about 30 acres in crops. As stump and brush removal costs approximately $100 per acre, only alluvial soils are cropped.

The lack of large urban markets and the seasonal nature of production encourage the sale of bulk milk to cheese factories and creameries. Tillamook, Coos, and Curry counties in Oregon are noted for making cheese.

Tillamook County, one of the most distinctive dairy areas of the Northwest, forms a unit in the coast region. In this county, which is populated by farmers of Swiss ancestry, dairying is predominant, with four-fifths of the arable land in grass, and more than 90 per cent of the farm income derived from milk. More than three-fourths of the milk is made into cheddar cheese in a modern cheese plant, one of the largest on the Pacific Coast.

British Columbia Farming (Fig. 14, Chapter 13). Farming in the Pacific Borderlands of British Columbia involves a few pockets of land topographically, climatically, and pedologically suitable for agriculture. The largest and economically the most important are the Lower Fraser Valley and the East Coast Lowlands of Vancouver Island. Other sections, largely undeveloped, include several disconnected lowlands.

The Lower Fraser Valley includes two sections, low-lying ground under 50 feet high and higher elevations averaging 300 feet above sea level. The lowland must be diked against annual flooding, and because of poor natural drainage, pumping stations and drainage canals are necessary. Upland surfaces are hilly and have less fertile soils than those on the lowland. Rainfall varies from 35 to 100 inches with a winter maximum. The production of whole milk for the Vancouver market is the leading industry. Approximately 40 per cent of the farm land is either in natural or controlled pasture, but about 30 per cent is used for the growing of grain, most of which is fed to dairy cattle and poultry. Egg production is consistently high throughout the year, principally because of the lack of temperature extremes. Vegetables and small fruits are raised mainly on the lowland soils, orchard fruits on the uplands. Temperatures rarely fall below zero degrees F., thus minimizing the danger of winterkilling to sensitive middle latitude orchard fruits.

The East Coast Lowlands of Vancouver Island and the Gulf Islands contain approximately 80,000 acres of cultivated land. The most productive farm lands have a discontinuous distribution and are associated with postglacial deltas and lake bottoms. Climate, soils, and terrain are similar to those of the Lower Fraser Valley and encourage dairying, poultry raising, and the cultivation of fruits and vegetables. The growing of spring flowers, such as daffodils and narcissi, for the distant central and eastern Canadian market in late March and early April is an economic expression of the early spring season in the region.

The remaining arable pockets of the British Columbia Pacific Border-lands comprise less than 20,000 acres of improved farm land. Practically all farms are subsistence in character and many are worked on a part-time basis; fishing and forestry supplement the meager farm income. A large area topographically suitable for farming is the Graham Island Coastal Plain. Nearly a million acres could be used for agriculture. But need for farm products will be much greater than now before expensive clearing, diking, and drainage prepare the land for pasture, grasses, root crops, and small fruits.

Alaska Farming (Figs. 11, 12, 13, 14). In 1950, the Department of Agriculture in cooperation with the Alaskan Agricultural Experiment Station published a progress report entitled *Some Economic Aspects of Farming in Alaska.* Although the report dealt with agricultural possibilities throughout the state, most of the study focused on five areas, the Kenai Peninsula, Anchorage, Kodiak Island and the Aleutians, Matanuska, and Fairbanks, and the Tanana Valley. The first four of these areas belong to the Pacific Borderlands; Fairbanks and the Tanana Valley were described with the Intermontane Plateaus.

Most of Alaska's land cleared for agriculture, three-fourths of the 12,000-acre total, is in the Matanuska Valley. This site of the Matanuska colony established in 1935 by the federal government was originally covered

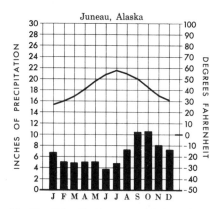
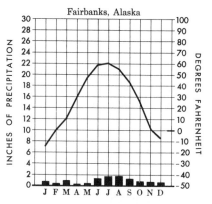

Fig. 11. Climatic Contrasts, Alaska. Juneau (58° 18′ N., 134° 35′ W.; altitude 80 feet; mean annual temp. 42° F.; mean annual precip. 79.54 inches); Fairbanks (64° 51′ N., 147° 52′ W.; altitude 50 feet; mean annual temp. 25.6° F.; mean annual precip. 11.74 inches). Great contrasts exist between the climate of coastal Juneau and interior Fairbanks. The former, in the Pacific Borderlands, has a marine climate; the latter, in the Intermontane Plateaus, has a continental one. Notice particularly the differences in temperature range and total precipitation.

Fig. 12. Matanuska Valley, Palmer, Alaska. Spring wheat in the shocks near Pioneer Peak, $4\frac{1}{2}$ miles southeast of Palmer. (U. S. D. A. photograph.)

by a stand of small timber. Soils are derived from fine sand and silt blown up from the bed of the Matanuska River. The nearly level to gently rolling surface may suffer wind and water erosion, and commercial fertilization is necessary for crop growth.

Rainfall averages less than 16 inches, the low amount influenced by location between the Chugach and Talkeetna Mountains. Spring may be too dry for vegetable seeding in an area where maximum precipitation comes in July, August, and September. In those months, cloudiness may reduce growth advantages of the long daylight period, and rainfall and high humidity hinder curing hay and the storage of grain. Possible sunshine ranges from 14 hours on April 15th and August 15th to 20 hours by the middle of June. The short growing season of about 108 days permits such crops as oats, peas, and vetch for silage or hay, small grains, potatoes, head lettuce, and celery; but these may be damaged by winds or by late spring or autumn frosts. Potatoes are the most important cash crop and are grown on three-fourths of Alaska's farms. In spite of the fact that it requires 6.8 acres to produce necessary feed for a cow, dairying is the most important farming activity.

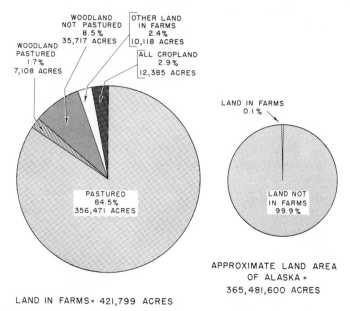

Fig. 13. Use of Alaskan Land for Farms. Alaska farm land comprises an extremely small part of the state, and more than five-sixths of the farm area is in pasture. (Courtesy U. S. Department of Agriculture.)

Crops grown in Matanuska, with the exception of grains, can be grown on the Kenai Peninsula; prevailing overcast, rainy weather, and lower summer temperatures discourage cereal growth. Kenai climate is typically West Coast marine in character, neither extremely cold in winter nor hot in summer. The newly completed highway to Anchorage will help Kenai farmers deliver crops to their nearest local market.

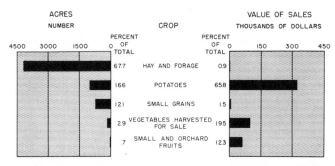

Fig. 14. Relative Importance of Specified Alaskan Crops. Hay and forage crops for dairy feed account for two-thirds of the acreage in crops harvested. Irish potatoes account for three-fifths of the value of crops sold. Dairy products account for approximately two-fifths of the farm produce sold. (Courtesy U. S. Department of Agriculture.)

Anchorage, the hub of Alaskan air transport, the home of Fort Richardson, and Alaska's largest city, over 30,000 population, has a small amount of agricultural production on the outskirts of the city. Climatic conditions are similar to those of Matanuska, but soils are not so well suited for farming. The growing of hay for dairying, the raising of vegetables, especially potatoes and the rearing of hogs and chickens are major farm enterprises. Feed for hogs and poultry comes largely from the garbage of Fort Richardson.

Temperatures on Kodiak Island and on the Aleutians are not a serious handicap to farming, but snowfall averages about 48 inches and covers native feed at times. On the lower slopes of mountains, heavy growth of grasses and mosslike plants offers good summer range for livestock. Beach rye and sedges at the heads of bays provide hay and silage, but curing hay is difficult in an area with an annual precipitation as high as 60 inches. Winter feeding is necessary on Kodiak, but year-round grazing is possible on some islands to the west; cattle are grazed on Chirikof, and sheep have been raised on Umnak, Unalaska, and on other islands. Handicaps to southwest Alaska's livestock industry include predatory animals, distances to markets, lack of slaughter houses, absence of cold-storage facilities, and inadequate transport for moving products to far-away consuming centers.

If stock raising ever proves valuable enough to expand, predatory animals can be eliminated from the limited space of these small islands. On the other hand, elimination of predatory beasts on the Alaskan mainland is almost impossible because the Alaskan mainland is part of the huge continental land mass. Wolves were exterminated centuries ago on the island of Great Britain, but they still remain a menace on the large European land mass across the English Channel.

QUESTIONS, EXERCISES, AND PROBLEMS

1. What conditions set the area apart as a region? With a good atlas, study the various topographic divisions which make up the region. Describe regional land forms, climates, vegetation, and soils. Sketch a vegetation profile for the western Sierra Nevada. Show how both altitude and latitude influence the height of the tree line. Describe specific forest units of California, Oregon, Washington, British Columbia, and Alaska. Comment on the great variety of California soils.

2. Describe the agriculture during California's Mission period, the gold rush era, and at the present time. Point out the important characteristics of California fruit, vegetable, and nut production. Tell of the state's field crops and livestock.

3. Compare the advantages of the Willamette Valley and the Puget Sound Trough for farming. Read carefully Edward Higbee, *American Agriculture,* Chapter 13, "The Willamette Valley." Describe the agriculture of coastal areas in Oregon, Washington, British Columbia, and Alaska. Read outside references and tell of the planned settlement of the Alaska Matanuska area in the 1930's. How does this settlement compare with that of the Metlakatla Indians along the Alaskan coast?

4. Roland Atwood, an Anchorage, Alaska, publisher, recently stated that Alaska is not only the largest state in the Union, but that it will be the richest of the states. Analyze Mr. Atwood's prediction critically.

5. A prediction has been made that California will soon be the most populous state. Even now, authorities are concerned about the invasion of the state's citrus groves by urban developments. Consult outside readings on these questions.

6. Identify the following: physical regions of California, Oregon, Washington, British Columbia, and Alaska; Mediterranean climate, West Coast marine climate, indefinable land grants, William Davis, caldera, highest mountain in North America, Lassen Peak, Mt. Whitney, antecedent stream, Tehachapi, Kettleman Hills, Central Valley project, Tamarack, Tongass, Tillamook, Palisade glacier, Inside Passage.

SELECTED REFERENCES

Atwood, Wallace W., *The Physiographic Provinces of North America,* Ginn and Co., 1940, pp. 439–518.

Baugh, Ruth E., "Geographic Factors in the Evolution of California," *Journal of Geography,* March 1955, pp. 133–139.

Brown, Ralph H., *Historical Geography of the United States,* Harcourt, Brace and Co., 1948, pp. 83–86.

Dutro, J. T., Jr., and T. G. Payne, *Geologic Map of Alaska, 1:2,500,000,* U. S. Geological Survey, 1954.

Freeman, Otis W., and Howard H. Martin, editors, *The Pacific Northwest, an Over-All Appreciation,* John Wiley and Sons, 1954, pp. 3–120 and 285–378.

Geographical Record, "Alaska Water Supply," *Geographical Review,* January 1951, pp. 156–158.

Gregor, Howard F., "A Sample Study of the California Ranch," *Annals of the Association of American Geographers,* December 1951, pp. 285–306.

Gregor, Howard F., "The Local-Supply Agriculture of California," *Annals of the Association of American Geographers,* September 1957, pp. 267–276

Gregor, Howard, F., "The Southern California Water Problem in the Oxnard Area," *Geographical Review,* January 1952, pp. 16–36.

Highsmith, Richard M., Jr., "Irrigation in the Willamette Valley," *Geographical Review,* January 1956, pp. 98–110.

Kuchler, A. W., "The Broadleaf Deciduous Forests of the Pacific Northwest," *Annals of the Association of American Geographers,* Vol. 36, 1946, pp. 122–147.

Lantis, David W., "California," *Focus,* October 1957.

Large, David C., "Cotton in the San Joaquin Valley," *Geographical Review,* July 1957, pp. 365–380.

Leighly, John, "Settlement and Cultivation in the Summer Drylands," *Climate and Man,* Yearbook of Agriculture, 1941, pp. 197–202.

Lemons, Hoyt, and Rayburn Tousley, "Washington Apple Industry: Its Geographic Basis," *Economic Geography,* Vol. 21, 1945, pp. 161–182.

Marts, M. E., "Upstream Storage Problems in Columbia River Power Development," *Annals of the Association of American Geographers,* March 1954, pp. 43–50.

Matthes, Francois E., *The Incomparable Valley, a Geological Interpretation of the Yosemite,* University of California Press, 1950.

Miller, David H., *Snow Cover and Climate in the Sierra Nevada, California,* University of California Press, 1955.

Miller, Elbert E., and Richard M. Highsmith, Jr., "The Hop Industry of the Pacific Coast," *Journal of Geography,* February 1950, pp. 63–77.

Minister of Education, Province of British Columbia, *Geography Manual, British Columbia,* 1954.

New York Times, "California Maps Vast Water Plan," March 18, 1956, p. 42.

Renner, George T., 3rd, "The Halfmoon Bay Littoral of Central California," *Journal of Geography,* April 1954, pp. 164–171.

Rude, Gilbert T., "Our Last Frontier, The Coast and Geodetic Survey's Work in Alaska," *Geographical Review,* July 1957, pp. 349–364.

Smith, Philip S., "Areal Geology of Alaska," *Geological Survey Professional Paper 192,* U. S. Department of the Interior, 1939.

Thomas, Louis B., "Development of Chula Vista, California," *Economic Geography,* January 1950, pp. 65–76.

Ullman, Edward L., "Rivers as Regional Bonds: The Columbia-Snake Example," *Geographical Review,* April 1951, pp. 210–225.

U. S. Weather Bureau, "Fruit Frost Service," *Daily Weather Map,* Washington D. C., Feb. 15, 1956.

U. S. Weather Bureau, "Raisins and Rain Warnings," *Daily Weather Map,* Washington, D. C., Sept. 11, 1952.

U. S. Weather Bureau, "Weather and Fruit Growing," *Daily Weather Map,* Washington D. C., Aug. 22, 1947.

Zierer, Clifford M., *California and the Southwest,* John Wiley and Sons, 1956, pp. 1–96, 97–121, 122–192.

15 · The Pacific Borderlands Part 2

Minerals and Power Resources

Minerals. The story of minerals and power resources may begin with the California Gold Rush; for gold was one of the first metals discovered, and it was gold and the Mexican War which made California a part of the United States.

The discovery came on January 24, 1848 when James Marshall, who was building a mill for Johann Sutter, a Swiss pioneer, first saw the metal in the south fork of the American River near Coloma. This stream, and other tributaries of the Sacramento and the San Joaquin, rushing at great speed down the mountains eroded gold from the original formation and moved it out to the adjoining plain, where loss of carrying power encouraged stream deposition.

Nearly 100,000 people reached San Francisco in 1849, by various routes. They came by way of the long journey around Cape Horn; by sea for a shorter distance to Panama where they crossed the isthmus and boarded other craft for San Francisco; some came by prairie schooners over the Oregon Trail to the Willamette Valley, and then through the Klamath mountains to the gold fields; others journeyed by ox team through the West by way of the Santa Fe Trail and on from New Mexico to California.

On arrival in California, immigrants saw the cities almost deserted. All, or nearly all of the male inhabitants had gone to the mines. Soldiers deserted their ranks, sailors their ships, and men their employment to speed to the gold fields. Along the route to the diggings, mills were lying idle, fields of wheat were open to cattle and horses, houses were vacant, and farms were going to waste. The California Gold Rush emphasizes the principle that man will go anywhere and endure any privation for a chance to secure precious metals.

Methods of mining varied with the passage of time. At first everyone used a pan, a rocker, or a cradle—all simple methods of placer mining. Miners took advantage of the principle that gold, being heavier than the surrounding gravels, will sink to the bottom when water, gravel, and gold are shaken in a pan.

As the stream gravels became worked out, miners devoted their efforts to dry placers, or gravels laid down by geologically old streams, now extinct. This involved a more complex type of the placer principle, hydraulic mining. By this method, water under pressure in long hoses, was directed against ancient river valley deposits to dislodge the gold-bearing gravels. These moved into flumes, some a mile or more long, where separation of the gold took place. Thousands of fertile acres were ruined by the waste brought down from the early hydraulic operations. Ill feeling and outright antagonism developed between farmers and miners. An 1884 statute forbade hydraulic mining when in conflict with other interests. By 1860, shaft mining became more important than panning, hydraulic mining, and dredging, and continues as the dominant type today.

California's 1952 gold production, mostly from the Sierra Nevada Range, amounted to 258,176 fine ounces, giving the state third rank in production—behind South Dakota and Utah. The 1952 total for both Washington and Oregon was only about one-fifth as much as that for California. British Columbia gold production amounted to $12,000,000 in 1951, not all, from the Pacific Borderlands. Production for the entire territory of Alaska in 1952 was 240,557 fine ounces, only a little less than that for California.

California also produced over a million fine ounces of silver in 1952; figures for Oregon and Washington in the same year were 4,000 and 300,000 fine ounces, respectively. The yield of the three states is low compared to the 15,000,000 fine ounces for Idaho, leading United States producer. Alaska mined but 32,986 fine ounces in 1952.

Gold and silver are high-value, low-volume minerals in Alaska whose production can stand high transport and labor costs. Alaskan iron, lead, and zinc do not belong to the class of precious metals. Thus, it is not the quantity of minerals that will determine exploitation in the state, but the quality of the deposit. Richness of the ore and the cost of extraction and transport will determine the future of Alaska mining. Minerals occurring along Alaska's Pacific Borderlands will have an advantage in their greater accessibility to transport.

Many other minerals besides gold and silver occur throughout the Pacific Borderlands. The largest quantity of copper comes from British Columbia, north of Vancouver on Howe Sound and at Copper Mountain, 100 miles east of Vancouver. About 900,000 tons of ore are concentrated annually at Britannia Beach. British Columbia copper production amounts to about 50,000,000 pounds of refined copper a year; not all of this comes from the Pacific Borderlands. Cadmium, gold, lead, zinc, and pyrite are also found in association with copper.

California has valuable iron resources at Eagle Mountain, northeast of Indio, where proven reserves of a magnetic deposit—30 to 50 per cent metallic content—approximate 50 million tons; of course, these reserves are small when compared with the Lake Superior, the Labrador, and the Birmingham, Alabama, resources. Small deposits of iron ore also occur on Vancouver Island, Texada Island, and along the mainland coast of British Columbia.

Lead and zinc are produced in appreciable amounts in California and in British Columbia. In 1953, California accounted for over 5,000 short tons of zinc, mostly from the Richmond mine in Shasta County and from the Coso Mountains in Inyo County. The Coso district also produced over 8,000 tons of lead in the same year.

Large reserves of subgrade chromite occur in the ancient and modern black beach sands of the Oregon coast. Production in 1953 amounted to about 6,000 tons. California accounted for 25,000 tons in the same year.

The largest United States production of mercury comes from California, where it has been mined at 50 different sites. In 1953, the state produced 9,290 seventy-six pound flasks, much of it coming from the Mt. Jackson mine in Sonoma County. Oregon accounted for only 648 flasks in the same year. California also leads in the mining of tungsten, which comes mostly from the Pine Creek mine in the Sierra Nevada Range. The Bishop reserves are the largest known tungsten resource in the United States.

Other minerals in the Pacific Borderlands include gypsite, occurring in the southwest portion of the San Joaquin Valley; iodine, the entire United States supply coming from brines in California's oil well wastes; diatomite, most of which comes from California; lime sand, gravel, and building stone, all of which are widespread; and many other minerals.

Power Resources (Fig. 1). Commercial production of petroleum in 1865 came a few years after the first gold strike in California. The black gold, like the real metal, has given thousands of jobs to oil workers, stimulated manufacturing, farming, and many other industries, and provided the state with a major export.

California [1] has estimated proven reserves of liquid hydrocarbons (1954) of 4,218,837,000 barrels, which place the state second in rank behind

[1] In California, minerals have less direct importance than manufacturing, commerce, and agriculture. Excluding petroleum and natural gas, the tourist trade of southern California alone was worth more than twice the value of mineral commodities of the state during the early 1950's. Oregon mineral production amounts to approximately $5,000,000 annually, but the figure for Washington reaches more than $25,000,000 yearly. Minerals are a great economic resource of British Columbia, contributing over $125,000,000 each year to provincial economy.

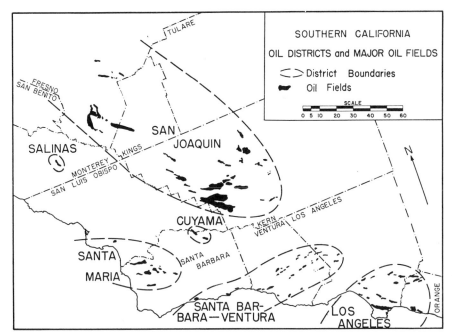

Fig. 1. Oil Districts and Major Oil Fields of Southern California. In 1954, California ranked 2nd in estimated proved reserves of liquid hydrocarbons. Texas is far in the lead of other states. (Source: Clifford M. Zierer, *California and the Southwest,* John Wiley and Sons, 1956.)

Texas. California's 9,026,603 million cubic feet of recoverable natural gas place the state sixth in natural gas reserves. Oil and gas fields occur around Los Angeles, north of Los Angeles along the coast, and in the San Joaquin Valley. Since 1940, California has accounted for one-sixth to one-fifth of the United States output of both crude oil and refined products. Most of the crude has an asphalt base and occurs in Tertiary formations of great complexity. Source rocks are highly faulted, fractured, and folded, and the traps frequently combine structural and stratigraphic features.

Other parts of the Pacific Borderlands possess no significant known resources of oil and gas. Possibly as much as 10 to 15 per cent of Alaska may be classified as geologically favorable for gas and oil. Oil corporations find rentals lower than in the United States and royalties are also less for the first discovery on unexplored land. On the other hand, transport costs for supplies are greater, food is more expensive, higher prices are necessary for driller's mud, and labor demands more wages. These and other charges make Alaskan oil drilling several times more costly than that of Texas or Oklahoma.

In spite of high expenses, United States oil companies are prospecting for petroleum. Phillips Petroleum Corporation has leased about a million acres along the Gulf of Alaska, 300 miles north of Juneau, in the Katalla-Yakataga area. Oil seepages are present in the district and petroleum has been produced commercially. The greatest holding of oil land in Alaska [2] is that controlled by the Navy along the Arctic Coast.

Useful quantities of coal occur in Oregon, Washington, Alaska, and British Columbia. Metallurgical coking coal and bituminous of good grade are present in both western Washington and British Columbia; lignite is found near Coos Bay, Oregon; and semianthracite occurs in quantity in Washington's western Cascades, especially in Lewis county.

Coal is mined extensively on the Puget Sound Lowland near Bellingham and at several centers in King, Pierce, and Thurston counties. Washington's production in 1950 was a little over a million tons, some of which was exported to Japan. In the same year, nearly 2,000,000 tons were mined in British Columbia, most of it from the Vancouver Island and the Nicola-Princeton districts. The main reasons for the limited exploitation of Northwest coal are the cheapness of imported petroleum and the easy availability of water power.

Coal is present in Tertiary and Cretaceous rocks throughout Alaska (Fig. 2). In the Pacific Borderlands, coal appears in the Tertiary sedimentary rocks of the Matanuska district, which is one of the state's principal productive bituminous fields. The better grades are found in areas that have experienced the greater amount of deformation and intrusion. Coal for local needs has been mined west of Cook Inlet and on Admiralty Island in Alaska's Panhandle. Beds ranging in quality from semibituminous to anthracite occur in the Kushtaka formation near the Gulf of Alaska. Deposits are extensive, and although they may be costly to mine and develop, they are among the valuable resources of the state.

If coal is limited in northwest continental United States, hydroelectric power more than makes up the deficit. Forty per cent of the country's potential water power is in the Pacific Northwest; of this, several million horsepower have been developed already. Sites in mountain canyons and in deeply eroded valleys of the lava plateau offer excellent locations for reservoirs and dams, of which those of the Columbia River at Bonneville and the Grand Coulee are the best known.

British Columbia also has an enormous amount of potential water power. Recently an important segment of that potential has been realized. Because it takes 10 kilowatt-hours to make a pound of aluminum, a reduction plant can be located with profit in a remote part of the earth if only power is cheap enough. Cheap power is the reason the Aluminum Company of Canada has built the world's largest aluminum project near Kitimat

---

[2] For a good short treatment of Alaskan oil production and resources see Raymond J. Schrick, "Alaskan Oil Rush," *Wall Street Journal,* June 16, 1958.

Fig. 2. Coal Beds in Alaska's Healy River Valley. Bituminous coal is interstratified with Tertiary sandstone and shale. (Source: Philip S. Smith, and U. S. Geological Survey, *Areal Geology of Alaska*, 1939.)

in northern British Columbia, a far away part of the world. The water for Kitimat's power is dammed in a chain of lakes that make a reservoir 150 miles long on British Columbia's Intermontane Plateau. At the west end of the chain, a 10-mile tunnel conducts water through the Pacific Borderlands and lets it fall 2,600 feet, 15 times Niagara's drop, to the hydroelectric plant located at Kemano (Fig. 3).

The Alaskan Pacific Coast has excellent water power potential for at least two reasons: (*a*) great differences in elevation exist between mountain top and tidewater; thus sufficient head is easily available; and (*b*) mountains contribute to the heavy, well-distributed precipitation. They act as barriers to the prevailing westerlies and trigger off moisture from air masses traveling long distances over the Pacific Ocean and the N. Pacific Current.

In 1949, the United States Bureau of Reclamation completed a recon-

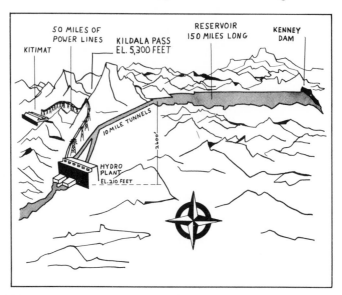

Fig. 3. British Columbia Power for Kitimat Aluminum. The direction of the east-flowing Nechako River was reversed by building Kenney Dam; and the water, now flowing west, develops enormous hydroelectric power by dropping about 2,000 feet over the western slopes of the Coastal Range. (Courtesy International Harvester Company.)

naissance survey of 200 potential water power sites in Alaska, and found that, if developed, they would have a capacity of more than 8 billion kilowatts—almost half the capacity of all the hydroelectric installations in contiguous United States.   But potential water power and actual water power are far different in Alaska.   In 1953, only three small hydroelectric installations were in operation—all on the Pacific Borderlands—one at Juneau, another at Ketchikan, and another at Anchorage.

Aluminum Company of America announced in 1952 that it intended to build a mammoth aluminum reduction plant at the head of Taiya Inlet. The project envisaged damming the headwaters of the Yukon River just across the Canadian border, reversing the river's flow, and piercing the coastal range with a 15-mile tunnel to achieve a head of 2,000 feet above the proposed plant.   The plant itself could have an ultimate aluminum capacity of 400,000 tons, or about two-fifths of the domestic aluminum output at that time.

Alcoa's plan, however, was stopped soon after it became public.   The Canadian government, falling back on a parliamentary act of 1907, refused to permit the exportation of any power that might be needed for future Canadian development.   Behind that refusal was an alternative proposal for the utilization of the Yukon's water resources within Canada for a major metallurgical development.   Although American enterprise appears to have been checked at least temporarily by this move, the ever-widening search for favorable power sites foreshadows the growth of electrometallurgical industry in Alaska.

The Forest Industries

(Figures 4, 5)

The Pacific Borderlands, with the exception of southern California and Alaska, have depended almost from the beginning of permanent settlement more on forest products than on any other resource. It was the demand for lumber in California that sent lumber schooners along the Straits of Juan de Fuca and into Puget Sound in the early 1850's. It was lumber more than any other resource that led to the rapid economic development of most of the region through the second half of the nineteenth century.

Approximately one-half of the remaining saw timber in the United States grows in the Pacific Borderlands. Furthermore, there are few regions in the world where timber can be produced more easily or where it will grow faster. The distribution of rainfall—only a small portion occurs in summer—discourages plant diseases which normally flourish in a warm humid climate. The soils, except for the alluvial lowland areas, are either glacial gravels or leached forest soils less favorable to agriculture than to tree growth. The topography over much of the area is more discouraging to farming than to growing wood. However, large areas of rough ground and steep slopes do provide serious problems in forest exploitation.

Fig. 4. Mechanized Forestry. A tractor, equipped with winch and "arch," is pulling sugar pine logs to the landing in the California pine region. Many operators equip each such "yarding" tractor with a bulldozer blade to help clear the way through obstructions. The forest in the background has been selectively logged. (Courtesy Caterpillar Tractor Company.)

Fig. 5. Seed Block. Because little Douglas fir trees will not grow in shade, block-cutting like this is the best harvesting method; selective cutting will not work for some types of trees. In the above illustration, parent trees for the thriving young Douglas fir seedlings on the slopes are the big trees in the background. They were left as a seed block by the loggers who have harvested this area. Young trees, if protected from fire and disease, will replace the ripe forest that was removed. The trees that become overripe lose value and add growth slowly. Younger trees grow faster. (Courtesy American Forest Products Industries.)

Most of the forest occurs in relatively pure stands; and many of the trees, such as the giant redwood, the state tree of California, and the Douglas fir, the state tree of Oregon, are extremely large. The former is one of the largest and oldest living trees in the world, and the latter may reach a height of nearly 200 feet. Large size brings transport problems and tree trunks may be sawed into several parts before movement on trucks or rail cars is possible.

Like most modern industries, logging has undergone many changes from the days when the trees were felled with axe and handsaw, then hauled out on skid-roads by teams of horses or oxen to tidewater. The power chain-saw fells the tree at a rapid rate. It cuts a wedge in one side of the tree, much closer to the ground than would be possible with axes. This wedge is broken out, and a cut through from the opposite side sends the tree crashing to earth. *Bucking,* the logging term for cutting a fallen tree into convenient lengths for handling, is also accomplished with a power saw.

Power-bucking is ten times faster than old-time hand-bucking, requires considerably less effort, and greatly reduces the hazard. Awkward branches are lopped off with the same saw.

The "sky-line," rigged to two spar trees with a donkey engine (steam or diesel) to do the hauling, does the "yarding" or assembly of the logs for the larger stands on steep slopes or rough ground. Sometimes only one "spar tree" is necessary, in which case it is known as the "high lead" method. For the smaller stands where "selective" logging is necessary, the caterpillar with trailer arch is used not only to drag out the logs but to make its own road for the purpose.

Certain of the trees may be left standing purposely for natural seeding, and sometimes the area is replanted to seedlings. Tree farming has replaced mining of the forests, so characteristic of American forestry several decades ago. Years hence the loggers will come back on a schedule planned with businesslike foresight.

As the more accessible timber is cut and operations go farther from the sea, logging railroads and logging trucks are needed to bring the logs to the booming grounds at the coast, where the tugs take over and tow the booms to the sawmill or the pulp mills.

One of today's major logging problems is transportation, with good roads a controlling factor. Winter road conditions of the Pacific Borderlands are different from those in the same latitudes of eastern North America. On the Pacific Coast, cool season precipitation is greater than that of the Eastern seaboard and comes largely as rain or wet snow; this may cause road deterioration and wash out bridges. In the East, most winter precipitation comes in the form of snow, causing less serious transport problems in forest operation.

Trucks have become the most important means of moving forest products out of the woods in both East and West. In the latter region practically all mills are located at tidewater. If forest roads do not lead directly to the mill, logs may be floated the remainder of the route to the processing plant. Use is made of the many stretches of open water for towing huge rafts of logs to the mills. Diesel-powered tugs on Puget Sound haul log rafts containing as much as 2,500,000 board feet against the drag of wind and tide. In some cases tide and wind are favorable; moreover, the many islands and peninsulas provide protection from occasional strong winds and high waves.

Paralleling the ability to cut down and handle large trees through powerful mechanized equipment, the variety of cutting and trimming machinery in the mill is also able to take care of all sizes of logs. Like the old-time machine shop, early sawmills were a maze of overhead shaftings and slapping belts. Electricity runs most of the sawmill machinery today, with a main steam-electric or diesel-electric plant furnishing the power. Power also comes into play when lumber is placed in storage yards for curing. To save space it is stacked high by means of fork trucks instead of the old hand-stacking method. Delivery to local yards, railroads, or docks again is handled by trucks.

Mills that are processing the region's tree harvest into lumber, plywood, paper, veneer, and other forest products are numerous along the coast. Eureka and Humboldt in California; Portland and Bend in Oregon; Seattle, Everett, Tacoma, Bellingham, Longview, Chehalis, and Grays Harbor in Washington; Vancouver, New Westminster, and Prince Rupert in British Columbia; and Sitka and Ketchikan in Alaska.

Products from the mills move to markets in all parts of the world. When the author visited Shanghai, China, in 1936, one of the first cargoes he noted was that of a freighter from Seattle unloading lumber. Northwest wood products move to Chile and Bolivia for mine props; softwoods travel to Australia, a nation now using local forests faster than tree growth replaces them; the tree-hungry British Isles purchase lumber from the Pacific Borderlands; and forests of the Northwest supply markets all over the United States. The digging of the Panama Canal was a boon to the Pacific Northwest. The canal shortened the route from West to East, and it encouraged railroads to lower rates for overland transport.

In spite of many regional advantages for successful tree growth, Pacific Borderlands forests face problems. The most accessible areas already are cutover; for example in British Columbia over a period of ten years, 1935–44, 87 per cent of the timber was cut from the coastal lands and 13 per cent from the interior. Interior forests will be more expensive to exploit.

Fire is a hazard to Pacific forests, especially in the summer, the season of least precipitation. Next to fire, the deadliest enemies of the forest come from nature itself. Much research has been done on disease and insect pests, so hazardous to the forest industry. A specific example will illustrate conservation practices followed. In the late 1940's, the hemlock looper, one of forestry's most energetic enemies, began to do serious damage to the trees in Oregon's heavy timberlands. With the aid of the experts from the United State Bureau of Entomology, a dusting treatment was planned that proved deadly to the looper but harmless to other winged wildlife of the area. It required more than 900 plane flights at low level over the forests to apply the treatment.

Proper taxation may increase the practice of tree farming, mentioned previously as good conservation in forest management. Because tree farming is a long-range process, a landowner must invest money in fire protection and carrying charges over an extended period. Excessive annual taxes can render such investments uneconomical. Some authorities suggest establishing a nominal tax on harvested timberlands and providing a more substantial yield tax to be paid at the time of the next harvest. Such a system encourages continuous yield management.

At this point it may be useful to look at forest data on each of the several political units included in the Pacific Borderlands.

California. The state has a total land area of 100,314,000 acres, with 42,541,000 acres of forest and brush. Commercial forest occupies 17,317,000 acres and the non-commercial type 25,224,000 acres. California's forests produce more than one-eighth of the annual lumber output of the United States, employ more than 100,000 workers, and supply raw material for industries, which together rank third among manufacturing industries in the state in average number of employees, salaries and wages paid, and in value added to raw material through manufacture.

Oregon. Oregon's land area, 61,477,769 acres, and forest area, 29,596,960 acres, are less than similar acreages in California; but the former has a far larger acreage in commercial forests, 26,100,000 acres, than the latter. Oregon has more standing saw timber and produces more logs, lumber, and plywood than any other state in the Union. Forest industries employ directly 90,000 workers, produce goods worth a billion dollars annually, contribute 45 per cent of the state's manufacturing payroll, and sixty cents of every dollar of Oregon's income. There are two distinct commercial forest regions, the Douglas fir area, west of the Cascades, 14,700,000 acres, and the Western Pine region, east of the divide, 11,400,000 acres.

Washington. This state has over half of its area in forests, 23,868,000 acres out of a total of 42,743,000 acres. Commercial forests occupy 19,490,000 acres and non-commercial forests comprise 4,378,000 acres. Just as in Oregon, forests are the foundation of Washington's economy. They provide year-round jobs for nearly 70,000 workers and one-third of the state's manufacturing payroll. Washington leads the nation in the production of wood pulp, wood shingles, and wood doors. As in Oregon, there are two distinct commercial forest areas, the Douglas fir forest west of the Cascades and the pine forest east of these mountains.

British Columbia. The province produces about one-half of the lumber cut in Canada, and most of it is taken from the tall straight forests of Douglas fir, cedar, hemlock, spruce, and pine in the Pacific Borderlands. As might be expected, lumbering is the most valuable primary industry, and much of the product enters foreign trade. Out of a total of 229,938,000 acres, 158,294,000 are forested. Total productive forests add up to 78,833,000 acres with 55,183,000 acres accessible. The net value of all forest industries in 1949 reached $292,259,830, while the value of lumber production alone in the coastal forests for 1950 totaled $142,141,480.

Alaska. Alaska's Pacific Borderlands possess certain favorable factors for the growth and exploitation of trees. In the Tongass and Chugach National forests, growth of hemlock, Sitka spruce, and western red cedar is sufficient to permit cutting one billion board feet annually. Largely because of numerous indentations of the fiord-and-island coast line, and the low elevation of the timber line, at least three-fourths of the Panhandle's commercial timber lies within two and a half miles of ice-free tidewater. And southern Alaska's climate, with moderate winter temperatures and precipitation up to 150 inches, encourages tree growth comparable to that in Washington and British Columbia.

However, in 1950, largely because of inadequate transport and high labor costs, only three stationary sawmills and several semiportable ones were active in Alaska's Pacific forests. Ocean freight rates along the Inside Passage are so high that Alaskan lumber (except Sitka spruce, which is needed for the aircraft industry) cannot compete on the contiguous United States market; and in the Anchorage-to-Fairbanks rail belt, Alaskan lumber loses out to Washington Douglas fir because wages in the Puget Sound area are lower.

The use of Alaskan forests for paper pulp may hold greater promise than the use for lumber. In 1954, Puget Sound Pulp and Paper Company completed a $56,000,000, 500 ton a day pulp mill at Ward Cove near rainy Ketchikan. Four hundred men are employed at the plant and between 500 and 600 in the forest. A 50-year contract between the paper company and the Forest Service specifies cutting practices that will maintain production indefinitely on the basis of an 80-year rotation; the government concession also provides for the safeguarding of salmon spawning streams, the prevention of pollution, and the preservation of the region's scenic attractions. It is significant that the output of the Tongass and Chugach National forests is big enough to sustain permanently five more mills of the same size.

The Ketchikan paper pulp factory may have set the pattern for pulp mills to be constructed in the Sitka, Juneau, Petersburg, and Wrangell areas. Foreign capital has entered Sitka already with one of the largest Japanese overseas investments for a pulp mill. The factory is being built by Alaska Lumber and Pulp Company, owned by several Japanese paper and trading corporations. When the plant is completed in 1959, it will produce 100,000 tons of pulp annually, supplying about one-fifth of Japan's total needs. Cheap Japanese labor and transport may be the answer to Alaskan labor and transport problems. But expanding Japanese industrial development could bring serious political problems.

Fisheries

(Figures 6, 7, 8)

The Pacific Borderlands of North America, like the northeastern coasts of the continent, lie near one of the world's great fishing grounds. But

Fig. 6. Catching Tuna Fish. Nearly 200 ships of the Clipper Fleet prowl Pacific waters as far south as Peru for tuna. The fleet, with up-to-date equipment for freezing hundreds of tons of fish in each ship's hold, accounts for more than half the annual catch. (Courtesy National Steel Corporation.)

the borderlands lie much farther away from the great consuming market than do fisheries of the Northeast, the North Sea Banks, and the Japanese Banks.

Natural conditions of Northwest coastal waters favor an abundance of marine life. The environment includes a broad continental shelf over which there is a mixing of warm and cold ocean currents, ideal for the growth of phytoplankton and zooplankton, sometimes called the pastures of the sea.

Again, from Cape Blanco, Oregon, to the tip of Alaska's Aleutian chain, there are hundreds of coastal indentations, islands, fiords, inside passages, protected bays—all ideal habitats for fish and all helpful to man in the various activities of fishing; and headwaters of great rivers like the Columbia and the Fraser provide good spawning grounds for anadromous fish. The fact that some of the partly enclosed seas are deep and cold like Puget Sound and others are shallow and warm like Willapa Harbor is another fishing advantage. Moreover, the great latitudinal extent of the coast, from 40° north to 60° north, a distance well over a thousand miles, provides considerable variety in marine conditions.

With such an ideal and diverse environment for ocean life, it is not surprising that commercial fish are caught in great numbers and in great variety. In fact, quantity is sufficient to give world leadership in salmon and halibut fishing; and diversity permits whaling around Bering Sea as well as tuna fishing in the more southerly waters.

Many harbors contain fleets of trollers, trawlers, seiners, and all other equipment necessary for a successful fishing industry. Astoria, Oregon, and Ketchikan, Alaska, have very heavy per capita investments in canneries, icing plants, and reduction works. Fisheries are also significant at Prince

Fig. 7. Fishway at Bonneville Dam. A fishway may consist of a water-filled lock, channel, or a series of connected pools, by means of which fish may swim past a dam or a natural barrier. The photograph gives an upstream view of a fish ladder which aids salmon in reaching their spawning grounds. (Courtesy Fish and Wildlife Service.)

Fig. 8. Pribilof Island Seals. This fur seal herd, mostly pups and cows, gathers on the beaches of St. Paul, Pribilof Islands, Alaska. Notice the large number in the bay bordering the barren island. (Courtesy E. P. Haddon, U. S. Fish and Wildlife Service.)

Rupert, British Columbia, at Bellingham and Aberdeen, Washington, and at many other coastal cities. However, more fishing craft are based on Seattle than on any other port; here, Fisherman's Terminal can accomodate 1,000 vessels in Salmon Bay's expansive area of 84 acres.

Salmon. Salmon provide an important per cent of the North Pacific catch. One habit of this fish, a migration for spawning, makes it extremely easy to exploit. During their life span, the five varieties of true Pacific salmon spawn only once in shallows at the headwaters of freshwater streams. The young fish,[3] when about an inch long, leave their home in the stream gravels to feed on insects and other water life. When several months old, they migrate to the open sea. At maturity, reached at different ages for the various species, they return to the fresh-water streams in which they had their origin and ascend in vast schools to the spawning grounds. Once started upstream, they struggle against all obstacles, swimming up swift rapids and jumping considerable falls, in their instinctive urge to

[3] The five varieties of true Pacific salmon include the sockeye or red salmon, which weighs from 4 to 10 pounds and which is an ideal cannery fish; the chinook or king salmon averages over 20 pounds—some weigh 100 pounds—and is sold fresh as well as in cans. Coho or Silverside are less popular because of their light colored flesh; humpback are pink, weigh from 3 to 5 pounds, and are caught in large quantities, especially in southeastern Alaska. Finally, chum or Keta are light in color, and although they were once considered inferior they are now processed by many canneries.

reach their spawning grounds. It is at this time that man takes them by the hundreds of thousands.

Since a certain percentage of breeding stock must be allowed to reach the spawning grounds in order to maintain salmon fisheries, the fishing season is closed during part of the migrations, and limitations are placed on the length of nets and traps.

Such control of Northwest fisheries is a comparatively recent development. In fact, in the early days of Northwest salmon fishing, no one thought of a conservation policy, or if anyone did, nothing was done to put it into effect. Some streams were blocked completely by traps so that no salmon reached the spawning beds. Important changes in this attitude came as follows.

The White Bill of 1924 gave the United States Fish and Wildlife Service supervisory and enforcement powers over all Alaskan fishing. The bill's most important feature was a provision for at least a 50 per cent escape of all salmon entering a stream to spawn. A second important conservation advance came in 1937 with the ratification and creation of the International Pacific Salmon Fisheries Commission. A major aim of the commission is the application of salmon conservation policies to the entire Fraser River Basin, probably the greatest salmon spawning grounds in the world.

Other activities aiming to conserve salmon include the building of fish ladders around power dams, and artificial propagation at fish hatcheries and later stocking of depleted streams with fingerlings.

Although part of the salmon catch reaches the market fresh or frozen, most of it is packed in tin cans. Canning salmon is a highly mechanized operation; much of the canning machinery is rented to the salmon packing plants by can producing companies, such as American Can Company and Continental Can Company, on a basis somewhat similar to that employed between the United States Shoe Machinery Company and shoe factories.

A long string of salmon canneries, built near the source of fish supplies, extends from northern California to the Aleutian Islands. Each cannery possesses loading and unloading platforms for fishing boats to move along the side. Fresh water, so necessary in canning operations, is easily available in the humid West Coast marine climate; and sufficient tidal range or stream current is present to carry away refuse dropped into the water from the floor of the cannery.

Since 1950, there has been a trend to use large freezer ships which go north from Washington and Oregon to process salmon in Alaskan waters. On these fishing craft, salmon are frozen in brine and stored until they can be processed in packing plants farther south. Some ships have a combination of freezer and cannery facilities. Freezer ships have greater flexibility in operation than that found in the shore cannery and their utilization is less seasonal. After the Alaskan fishery season, the freezer can handle the tuna run in southerly waters, a run which comes at a different time of the year.

Seasonal workers for the Alaskan fisheries no longer travel north by steamer or cannery tender, but usually move by air. The annual salmon airlift of about 4,000 cannery workers, fishermen, and machinists begins in mid-May to take care of the salmon run starting in July and ending in September.

Halibut. A fish second only to salmon in the fishing economy of the Pacific Northwest is the halibut. Coastal waters from Cape Blanco, Oregon, to Dutch Harbor, Alaska, as well as in the Bering Sea, are favorable for the fish;[4] there are extensive zones of gravel sea bottom under 150 fathoms deep; cool waters with temperatures in the 40's abound; food in abundance is at hand in the form of cod, herring, and sand launces; the large size of the mature halibut protects it from other fauna except seals, sea lions, and sharks.

The halibut is similar to the salmon in possessing the habit of migration for spawning, but differs from the salmon in many other ways. In the first place, halibut mature in twelve to fifteen years, in contrast to the salmon in four to five years. The latter migrate to fresh water for spawning, whereas halibut congregate at the outer edge of the continental shelf for spawning. The halibut weighs from 4 to 200 pounds, some over 300, which makes it much larger than most of the salmon.

Many salmon are pelagic fish, surface feeders, in contrast to the bottom feeding, or demersal halibut. Thus, salmon may be caught with purse seines, but halibut are caught on long bottom lines strung with shorter lines baited with herring; this type of gear is called a "skate" and is usually set at depths of 300 to 1,000 feet. Modern fishing vessels operate as many as eight miles of lines carrying several thousand hooks; and boats raise and lower the heavy gear with a power-driven winch.

Another difference between halibut and salmon concerns methods of marketing. Over half the halibut catch is sold fresh in contrast to the many salmon which reach the market in cans. Dressed almost as soon as they are taken from the hook, halibut are packed in crushed ice until arrival at a port, such as Seattle or Prince Rupert. Once in port they are handled so efficiently that the fish may be on the way to the Eastern market by fast transcontinental refrigerator express the same day it arrives on land. The flesh of the halibut is firm and the price per pound is relatively high, so that it is well suited for long distance transport. Shipments to the big

---

[4] The Bering Sea halibut fisheries, north of the Aleutians, have experienced little commercial development because of their isolated location.

Eastern market have increased steadily since 1890, when fast transcontinental rail service between Puget Sound and eastern United States was started.

Overfishing has taken place in halibut fisheries just as in salmon fishing. In fact, halibut of North America's northeastern coast have been depleted so much that the Pacific catch exceeds that of the Atlantic by a wide margin. Thus, man realized the need for conservation too late. Pacific Borderlands fishing for halibut is now controlled by the International Pacific Halibut Commission, which includes three members from Canada and three from the United States. This commission seems likely to conserve an important Northwest industry.

Largely because of overfishing, and consequent lower catches of halibut and salmon, North Pacific fisheries are showing more diversity. Fishermen are seeking more cod, crab, flounder, oysters, rock fish, shark, sole, and many other varieties.

In any study of Northwest fishing, mention should be made of Pribilof Islands sealing. The history of Pribilof sealing goes back to the discovery of five volcanic isles by Gerassim Pribilof in 1786. From 1786 to 1834, the Russians took about 2,000,000 pelts from the islands; but careless killing and lack of conservation reduced the herd so seriously that between 1835 and 1867, only 600,000 were taken. After Russia's sale of Alaska in 1867, the United States leased rights for seal pelts to private enterprise. In 1910, control of exploitation passed to the government largely because of much needed conservation. Between that year and 1948 the seal herd increased to nearly 4,000,000 in spite of the killing of nearly 1,500,000 seals. Numbers have been lowered slightly since the late 1940's.

On December 15, 1911, an international agreement was signed by the United States, Russia, Canada, and Japan, which prohibited pelagic sealing. To obtain this agreement, the United States conceded a percentage of the profits on sealskins to Canada and Japan. Russia was a signatory to the treaty only in the interest of the seal herd on her side of the Pacific. This treaty had a great deal to do with the increase in seal numbers from 1910 to 1950.

At present, the Fish and Wildlife Service is conducting active research on a series of sealing problems. These include the following: Where do Pribilof seals go on the annual migration from the islands? What species of marine life do they eat? In what proportion do they consume this food on their migrations? Are they an economic hazard to commercial fishermen? To what extent does the killer whale prey on pup seals when they take to the water?

California Fishing. In contrast to salmon and halibut, leading products of Northwest fisheries, tuna, sardine, and mackerel dominate the California catch. All are pelagic fish, but not all are caught with purse seines. In fact, most of the tuna are caught with pole and line. Members of the fishing crew, with eight-foot bamboo poles and three-foot lines with wire leaders, fish from racks over the guard rail after bait has been tossed out to attract a school of tuna alongside. For heavier fish, two or three or even four poles are used to one leader and hook so that the big fish may be swung aboard. Fishermen designate the size of a tuna as a one-, two-, three-, or four-pole fish. Tuna fishing occurs over such a wide area of tropical waters that there is no limited season and deliveries to canneries are made the year around. Two tropical species, yellowfin tuna and skipjack make up about four-fifths of the catch.

Sardines may be caught more easily at night, because the phosphorescent glow they give off makes them easy to locate and capture as they swim near the surface. But there has been a serious decline in the catch since 1945; this decline may be a result of overfishing.

Purse seines are important in both sardine and mackerel fishing. The long wall of webbing, 1,200 to 1,800 feet long, is circled about a school, and the bottom is closed by pulling a purse line which is threaded through rings along the bottom of the net. Like the coins in a money pouch, the fish are safely confined in this purse when the drawstring is pulled. For the past several decades in California, it has been chiefly the purse seine that has made possible the landing of fish in such overwhelming volume, especially sardine and mackerel, which form dense schools in local waters. The purse seine also accounts for 10 to 15 per cent of the tuna catch.

In the early 1950's, 93 per cent of the huge tonnage caught by California fishermen was delivered to canneries. California's 1950 catch was 1,350,000,000 pounds. Sardines constituted 53 per cent of the 1950 total, tuna 28 per cent, and mackerel 12 per cent.

Seafoods sold on the fresh-fish market constituted only 7 per cent of the total. Among them, mollusks and crustaceans made up less than 2 per cent of the landings; the group of flat fishes (halibut, sole, flounder, etc.), caught chiefly by trawling, contributed a little over 2 per cent; and what was once the most important fishery, that for two species of salmon, had dropped to about one-half of 1 per cent in 1950. In the early 1950's California stood first among states of the Union in volume and value of marine fisheries, and ocean products constantly rank fourth or fifth among the state's resources.

Manufacturing and Commerce

Manufacturing centers extend from southern California in the south to Kitimat, British Columbia, and Sitka, Alaska, in the north; and the number of factories is constantly increasing. The region possesses great natural resources and a wide variety of local raw materials that need processing; and raw material needed for manufacturing that are not available locally can be obtained easily from world resources because of proximity to the ocean. The very name *Pacific Borderlands* suggests nearness to the world's largest ocean, whose area is greater than the earth's entire land surface. Ocean side location also contributes a world market. Indeed, commerce has aided industrial progress greatly; all of the large manufacturing centers are coastal cities; all have good harbors; and all have steamship lines which radiate outward to Mexico, the Panama Canal, South America, Australia, East Asia, and to other parts of the world. Forest products, grain, fish, petroleum, fruit, and manufactured goods form major exports; metals, bauxite, and other raw materials used in factories dominate imports.

Three wars and a great increase in population, and in consequent labor supply and local markets, have aided industrial expansion. War encourages a country to decentralize industry where possible; moreover, World War II and the Korean War placed the Pacific Borderlands close to the scene of the conflict. Some of Alaska's Aleutians were taken by the Japanese in World War II.

In regard to population increase, changes in California's population during the last ten years will serve as an example; whereas population for the United States as a whole (between 1940 and 1950) showed an increase of 20 per cent, that for California jumped almost 50 per cent and is still increasing rapidly.

Five major industrial areas stand out in the Pacific Borderlands. From south to north, they are the Los Angeles, San Francisco, Portland, Seattle-Vancouver, and Prince Rupert-Kitimat factory districts.

The Los Angeles District. The Los Angeles urban district, according to the Bureau of Census, includes Los Angeles and Orange counties with more than 5,000,000 people. The city itself sprawls over 453 square miles and numbers over 2,000,000 persons.

Motion pictures have been associated with the Los Angeles area for many years. Physical conditions were ideal for the birth of the industry. Within a few miles, almost any type of land form, climate, vegetation, or water body may be found. The local Mediterranean climate is favorable to outdoor photography. The physical environment greatly encouraged the movie industry.

However, motion pictures provide employment for only a small per cent of Los Angeles factory workers—33,000 early in 1955, whereas 700,000 were employed in other industrial pursuits, including aircraft manufacturing, petroleum refining, petrochemical processing, metalworking, making machine tools, assembling automobiles, producing synthetic rubber and products from both natural and synthetic rubber, food processing,[5] and many other types of manufacturing.

Aircraft production is aided by the relatively warm, dry climate, which

---

[5] The farm income of California exceeds $2,000,000,000 annually and processing adds another $1,000,000,000. In total, food processing accounts for about one-fifth of California's manufacturing.

favors testing planes and the outdoor storage of parts. Moreover, national decentralization of the strategic industry seems advisable under modern methods of warfare. In 1954, nearly 225,000 workers were employed in California's aircraft and parts industry; Los Angeles employed 80 per cent of these workers, who comprised 28 per cent of all the employees in the manufacturing industries of metropolitan Los Angeles.

Large supplies of petroleum in the Los Angeles Basin and in the San Joaquin Valley furnish a base for oil refining and for the fast growing petrochemical industry. Local gas and oil are also a great advantage in a region far removed from a major coal field.

War encouraged the establishment of a West Coast iron and steel plant at Fontana, a few miles from Los Angeles. Fontana gets most of its coking coal from Sunnyside, Utah, 800 miles away; iron ore comes from Eagle Mountain, about 160 miles distant; limestone may be obtained from Colton, 12 miles away; Nevada supplies some manganese; Arizona has fluorspar; much commercial scrap iron may be purchased locally. It is worth noting that before the Fontana development, California exported nearly 500,000 tons of scrap iron annually; now the state is a deficiency area for scrap (Fig. 9).

Although no large supply of nearby iron and coal is available, the coastal location of Los Angeles gives opportunity to procure these necessary materials from many world sources. Baltimore and Philadelphia, on the Eastern seaboard, have achieved success in the manufacture of iron and steel at the Sparrows Point and Fairless plants; thus, a steel plant near or at Los Angeles should succeed.

California's large population of more than 12,000,000 people and the state's location thousands of miles away from eastern centers of automobile manufacture are two good reasons for local automobile[6] assembling plants and for the manufacture of tires and other rubber goods. These two reasons also favor an expanding manufacture of clothing and meat products. Many of the animals supplying the meat packing industry graze on arid pastures of the Intermontane Plateau states bordering California to the east. When these animals have attained sufficient growth on plateau grasses they are shipped to California's Great Valley for fattening. West Coast markets are depending less and less on the Corn Belt for fat cattle.

The San Francisco District (Figs. 10, 11). The city of San Francisco has only about one-third the population (800,000) of Los Angeles, but the less-than-a-million people are crowded into a smaller area, 91 square miles, of which only about 45 square miles are dry land. The population of San Francisco's metropolitan district is also smaller than that of Los Angeles;

---

[6] At the close of 1954, 36,000 people were employed in California's automobile assembly plants. Los Angeles is second only to Detroit among auto manufacturing centers of the world; there are seven major assembly plants with a capacity of 650,000 cars annually.

Fig. 9.   California Steel Plant.   The Kaiser Steel plant at Fontana, California, has been oper-
ating at almost full capacity since it was built in 1942 to supply steel to the rapidly expanding
West Coast market.   Located in the San Bernardino Valley, 45 miles east of Los Angeles, the
mill's 9 open-hearth furnaces have an annual capacity of 1,536,000 tons of steel.   During World
War II, when the plant was built, an inland location was deemed safer than a coastal one.
(Courtesy Kaiser Steel Corporation.)

a total of approximately 2,500,000 people in San Francisco's six surrounding counties is only about half the number of Orange and Los Angeles
counties.

Although manufacturing has quadrupled since 1919, it is still far behind
that of Los Angeles.   Like its southern rival, San Francisco has no local
coal or iron for heavy manufacturing.   Hydroelectric power is carried by
wire from waterfalls in the Sierra Nevada Range.   Petroleum and natural
gas from the San Joaquin Valley are also needed to supply energy for the
city's industries.

Many industrial establishments may be classified as light manufacturing.   These include printing and publishing, the processing of agricultural
products from the Great Valley to the east,[7] the refining of cane sugar mov-

[7] The San Francisco Bay area, with more than 75 canneries, leads the entire Southwest in the
canning of fruits and vegetables.   Most of these products come from the Santa Clara Valley and
from the delta lands of the Sacramento and San Joaquin rivers.   Since the industry is so highly
seasonal in character, workers include housewives and students from colleges and high schools.

ing by ship from Hawaii's cane fields, the manufacture of chemicals from nearby oil fields, as well as the refining of the oil.

San Francisco has a cooler, more energizing climate than Los Angeles. This may favor worker efficiency over that of the southern city. Summer temperatures[8] are decidedly more pleasant for hard work; and winters, although cooler and damper than those of Los Angeles, are not a handicap for working.

San Francisco's Golden Gate provides one of the best natural harbors in the world. In 1953, the value of San Francisco imports was $361,000,000;

Fig. 10. The Port of San Francisco. The bridge in the distance spans the Golden Gate, the best known and most significant break in the California coast line. The Golden Gate and the adjoining bays, San Francisco and San Pablo, make up one of the world's best natural harbors. (Courtesy San Francisco Chamber of Commerce.)

[8] San Francisco's summer temperatures are among the coolest in the world for that latitude. The city is located at one of the few breaks in the Coastal Ranges. The Great Valley to the east, almost completely surrounded by mountains, may develop a local low-pressure system during the high-sun period. With pressures on the nearby seas higher, cool sea air moves through the San Francisco break towards the Great Valley low-pressure area; this creates cool summer temperatures in San Francisco. The city receives its highest temperatures in the autumn, after the dissipation of the Great Valley low-pressure area. Cool summers and mild winters make conditions favorable for man's mental and physical activities.

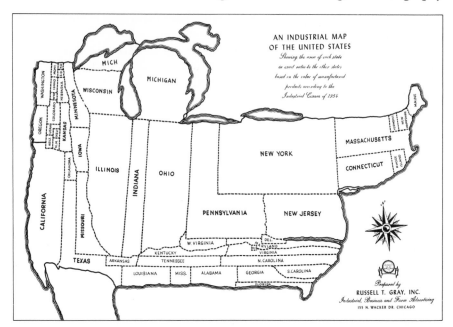

AN INDUSTRIAL MAP
OF THE UNITED STATES
*Showing the area of each state
in areal ratio to the other states
based on the value of manufactured
products according to the
Industrial Census of 1954*

Prepared by
RUSSELL T. GRAY, INC.
Industrial, Business and Farm Advertising
155 N. WACKER DR. CHICAGO

Fig. 11. Manufacturing in the United States. The above map shows the relation of each state to all the other states, based on the value added by manufacture. It may be noted that the North American Ruhr, the area around the Great Lakes, shows unquestioned leadership. But California compares quite favorably with states like Illinois, Ohio, and Indiana. (Courtesy Russell T. Gray, Inc.)

exports $370,000,000. Petroleum is the most important export in tonnage; other important outgoing products include fruit, rice, barley, canned vegetables, canned fish, dairy products, and cotton. Coffee is San Francisco's most valuable import and others are sugar, copra, bananas, canned pineapple, newsprint, vegetable oils, and ores. During 1953, a total of more than 5,000 ships arrived at the ports on San Francisco Bay.

In 1953, Los Angeles imports were valued at $261,000,000 and exports at $270,000,000. This harbor is primarily concerned with coastal and intercoastal shipping, but it also shares in the Far Eastern and Latin American trade, as well as the Hawaiian and Pacific Island commerce. Petroleum has long dominated the Los Angeles Customs District export trade. Convenient location with respect to producing wells and refining centers is of paramount importance. Raw cotton, canned fish, borax, oranges, steel pipe, and machinery are other important exports. Crude rubber, lumber, copra, vegetable fibers, coffee, bananas, molasses, newsprint, and chemicals are major imports.

Each of California's big coastal cities has certain advantages over the other in regard to location. San Francisco lies nearer Hawaii, nearer Northwest coastal cities, nearer Alaska, and nearer the Orient.

Los Angeles is nearer the Panama Canal; and because of the Pacific Coast curve toward the east in the vicinity of Los Angeles, that city is closer to North America's Eastern seaboard. Moreover, east of Los Angeles, trains on the Southern Pacific and Santa Fe can head directly towards the Atlantic Coast and encounter no serious mountain barrier. On the other hand, trains heading directly east from San Francisco will face the formidable mountain topography of the Sierra Nevada range.

The Portland District. The Portland manufacturing section includes an area adjoining and lying west of the confluence of the Willamette and Columbia rivers. Several manufacturing cities lie on the river lowlands, factory centers such as Portland[9] and Astoria, Oregon, and Vancouver and Longview, Washington.

Although little local coal and oil are available, hydroelectric energy comes over wires from Bonneville Dam, where the Columbia cuts through the Cascades; and from the Grand Coulee, where the stream has eroded deeply into the lava plateau. The 1955 international agreement between Canada and the United States for Canada to supply the Northwest with gas from Canada's Peace River district has increased energy sources for the Portland region.

Industrial raw materials are dominated by forest and farm products. Wood processing is important with factories for lumber, paper, paper pulp, furniture, plywood, veneer, etc. Grain and livestock form the basis for flour milling, meat packing, and the manufacture of clothing. Portland is the largest United States market for nationally grown wool; and clothing factories furnish wearing apparel for the local population and for those of other regions. Climatic conditions favor manufacturing.[10]

The Seattle-Vancouver Region (Fig. 12). Tacoma, Bremerton, and Bellingham, all in Washington, may be added to the two cities which give their names to the region. All have excellent harbors and a favorable outlet on the Pacific, two encouraging factors for the development of commerce; and the growth of manufacturing is partly dependent upon trade. Overland outlet to the Eastern seaboard is not easy because of the mountain barriers

---

[9] In 1947, Oregon's industrial workers numbered 114,000 and those of Washington 159,000. Portland leads Seattle in textiles, lumber, furniture, and paper; but Seattle is far ahead in transport equipment. Portland is a river port with access to the country east of the Cascades by way of the Columbia gorge.

[10] Ellsworth Huntington, probably geography's greatest believer in the importance of an energizing climate for man's best work, chose the West Coast marine climate—that of coastal lands of Washington, Oregon, and British Columbia—as the most ideal for the development of great manufacturing regions and the progress of civilization. In general, this climate has cold, but not extremely cold, winters; warm but not hot summers; generally high relative humidity; ample well-distributed precipitation; and frequent changes in weather brought about by a constant sequence of west-east moving cyclonic storms. Huntington believed that such atmospheric conditions encourage the greatest mental and physical activity, two very important factors in man's successful operation of the complexities of modern industry.

Fig. 12.   Aerial View of Boeing Airplane Company's Renton, Washington, Plant.   Airplane plants are widely distributed in the United States; this is partly a defense measure.   (Courtesy Boeing Airplane Company.)

lying a short distance to the east.   This is especially true of the Washington cities.

In this area as well as in others of the Northwest, the processing of local raw materials features manufacturing.   The proximity to dense coniferous softwood forests gives a good base for the production of lumber,[11] furniture, mill work, paper, paper pulp, plywood, shingles, etc.   Large catches of salmon, halibut, and other fish encourage canning and freezing plants, as well as those which prepare the fish for shipment direct from the sea to the market.   Shipbuilding is stimulated by ocean location, local forest products, and the presence of the United States naval station at Bremerton.   Flour mills obtain wheat from the nearby Columbia Plateau; large quantities of flour as well as wheat are loaded for export.   Other industrial developments include factories for aircraft,[12] aluminum, clothing, machine tools, and the processing of fruits, vegetables, and other agricultural products.

[11] The Greater Vancouver area is the main sawmill center of British Columbia; mills are clustered around False Creek, the north shore of Burrard Inlet, and at Port Moody.   Pulp mills are located at Woodfibre, Port Alice, and Nanaimo.

[12] Boeing Aircraft Corporation has enormous plants and investments in Seattle.

Vancouver's food processing plants, vegetable and fruit canneries, butter and cheese factories, milk condenseries, and poultry and stock feed mills use the products of the Lower Fraser Valley. Cattle for slaughtering and meat packing are brought in from the Interior Plateau and from the grasslands of Alberta. Other Vancouver food industries include bakeries and breweries, which are found in all large cities. Unlike the other food industries, fish processing is not concentrated in Vancouver; on the contrary, fish canneries and processing plants are scattered along the coast in order to be near the fishing grounds.

Vancouver's petroleum refineries first obtained petroleum from California. Now oil comes by transmountain pipe line from Alberta. Coke and gas are made from local supplies of coal. In terms of value, almost 30 per cent of British Columbia's manufacturing is in Vancouver. In the early 1950's, the city ranked third in population among Canadian cities, but only fifth in manufacturing.

The Prince Rupert-Kitimat District. Mention has been made already (p. 418–20) of the enormous water power development at Kemano, a plant which furnishes hydroelectric energy for the ALCAN aluminum industry at Kitimat. So far, Kitimat is a one-industry town; but Prince Rupert, not far away, boasts of the Celanese Corporation cellulose plant, a large fish packing industry, and facilities for handling Canadian grain for Pacific Coast shipment. Prince Rupert's proximity to Alaska started a shipping boom for this northern port at the beginning of World War II. It has Eastern seaboard connections by rail, and lies much closer to militarily strategic Alaska than does Vancouver or Seattle.[13]

The Alaska District (Fig. 13). Little manufacturing occurs in Alaska. The small developments include the processing of forest products, the canning of various types of fish, and the preparation of foods such as bread for local consumption.

Commercial activities suffer many handicaps in the huge, sparsely populated peninsula. Perhaps Alaska's present transport and population cycle may be summarized as follows: sparse population leads to expensive transport; high charges for shipping encourage high living costs; high living costs account for higher-than-average expenses in production; expensive production and shipping make it impossible to establish many industries; the minimum number of industries, such as fishing, trapping, tourists, forestry, and mining which have a maximum activity in the summer, make for seasonal unemployment; seasonal unemployment and high costs of living discourage immigration and encourage emigration; all these conditions result in sparse population.

[13] For more information on the Prince Rupert advantage, see Richard L. Neuberger, "Seattle Ponders a Bad Dream," *Saturday Evening Post,* February 7, 1948.

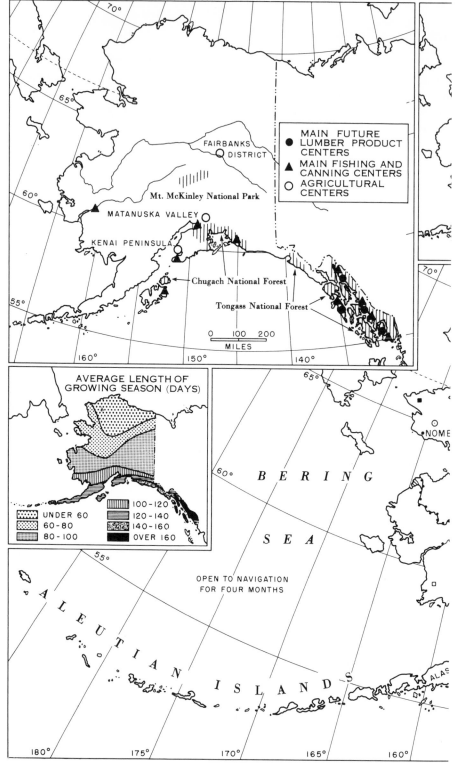

Fig. 13. Alaska. (After map, *Focus,*

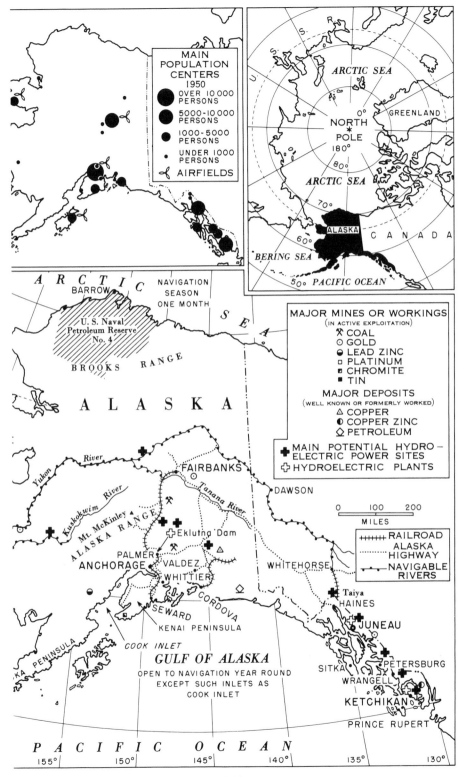

MAIN
POPULATION
CENTERS
1950
● OVER 10,000 PERSONS
● 5000-10,000 PERSONS
● 1000-5000 PERSONS
· UNDER 1000 PERSONS
⋈ AIRFIELDS

ARCTIC SEA

NORTH
*
POLE
180°
0°
GREENLAND
80°
ARCTIC SEA
70°
ALASKA
60°
C A N A D A
BERING SEA
50°
PACIFIC OCEAN

A R C T I C

NAVIGATION
SEASON
ONE MONTH

S E A

BARROW

U.S. Naval
Petroleum Reserve
No. 4

B R O O K S   R A N G E

A L A S K A

MAJOR MINES OR WORKINGS
(IN ACTIVE EXPLOITATION)
✗ COAL
○ GOLD
◕ LEAD ZINC
□ PLATINUM
▣ CHROMITE
■ TIN
MAJOR DEPOSITS
(WELL KNOWN OR FORMERLY WORKED)
△ COPPER
◐ COPPER ZINC
◇ PETROLEUM

✚ MAIN POTENTIAL HYDRO-ELECTRIC POWER SITES
✤ HYDROELECTRIC PLANTS

Yukon   River

Kuskokwim   River

FAIRBANKS

Tanana River

DAWSON

Mt. McKinley

ALASKA RANGE

✤ Eklutna Dam

PALMER
ANCHORAGE
VALDEZ
WHITTIER

WHITEHORSE

0   100   200
MILES

┼┼┼┼ RAILROAD
········· ALASKA HIGHWAY
━•━ NAVIGABLE RIVERS

SEWARD
CORDOVA
KENAI PENINSULA

Taiya
HAINES

JUNEAU

COOK INLET

GULF OF ALASKA
OPEN TO NAVIGATION YEAR ROUND
EXCEPT SUCH INLETS AS
COOK INLET

SITKA

PETERSBURG
WRANGELL

...KA   PENINSULA

KETCHIKAN

PRINCE RUPERT

P A C I F I C   O C E A N

155°   150°   145°   140°   135°   130°

American Geographical Society, September 1953.)

The Tourist Industry

(Figure 14)

Several basic conditions for a successful tourist industry have been mentioned before, but they may bear repeating. First, there must be attractive climate and/or scenery, either physical, man-made, or both; second, the tourist center must be relatively near a dense population with high standards of living; or transport facilities between the population and the tourist area must be rapid, comfortable, frequent, and within the budget of the tourist trade; and third, accommodations for tourists must be plentiful and priced within reach of the tourist dollar. It may be well to see how the Pacific Borderlands conform with respect to these conditions.

The Mediterranean climate of southern California is especially attractive to tourists during the months of November to April, inclusive. Although this is the rainy season, few rainy days occur to give the region its approximately 15-inch average annual rainfall. Clouds are at a minimum and sunshine at a maximum even in winter. Summers are sunnier than the winters, and the rain is almost nil, but the temperatures are high. Some tourists do not like the heat, although many minimize its disadvantages by frequenting the numerous bathing beaches or by driving to the nearby mountain resorts with their cooler temperatures.

Fig. 14. Juneau, Alaska. At the right is the mill for a large shaft-type gold mine sunk into the mountain side. Notice the limited amount of nearly level land between the steep Coastal Range and the Pacific Ocean. Similar site situations exist for the towns of Ketchikan, Wrangell, and Skagway, all located on the Alaskan Panhandle. (Courtesy U. S. Geological Survey.)

West Coast marine summers are most attractive to tourists. At that season there is little cloud or rain and temperatures seldom rise above the 70°F. mark. However, the winter climate can hardly be recommended. It is rainy, cloudy, and, although actual temperatures are high for the latitude, the sensible temperatures are far from pleasant.

The physical landscape is attractive throughout the entire region. The tourist can see mountains of every variety, including the Sierra Nevada fault block; this range contains the highest mountain as well as the only active volcano in the contiguous United States. Oregon contains beautiful Crater Lake, and numerous monadnocks occur in the tilted Klamath upland; there are the fold mountains of the Coast Ranges; and in Alaska, Mt. McKinley rises to the highest altitude of any mountain in North America.

The visitor may also see huge alluvial fans, some of which spread in an east-west direction almost across the Great Valley of California; the sea terraces, which evidence uplift along the Pacific Coast; the U-shaped valley of the Yosemite, formed by glacial erosion; beautiful waterfalls dropping from high elevations to lowland valleys; and the magnificent scenery of the downfaulted, subsiding Inside Passage leading to Alaska.

Most tourists are impressed by the region's beautiful forests. The oldest, largest, and tallest trees in the world grow in the Muir Woods near San Francisco and in Yosemite National Park on the Sierra Nevada Range. If the visitor seeks variety in vegetation, he can find everything from desert, in the central part of the Great Valley of California, to rainforest on the nearby mountains.

Man-made environments show diversity as well as attractiveness. These include the movies of Hollywood; displays of flowers such as the Pasadena Tournament of Roses; numerous national parks; famous universities such as those of California, Oregon, Washington, British Columbia, and Alaska; bathing beaches; abandoned mining towns of the gold rush days; orange groves and other evidences of subtropical agriculture; famous hotels like the Mark Hopkins in San Francisco, and the view of the Golden Gate from the top of the Mark; city parks like the famous Stanley Park of Vancouver; and many other places made attractive by man.

One handicap to tourism is the great distance that separates the Pacific Coast from the densely populated east. This disadvantage has been lessened somewhat by good federal and state highways; by coach and pullman accommodations over a variety of scenic cross-country railroad routes; by slower, but cheaper, bus service; and by frequent, fast, and relatively cheap air travel. Numerous hotels and motels in all price ranges are available.

In the future, the Pacific Borderlands may not have to depend so much on tourists from regions to the east. With the great increase of local population, significant intraregional tourist movement is already taking place.

Regional Summary

The physical environment of the Pacific Borderlands shows a certain unity in (*a*) the long northwest-southeast stretch of mountains; (*b*) a long band of forests extending in the same general direction; (*c*) a long belt of metallic minerals associated with the mountains or carried onto the plains by streams eroding the mountains; (*d*) a long fringe of ocean bathing the Pacific shore of the entire region; and (*e*) a long list of northwest-southeast trending valleys with extensive level lands.

Man's adjustments to the elongated north-south physical features also show considerable regional unity. The long band of forest is utilized for many types of wood products; the long belt of metallic minerals has been tapped by numerous mining centers; the long fringe of Pacific Ocean encourages fishing and both foreign and domestic commerce; and the long list of valley lands provides one of the richest farming areas in North America.

Products of the farm, the mines, the sea, and the forests contribute materials for manufacturing centers extending over a wide expanse of latitude. And finally, mountains, valleys, forests, and sea contribute an extremely attractive landscape for a long string of tourist resorts.

QUESTIONS, EXERCISES, AND PROBLEMS

1. Trace the history of California mining. What routes were traveled to the gold rush? What influence did the discovery of gold exert upon other California industries? List and give the location of mineral resources in the Pacific Borderlands. Do the same for the oil, gas, coal, and hydroelectric power resources.

2. What relationships exist between forest cover and the physical environment? What major tree types furnish most of the forestry products? Describe the various phases of forestry throughout the region together with the products resulting from forest exploitation. Name and analyze major forest problems. Read carefully Edward Higbee, *American Agriculture,* Chapters 5 and 6, on the geography of Western forests.

3. Tell of the salmon and halibut fishing industries. How do habits of the fish as well as the physical environment influence methods of fishing? Comment on California fishing. What conservation practices have been employed in the fishing industry? Have they been successful? Comment on the topic of conservation for all Pacific Borderlands' natural resources.

4. Study the background, development, and character of manufacturing, in general, for the region; describe manufacturing specifically in the Los Angeles district; in San Francisco; in the Portland area; in the Seattle-Vancouver section; in Prince Rupert and Kitimat; and in the Alaska district. Study tourist possibilities for the Pacific Borderlands.

5. Comment on the political geography of Alaska. Describe Alaskan transport facilities and their relation to the environment; how do they affect the state's economy?

6. Each of the following cities has approximately 100,000 people or more in its urban district: Berkeley; Fresno; Glendale; Long Beach; Los Angeles; Oakland;

Pasadena; Richmond; Sacramento; San Diego; San Francisco; San Jose; Stockton; Portland; Seattle; Tacoma; Vancouver, British Columbia. Name major activities encouraging the growth of each of the above population centers.

7. Locate the following towns and cities and indicate the most important economic activities for each: Anchorage; Astoria; Bellingham; Bremerton; Eagle Mountain; Eugene; Eureka; Everett; Fontana; Howe Sound; Juneau; Kemano; Ketchikan; Longview; New Westminster; Prince Rupert; Salem; Seward; Sitka; Vancouver, Washington; Victoria, British Columbia; Wrangell.

8. Describe carefully the regional distribution and growth of the population. What economic and political responses will result from the rapid population growth?

9. Identify the following: Sutter's mill, sequoia, Douglas fir, plywood, Sitka spruce, bucking, chain saw, Iron Chink, three-mile limit, Bonneville, smog, placer mining, Alcoa, spar tree, White bill, fish ladder, freezer ship, skate, hemlock looper, causes for San Francisco's cool summers, Japanese investments in Alaska, Pribilof Islands.

SELECTED REFERENCES

Allen, Edward W., "Fishery Geography of the North Pacific Ocean," *Geographical Review,* October 1953, pp. 558–563.

California Division of Mines," Geological Formations and Economic Development of Oil and Gas in California," *Bulletin 118,* April 1943.

Cunningham, William Glenn, *The Aircraft Industry: A Study in Industrial Location,* L. L. Morrison, Los Angeles, 1951.

Day, Albert M., "Old Man of the Pribilofs," *Scientific Monthly,* May 1949, pp. 329–337.

Eiteman, Wilford J., and Alice Boardman Smuts, "Alaska Land of Opportunity Limited," *Economic Geography,* January 1951, pp. 33–42.

Fields, Paul E., "Guiding Migrant Salmon," *Scientific Monthly,* July 1957, pp. 10–22.

Forbes, "Fontana Steel Plant," June 15, 1956.

Freeman, Otis W., and Howard H. Martin, *The Pacific Northwest,* John Wiley and Sons, 1954, pp. 121–284 and 389–438.

Geographical Record, *Geographical Review:*
"The San Francisco-Oakland Metropolitan Area," April 1955, pp. 264–265;
"The Western Hardboard Industry," July 1957, pp. 427–428;
"Urbanization and Water in Southern California," July 1954, pp. 422–423.

Griffin, Paul F., and Ronald L. Chatham, "Population: A Challenge to California's Changing Citrus Industry," *Economic Geography,* July 1958, pp. 272–276.

Gruening, Ernest, "The Political Ecology of Alaska," *Scientific Monthly,* December 1951, pp. 376–386.

Highsmith, Richard M., Jr., and John L. Beh, "Tillamook Burn: The Regeneration of a Forest," *Scientific Monthly,* Vol. 75, 1952, pp. 139–148.

Janssen, Richard F., Jr., "Saving the Trees," *Wall Street Journal,* July 16, 1957.

Jenkins, Olaf P., *Mineral Commodities of California,* Department of Natural Resources, Division of Mines, 1957.

Lincoln, Freeman, "Frank McMahon's Pipe Dream for Gas," *Fortune,* January 1958.

McKibben, Gordon C., "A City Fights to Keep Pacific from Its Doors as Harbor Sinks, Long Beach," *Wall Street Journal,* May 6, 1957.

Power, E. A., and C. E. Peterson, *Fisheries of the United States and Alaska, 1955,* Fish and Wildlife Service, U. S. Department of Interior, March 1956.

Siddall, William R., "Seattle: Regional Capital of Alaska," *Annals of the Association of American Geographers,* September 1957, pp. 277–284.

Smith, Richard Austin, "Alaska: The Last Frontier," *Fortune,* September 1955.

Smithsonian Institution, "Kitimat and Kemano," *Annual Report, 1956,* pp. 355–362, U. S. Govt. Printing Office, 1957.

Standard Oil of California, "Power Logging," *Bulletin,* January 1952.

Stone, Kirk H., "Alaskan Problems and Potentials," *Journal of Geography,* May 1951, pp. 177–188.

Stone, Kirk H., "Populating Alaska: The United States Phase," *Geographical Review,* July 1952, pp. 384–404.

U. S. Department of Commerce, *Alaska,* 1954 Census of Manufactures, 1957.

U. S. Weather Bureau, "Weather and Forest Fires," *Daily Weather Map,* Washington, D. C., July 22, 1954.

Wall Street Journal, "Alaska's Timber," June 20, 1953.

Winther, Oscar Osburn, "Los Angeles: Its Aquatic Life Lines," *Journal of Geography,* February 1950, pp. 45–62.

Young, Robert N., and Paul F., Griffin, "Recent Land-Use Changes in the San Francisco Bay Area," *Geographical Review,* July 1957, pp. 396–405.

Zierer, Clifford M., editor, *California and the Southwest,* John Wiley and Sons, 1956, pp. 192–360.

Zierer, Clifford M., "Tourism and Recreation in the West," *Geographical Review,* July 1952, pp. 462–481.

16 · North America: Outlook

A few centuries ago, Christopher Columbus made a long voyage seeking a new route to the riches of the East Indies. He failed to attain his goal. Instead he discovered a continent which in Columbus' day was much less valuable than the East Indies he sought, but which today is far richer than his long dreamed of Oriental islands.

In fact, North America, with 6.6 per cent of the world's population and 14.8 per cent of the earth's land mass, now produces 15.9 per cent of the agricultural output, in value (12.1 per cent of the vegetable products and 20.3 per cent of the animal products); 40.5 per cent of the metals and mineral fuels (34.4 per cent of the metals and 47.1 per cent of the mineral fuels); 21.9 per cent of the non-metallic minerals; one-third of the textile fibers; more than one-fourth of the output from forests; and one-third of the manufacturing output.[1]

What are the reasons for the great changes that have taken place on the continent during the nearly 500 years that have elapsed since Columbus' discovery? We cannot ascribe the progress to a change in the physical environment. Climates are but little if any different from those experienced by the Indians who occupied the continent before the coming of the Europeans.

The rich Appalachian coal and high-grade Lake Superior iron had formed long before early man ventured across the Alaskan land bridge enroute from Asia to North America. The prairie grasses that Europeans found in what is now the American Corn Belt had been growing for thousands of years on land leveled and enriched by Pleistocene ice.

The same ice made the Great Lakes, which long carried nothing but Indian canoes. Now, the waters that border the Interior Seaboard carry

---

[1] All figures are taken from W. S. Woytinsky and E. S. Woytinsky, *World Population and Production,* The Twentieth Century Fund, 1953.

the greatest commercial tonnage of any of the world's waterways of similar size. Much of this commerce involves materials reaching the North American Ruhr, a manufacturing district which occupies the rimland of the Great Lakes. The Indian used this rimland as a fishing, hunting, and trapping range with only a few small plots planted to corn, pumpkins, and other vegetables.

Thus, if Columbus were to return to North America today, he might think he had discovered several continents. For in terms of productivity, his discovery is contributing many times the amount of goods and services which the civilization of 1492 produced.

If the changes in the continental land use during the past 500 years are not a result of alterations in the physical environment, what is the answer? Probably the truth is that man has a choice in making his adjustments with nature. The European immigrant did not want to continue to trap, hunt, and raise a few vegetables on a richly endowed continent like the Indian did. Instead he wanted to cultivate more of the rich farmlands and to farm them better; he desired to exploit some of the greatest power and mineral resources in the world; he wished to raise more and better domestic animals in one of the earth's best natural environments for domestic fauna; he hoped to build one of the world's greatest transport networks on generally favorable terrain. Nature gave the European newcomer this choice and he took full advantage of it.

Besides making the choice to draw greater productivity from the North American continent, the European had to contribute a significant supply of ingenuity and hard work, and ingenuity and hard work are still two of man's best allies for progress.

For example, during the last few decades the American farmer has increased corn production 25 per cent and more by the use of improved hybrids and by consistent fertilization with nitrogen, phosphates, potash, and other minerals. In 1957, corn yields for the entire United States averaged 46.8 bushels per acre, a new national record, against the average yield of 37.8 for the past 10 years.

The digestive processes of cattle, hogs, sheep, and poultry are being studied for clues to provide better and more economical meat. As a result feeding periods for livestock have been shortened and gains in weight have been cheapened.

Recent progress in crop yields and in cheaper and better meat has been aided by farm machines, increasingly automatic, which are replacing hand labor on the farm.

Perhaps the greatest change in agriculture is taking place in farm management. Farms are getting larger; farm population is declining; and more and more farming is done on a contract basis. It may work something like this: Meat packers furnish many farmers with young livestock, stipulate the manner and length of the feeding period, and pay a fixed fee, and incentive bonuses, for good management of livestock production. The contract technique enables farmers to turn out a large volume at a small margin of profit even though their capital is limited.

All these improvements in plant and animal production have multiplied and will continue to multiply food production enormously. At the 1952 meeting of the Association of American Geographers, a seminar on world population problems agreed that with North America's continued progress in production, the Mississippi Valley alone is capable of supporting a half billion people at relatively high living standards. Compare this figure with the few million Indians gaining a livelihood from the continent when Columbus first saw it.

North American progress is being made in other industries besides agriculture. Think of the problem which faced America directly after Pearl Harbor. The country was cut off from tropical rainforest rubber at a time when much American transport was dependent on rubber-tired wheels. Anglo-American manufacturers met this challenge, and today over half of the American rubber is synthetic—a synthetic that takes the place of rubber grown on trees. This development in manufacturing technique, and scores of others which could be mentioned, shows that progress in American manufacturing has been as great as that in farming. Favorable advances also have been made in other industries.

Americans have inaugurated tree farming to crop the forests rather than mine them. Inventors have developed means of handling low-grade ores like taconite to lengthen the life of continental metal deposits; technicians employ many methods of geophysical prospecting to discover and exploit hidden power and mineral resources.

Man is stocking rivers and lakes with fish, and building fish ladders around dams constructed for power and irrigation. He is conducting research for increasing fish production on North America's bordering continental shelves. He has invented thousands of labor saving devices to increase efficiency in fishing, farming, mining, forestry, manufacturing, transportation, marketing, and other industrial pursuits. Research in and increased peaceful uses of the atom will expand power facilities for this continent and all other continents. Anglo-America has enormous resources of uranium, a basic mineral for atomic power development, both in the United States and in Canada.

One change constantly taking place in Anglo-America, and one of particular interest to regional geographers, should be mentioned. With continued improvement in transport, with greater use of transportation by the general public, with a general rise in literacy, and with the elimination of the very rich and the very poor, we may find greater uniformity of customs, habits, and living standards taking place throughout the United States and

Canada.   Foreigners already speak of the great uniformity of Anglo-America.

This does not mean that regional differences will disappear entirely.   In spite of the progress man has made in conquest of his physical environment, there are still great contrasts in land forms, water bodies, soils and minerals, natural vegetation, and climates.   And, in the foreseeable future, man will continue (*a*) to employ a different land use for mountains from that developed on plains; (*b*) to make different economic adjustments on wet lands from those attempted on dry lands; (*c*) to exploit grasslands differently from forested areas; and (*d*) to use different economic practices on continental interiors from those employed on shorelands and coastal waters.   In short, different economic uses will appear in different physical regions in spite of man's vaunted progress in the control of nature, and in spite of the growing uniformity in the customs, habits, and living standards of Anglo-American people.

QUESTIONS, EXERCISES, AND PROBLEMS

1. In July 1958, President Eisenhower made a diplomatic journey to Canada to discuss certain misunderstandings between that country and the United States.   What geographic conditions and other factors favor the generally friendly relations which exist between the two countries?   What conditions cause friction in United States-Canadian relations?

2. Comment on the United States-Canadian and United States-Mexican boundaries and the problems associated with these borders.

3. Describe the trade that exists between the United States and its neighbors, Canada on the north and Latin America on the south.

4. Has geography anything to do with race troubles in the United States and Canada?   Study this topic, emphasizing the location of the major concentrations of the yellow and black races in Anglo-America and the causes for such concentrations.

5. Compare North America with the other continents in the production of agricultural products, minerals, power, textiles, forest materials, manufactured goods, automobiles and trucks, and airplanes.   How does the continent compare in railroad mileage, surfaced roads, and cargo ships?

6. How can Anglo-America's agricultural revolution be made to give greater benefit to the bulk of the Anglo-American people?

Index

Asterisks appended to page numbers refer to illustrations.

453